Theoretical Inorganic
Chemistry

Reinhold

Physical and Inorganic

Chemistry Textbook

Series

Consulting Editor:

Professor Harry H. Sisler

University of Florida

Gainesville, Florida

Consulting Editor's Statement

One of the principal developments which characterize modern chemical education is the tremendous increase in the importance of the theoretical aspects of the subject in the chemistry curriculum. This change has been particularly apparent in the field of inorganic chemistry. In this textbook by Professors Day and Selbin, the areas of chemical theory which are most important in the subject matter of inorganic chemistry have been carefully and expertly treated at a level appropriate to graduate and advanced undergraduate students. The authors, themselves expert and enthusiastic chemistry teachers, have prepared a volume which we are proud indeed to add to the REINHOLD PHYSICAL AND INORGANIC CHEMISTRY TEXTBOOK SERIES.

HARRY H. SISLER

University of Florida
Gainesville, Florida
February, 1962

Theoretical Inorganic Chemistry

M. CLYDE DAY, JR.
Associate Professor of Chemistry
Louisiana State University
Baton Rouge, Louisiana

JOEL SELBIN
Associate Professor of Chemistry
Louisiana State University
Baton Rouge, Louisiana

REINHOLD PUBLISHING CORPORATION, NEW YORK
Chapman & Hall, Ltd., London

Preface

There was a time when any attempt to comprehend natural chemical processes in terms of theoretical concepts was generally relegated to the physical chemist. We trust that this attitude is no longer prevalent. With the recent renaissance in inorganic chemistry, we find an ever-increasing emphasis on the theoretical aspects of the field. This is as it should be. Since a knowledge of theory permits the scientist to take the maximum advantage of his experimental data, we can see that the chemist would be derelict if he did not utilize every available tool in his research efforts. Obviously, such an attitude is not original with us. Most of the inorganic textbooks that have been written during the past decade have attempted to emphasize both the theoretical and the descriptive aspects of the subject. However, it is our personal feeling that it is not possible to adequately treat the theoretical side with only a portion of an inorganic chemistry textbook.

For some years, a course has been offered at Louisiana State University under the title of "Theoretical Inorganic Chemistry." It is generally intended as an advanced undergraduate and first-year graduate level course. As a guide for the course, the theoretical portions of several of the available textbooks have been used, but none of these seemed adequate. It was for this reason, along with a feeling that our experiences were not unique, that we were prompted to write this book. There will certainly be those who will question its classification as a textbook of inorganic chemistry, but on the other hand, we feel that there will be a large number of teachers and students who will welcome it. Even among those who generally favor this approach, there will be disagreement concerning the emphasis placed on various topics as well as the omission of others. In support of our choice of topics, we can only say that we have treated those which seemed to us to be most relevant to the modern inorganic chemist.

It might be noted that the level of mathematics we have used is somewhat higher than is customary in an inorganic textbook. However, nowhere have we used the mathematics for its own sake. Throughout the book we have attempted to develop the underlying principles of inorganic chemistry. So often these principles have no meaning except through the language of mathematics. In spite of the mathematical formalism, we feel that the complexity of the treatment is well within the abilities of a senior chemistry major. At the other extreme, we have given a relatively low-level treatment in Chapters 3 and 4. Although much of this material is covered in earlier courses, we feel that it is so fundamental to an understanding of inorganic chemistry that it is worthy of review.

It may seem somewhat inconsistent to have large sections of the book devoted to historical material and at the same time to place such heavy emphasis on advanced theoretical treatments. There are two reasons for this balance. To begin with, we feel that a well-rounded chemist should be aware of the historical as well as of the modern aspects of his field. Secondly, there are many concepts in modern chemistry that cannot be well appreciated unless an understanding is first had of the work that led to them. This is particularly true of the concepts underlying quantum mechanics. It is for this reason that the first chapter was written. This chapter is not intended to give the student a detailed discussion of the quantum theory. Rather, it is intended to present the ideas that inevitably led to quantum mechanics.

In writing a book of this nature, there are always many individuals who make contributions, both large and small. It would be very difficult to give credit without overlooking some one or more of these persons. As is undoubtedly the case with all authors, we sincerely appreciate their assistance and encouragement. We would like especially to single out Professors Paul Delahay, Sean McGlynn, and Robert Naumann, as well as Drs. Loys Nunez and Mohd Quereshi for reading various chapters and offering valuable comments and suggestions, and Professor Harry Sisler who read the entire manuscript. We would also like to express our sincere appreciation to Messrs. Adnon Shiblak and Samir Shurbaji for the drafting work, and to Mrs. Camille Delaquis for the preparation of the manuscript. Finally, we must recognize the patience and understanding of our wives.

M. Clyde Day, Jr.
Joel Selbin

Baton Rouge, Louisiana
February, 1962

Contents

1 | *Origin of the Quantum Theory*

One of the most interesting and also one of the most important problems in the early development of chemistry and physics has been the nature of radiant energy. Throughout the eighteenth century, the vast majority of physicists accepted the idea that visible light consisted of small particles that were emitted from the source like bullets. Such a corpuscular theory had been proposed by Sir Isaac Newton in a communication to the Royal Society in 1675, and the result was almost universal acceptance of his views throughout the scientific world. Yet, there was some dissention. Even before the work of Newton, Huygens had proposed an undulatory theory of light which was supported about that time by Hooke. They proposed that light possessed a vibrational character analogous to that of a water wave. As it turned out, some of the strongest support that is now known for the wave theory was used at that time to discredit it, and the corpuscular theory of Newton reigned until the nineteenth century.

There were few significant changes in the ideas of the nature of light until Thomas Young published his first attack on the corpuscular theory in 1800. At that time, he showed the superiority of the wave theory in explaining reflection and refraction. Then, in 1801, he discovered the phenomenon of interference and utilized it to explain the existence of Newton rings which Newton had earlier explained in terms of the corpuscular theory. Actually, the idea of interference was not completely original with Young, for Newton, himself, had used it in his theory of the tides. For the case of light, Young found that if a source of monochromatic light is focused on a double slit in a diaphragm such as that shown in Figure 1–1, a series of lines can be observed on a screen behind the slits. The positions of these lines can readily be explained in terms of the ideas

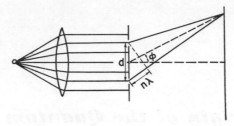

FIGURE 1-1. Diffraction of a Monochromatic Beam of Light at Two Narrow Slits.

of wave motion by means of interference and reinforcement. As the light rays pass through the two openings, the waves spread outward. When a crest of one wave coincides with a crest of another wave a reinforcement results, giving a bright line on the screen. However, when a crest of one wave coincides with a hollow of another wave, the result is complete destruction and, therefore, a dark line appears on the screen. From the geometry of the system, it is relatively easy to calculate where the lines will occur. If the difference in the paths from the two slits is an integral multiple of the wave length, the waves will be in phase and there will be a reinforcement; but when the path lengths differ by half a wave length, the waves will be exactly out of phase and there will be complete destructive interference. Thus, we find that a bright line will be observed when $n \lambda = d \sin \varphi$, and a dark line will occur when $(n + \frac{1}{2}) \lambda = d \sin \varphi$, where n is an integer such as $0, \pm 1, \pm 2, \ldots, \pm n$.

It would seem that the discovery of the phenomenon of interference should have been sufficient in itself to turn the tide in favor of the wave theory. However, in spite of his continued attacks on the corpuscular theory of radiation, Thomas Young failed to make any significant headway, and his reward was mostly ridicule by his fellow scientists. Then, in 1815, Fresnel rediscovered the phenomenon of interference and proceeded to put the wave theory on a firm mathematical basis. His work proved to be too much for the proponents of the corpuscular theory of radiation, and Huygens' wave theory was finally accepted more than a century after its author had died.

Throughout the remainder of the nineteenth century numerous other experiments were carried out on the nature of light, and they all gave further support to the wave theory. Thus, at the beginning of the twentieth century there was little doubt in the world of science that light is of a wave character, just as one hundred years earlier, there had been little doubt that it is corpuscular in character.

At the close of the nineteenth century there was a predominant sense of completion among the physicists. The classical fields of physics such as mechanics and electrodynamics appeared capable of describing all observable phenomena, and there appeared to be no new worlds to conquer. Then, suddenly out of this attitude of complacency came a succession of experimental discoveries of tremendous importance. Between 1895 and 1898, Roentgen discovered X rays, Becquerel discovered radioactivity, and Thompson discovered the electron. In three years physics had become a science that no one could have dreamed of a few short years before.

Along with these discoveries, an equally great realization came about very shortly thereafter with regard to electromagnetic radiation. Starting with *black body* radiation, a preponderance of experimental observations were accumulated that could not be explained in terms of the wave theory. This led to the development of a new quantum theory which has now permeated virtually all phases of physics and chemistry, not only from a structural and mechanistic standpoint, but also from a philosophical point of view.

BLACK BODY RADIATION

When a body is heated it emits *thermal* radiation, and the nature of this radiation depends on the temperature of the emitting body. Thermal radiation is a form of electromagnetic radiation just as is visible light. However, it usually consists of wave lengths that are longer, and therefore of lower energy, than visible light. It has been noted that the energy of the radiation from a heated body is spread over a continuous spectrum which is dependent upon the temperature of the body. At lower temperatures the spectrum consists mostly of low-energy radiation in the infrared region. However, as the temperature is raised it shifts toward the higher-energy region. This is readily indicated by noting that as a body becomes hotter it begins to radiate in the visible region. At first it becomes red, and as the temperature is raised, it approaches white such as may be observed in an incandescent light.

In order to study such radiation, it was found that a particularly desirable system was one known as a "black body." When radiation falls on a surface, some of the radiation is reflected and some is absorbed. The *absorptivity* of a surface is defined as the fraction of the light incident on the surface that is absorbed, and a black body is defined as one that has an absorptivity of unity. That is, it absorbs all of the radiation that is incident upon it. In addition, it has been shown (Kirchoff's Law) that the ratio of *emissive power*, E, to the absorptivity, A,

$$\frac{E_0}{A_0} = \frac{E_1}{A_1}$$

is a constant for a given temperature. Now, since the absorptivity of a black body has been defined as unity ($A_0 = 1$), we see that the total emissive power of any surface must be given by

$$E = AE_0$$

where E_0 is the total emissive power of a black body. Since A is necessarily less than unity for any surface other than a black body, it is obvious that no surface can emit more strongly than a black body. Therefore, it is seen that a black body is both the most efficient absorber and also the most efficient emitter of radiant energy.

Ordinarily the apparatus used for the study of black body radiation consists of a well-insulated cavity with a small opening in one of the walls. For instance, a long tube heated by means of an electric current flowing through a wire wrapped around the tube is often used. The radiation is observed as it passes out through a small hole in one of the walls. If this furnace is maintained at constant temperature, the enclosure is known as an *isothermal enclosure*. Through thermodynamic arguments, it has been shown that the radiation field inside such an enclosure has some very special characteristics. In 1859, Kirchoff was able to show that if the walls and contents of the cavity are kept at a common temperature at equilibrium, the stream of radiation in any one direction must be the same as that in any other direction, it must be the same at any point in the enclosure, and it makes no difference of what material the walls are composed. If this were not true, the second law of thermodynamics would be violated. Now, if we consider an isothermal enclosure that approximates also a black body radiator, it is obvious that it will have some very interesting properties.

Before the turn of the century, a considerable amount of work was being done on the problem of black body radiation. As early as 1879, Stefan had given an empirical relation for the rate of emission of radiant energy per unit area of a surface, which had the form

$$E = e\sigma T^4 \tag{1-1}$$

where E is the rate of emission of radiant energy per unit area or the total emissive power, T is the absolute temperature, σ is a constant known as the Stefan-Boltzmann constant, and e is the *emissivity* of the surface and is defined as E/E_0. For a black body, it is therefore seen that the emissivity has a value of unity.

A problem that was of considerable interest at the time was the distribution of energy in the spectrum as a function of wave length and temperature. Here, the monochromatic emissive power, E_λ, is of interest. This is the energy emitted between wave lengths λ and $\lambda + d\lambda$. Before any experimental determination of the energy distribution was made for a black body, theoretical attempts were made to calculate the shapes of the distribution spectra as a function of the wave length. In an attempt to find an expression for the monochromatic emissive power, Wien utilized the classical methods of thermodynamics to obtain the equation

$$E_\lambda = \frac{a}{\lambda^5}\, f\,(\lambda T) \tag{1-2}$$

where a is a constant and $f(\lambda T)$ is some function of the wave length and the absolute temperature. In order to determine the function, $f(\lambda T)$, it was necessary to consider the mechanism by which the radiation is emitted. Since Kirchoff had shown that the nature of the walls, and therefore the nature of the radiator, is not important in an isothermal enclosure, any reasonable model could be chosen. Wien chose oscillators of molecular size and applied the laws of classical electromagnetic theory. As a result, he obtained the equation

$$E_\lambda = \frac{a}{\lambda^5}\, e^{-b/\lambda T} \tag{1-3}$$

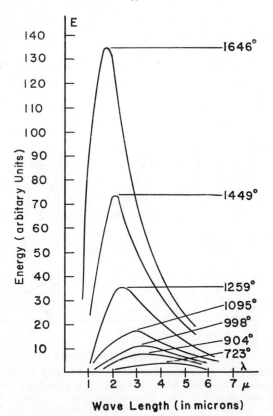

FIGURE 1–2. Energy Spectrum of a Black Body at Various Temperatures.

where a and b are constants. It was later shown that the distribution curves calculated from the Wien equation fit the experimental curves in the high-energy region (short wave lengths) extremely well, but the Wien equation failed completely to give a correct spectral distribution over all wave lengths.

Another theoretical attempt to determine a distribution law was made in 1900 by Rayleigh in which he applied the classical principles of equipartition of energy. The result was the equation known as the Rayleigh-Jeans equation,

$$E_\lambda = \frac{2\pi kT}{c\lambda^4} \tag{1-4}$$

This equation was found to give fair agreement with the observed spectral distribution in the low-energy region (long wave lengths), but it failed to even approach the observed data in the high-energy region of the spectrum.

It was in 1899 that Lummer and Pringsheim made the experimental determination of the energy distribution from a black body at various values of the temperature. Their results are shown in Figure 1–2. As can be seen in Figure 1–3, the Wien equation gives excellent agreement with experiment in the region of short wave lengths and the Rayleigh-Jeans equation appears to be asymptotically correct at very long wave lengths.

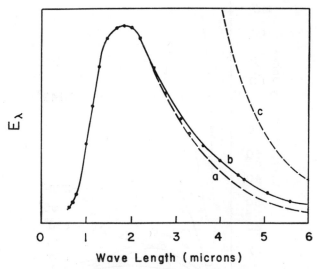

FIGURE 1–3. A Comparison with Experiment of the Three Radiation Laws: **(a)** Wien; **(b)** Planck; **(c)** Rayleigh-Jeans. The dots represent the experimental points. (From Richtmeyer, F. K. and Kennard, E. H., "Introduction to Modern Physics," 5th ed., copyright 1955, McGraw-Hill Book Co., Inc., New York, N. Y.)

However, neither of the equations is consistent with the experimental curves over the complete spectral range.

In an attempt to fit the total experimental spectrum for black body radiation, an empirical formula was at first sought that would fit the data from $\lambda \to 0$ to $\lambda \to \infty$. An example of one such formula is

$$E = cT^{5-\mu} \; \lambda^{-\mu} \; e^{-b/(\lambda T)^{\nu}}$$

from which, for $\mu = 5$ and $\nu = 1$, the Wien equation is obtained; and for $\mu = 4$ and $b = 0$, the Rayleigh-Jeans equation is obtained. Although a usable equation may be found, such an approach gives little intellectual satisfaction. Nevertheless, it was out of an attempt to determine such an empirical relation that Max Planck arrived at what was possibly the most revolutionary hypothesis of this era.[1]*

For the same reason that Wien was able to choose any type of reasonable energy radiator that he wished, Planck also was able to make such a choice. It had to be a system capable of emitting and absorbing radiation; and among the simplest types for the purpose of calculation is a set of simple harmonic oscillators. Now, according to classical ideas an oscillator must take up energy continuously and emit energy continuously. However, in order to find an empirical formula that would fit the experimentally determined spectrum of a black body radiator, Planck found it necessary to postulate that such an oscillator could not take up energy continuously as demanded by classical theory, but rather it must take up energy in discrete amounts. These amounts were integral multiples of a fundamental energy unit ϵ_0, i.e., $0, \epsilon_0, 2\epsilon_0, 3\epsilon_0, \ldots, n\epsilon_0$.

Using this idea, Planck was able to derive the equation

$$E = \frac{2\pi c}{\lambda^4} \; \frac{\epsilon_0}{e^{\epsilon_0/kT} - 1} \tag{1-5}$$

for the monochromatic emissive power of a black body. Here c is the velocity of light and k is the Boltzmann constant. Since Eq. (1–2) is of thermodynamic origin, and therefore basically correct, it is necessary for the distribution law of Planck to contain the temperature in the combination λT, or since $\lambda = c/\nu$, the combinations T/ν or ν/T are also acceptable. Consequently, it can be seen from Eq. (1–5) that the quantum of energy ϵ_0 must be proportional to $1/\lambda$, or what amounts to the same thing, proportional to ν. Therefore, we find that $\epsilon_0 = h\nu$, where h is a new constant known as Planck's constant, the presently accepted value being

---

* The superscript numbers refer to bibliographical references at the end of the chapter.

6.62 × 10^{-27} erg-sec. By making the substitution for ϵ_0, Planck's distribution law may now be expressed as

$$E_\lambda = \frac{2\pi hc^2}{\lambda^5} \frac{1}{e^{ch/\lambda kT} - 1} \qquad (1\text{–}6)$$

Whereas the energy distribution laws for black body radiation deduced from classical concepts had consistently failed to explain the experimental data, the quantum hypothesis of Planck succeeded. In Figure 1–3, is seen a comparison of the distribution curves of Wien, Rayleigh-Jeans, and Planck with the actual experimental data. The solid line represents the theoretical curve as determined by Planck, and the experimental curve is represented by the dots. Here it is seen that the theoretical curve determined by Planck coincides exactly with the experimental curve, while the classical curves as determined by Wien and Rayleigh fail at either one end of the spectrum or the other.

Planck's break with classical theory represented a real break. It involves no extension of classical ideas, but rather it is a radical change from the prevalent line of thought of that time. Quite in contrast to the classical idea that an oscillator can absorb and emit energy continuously from wave lengths of zero to infinity, Planck proposed that the energy must be emitted or absorbed only in discrete amounts. This implies that any system capable of emitting radiation must have a set of energy states, and emission can take place only when the system changes from one of these energy states to another. Intermediate energy states do not occur. Thus, we may find an oscillator with energy $2h\nu$, but we should never find one with an energy of 1.5 $h\nu$.

PHOTOELECTRIC EFFECT

In 1905, it was proposed by Einstein that the quantum properties should not be limited just to the process of absorption and emission of radiation, but they should also apply to the radiation itself. This means that electromagnetic radiation consists of particles, which we now call *photons*, that have an energy $h\nu$ and shoot through space with the velocity of light. Such radical changes in thought as proposed first by Planck and then by Einstein could not have been accepted without considerable experimental evidence to support them. This experimental evidence was available, and the success of the quantum theory was too great to be denied.

A satisfactory explanation by Einstein of the photoelectric effect was among the first triumphs of the quantum theory.[2] It had been found by Hertz as early as 1887, that if ultraviolet light is focused onto a metal surface, the surface becomes positively charged. This, of course, means that in some manner negative charge is being removed. Then, shortly after the discovery of the electron, it was shown that this charge was being carried away by electrons.

There are two important features of the electrons in the photoelectric effect that can be experimentally observed. These are the energy and the number of electrons emitted from the metal surface. When these were observed under controlled conditions, some very serious problems arose with regard to their interpretation. According to classical electromagnetic theory, the energy of the emitted electron should increase with an increase in intensity of the light used. Also, it would be expected that if light were permitted to shine upon the surface for a sufficient length of time, electrons would be emitted regardless of the frequency of the incident light. However, quite the contrary was observed. An increase in intensity failed to increase the energy at all, but rather it increased the number of emitted electrons, and in addition it was observed that if the frequency of the incident light were not above a certain value no electrons would be emitted regardless of how long the light was allowed to shine on the surface.

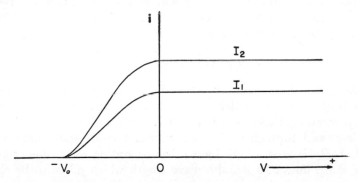

FIGURE 1–4. The Effect of Potential on the Photoelectric Current Produced by a Monochromatic Light Beam.

In Figure 1–4, it is seen that for a given intensity of light I_1 or I_2, a certain current, i, is obtained if a positive potential is placed on the electron collecting plate. However, as the potential is decreased to zero and then becomes negative, a point is finally reached where the current drops to zero. It is found that for light of a given wave length, no matter what the intensity, the current will drop to zero at some point V_0. Thus, we see that the number of photoelectrons emitted in unit time by the surface is directly proportional to the intensity of the light, but the stopping potential, V_0, is independent of the intensity. These observations are in complete disagreement with the predictions of classical theory.

For the photoelectric effect, as for black body radiation, the classical theory failed to explain the experimental observations. On the other hand,

Einstein was able to apply the quantum ideas of Planck with great success. According to the quantum theory, when a photon is incident on the surface of the metal it transfers its total energy to an electron in the metal surface. The electron then escapes from the metal surface with a kinetic energy equal to the energy of the incident photon minus the energy, w, necessary to escape from the surface. Since the energy of the photon is $h\nu$, the expression for the energy of the photoelectron becomes

$$KE = 1/2\ mv^2 = h\nu - w \qquad (1\text{--}7)$$

In terms of the quantum theory the curves in Figure 1–4, become quite reasonable. If the energy of the incident photon is greater than w, a photoelectron will be emitted, and the negative potential necessary to stop the photoelectron will be V_0. When the intensity of the light is increased, such as I_1 to I_2, a larger current, i, will be observed because the surface is being bombarded by a greater number of photons which yields a greater number of photoelectrons. If, on the other hand, the energy of the incident photon is less than w, no photoelectrons will be emitted. This is true regardless of the intensity or how long a period of time the light shines on the surface merely because an electron does not receive sufficient energy from a single photon to break away.

ATOMIC SPECTRA

At the same time that interest was being focused on the problems of black body radiation, a similar development was taking place in the field of atomic spectra. It had been found that if, for instance, an electric discharge is passed through an element in the gaseous state, light will be emitted. Analysis of this light by a prism or grating spectrometer gives a series of sharp lines of a definite wave length which prove to be characteristic of the particular element. In the case of a light element such as hydrogen, this line spectrum turns out to be fairly simple, as can be seen in Figure 1–5. However, for the heavier elements it is more likely to be extremely complex.

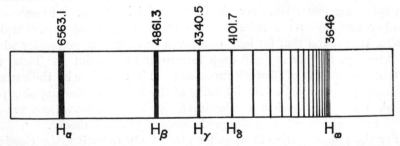

FIGURE 1–5. Spectral Lines of Atomic Hydrogen in the Visible Region.

During these first years a considerable amount of spectral data was accumulated, and as is commonly the practice, one of the first interests was to obtain an empirical relation to predict the sequence of lines. It was evident that the lines were not haphazard, but rather that they followed some sort of order. As early as 1883, Liveing and Dewar had realized that several possible series existed in the spectra of the alkali and alkaline earth metals. Although they were not able to discover an empirical equation to predict this order, they did recognize various repetitions of groups of lines and relations between groups that appeared to be either *sharp* or *diffuse*. Then, in 1885, Balmer discovered the equation

$$\lambda = \lambda_0 \frac{m^2}{m^2 - 4} \tag{1-8}$$

which related the nine lines of the hydrogen spectrum that were known at that time. In this case λ_0 is a constant with a value of 3646 angstroms, and m is a variable integer which can take on the values of 3, 4, 5, . . . , ∞. The agreement between the observed values of the hydrogen lines and their values calculated by the Balmer formula turns out to be extremely good.

Ordinarily, these equations are expressed in terms of wave number $\bar{\nu}$ instead of wave length. The frequency of a wave is given by $\nu = c/\lambda$ and represents the number of vibrations per second, and the wave number is $\bar{\nu} = 1/\lambda$ which is the number of vibrations per centimeter. In terms of wave number, the Balmer equation assumes the more familiar form

$$\bar{\nu} = R \left(\frac{1}{2^2} - \frac{1}{m^2} \right) \tag{1-9}$$

Or more generally, this can be expressed as

$$\bar{\nu} = R \left(\frac{1}{a^2} - \frac{1}{m^2} \right) \tag{1-10}$$

where R is a constant known as the *Rydberg constant*, a is a constant that depends on the particular spectral series, and m is still a variable integer as it was in Eq. (1–8). The Rydberg constant has been found to be a constant for a given element and very nearly constant for all elements. The difference in its value is due to the atomic weight of the element, and it has been found to have a value of 109,677.58 cm^{-1} for hydrogen.

At the time the Balmer series was discovered, the only portion of the spectrum that was known was the visible region. We now know that this represents an almost infinitesimally small portion of the total spectrum, ranging in wave length from about 4000 to 8000 Å, as can be seen in Figure 1–6. Thus, after the discovery of the Balmer series, it is not too surprising that other series of the same general type were subsequently

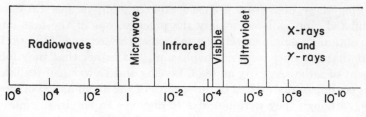

Wave Length in Centimeters

FIGURE 1-6. A Simple Division of the Electromagnetic Spectrum.

discovered in the hydrogen spectrum. The *Lyman* series was found in the ultraviolet region and the *Paschen, Brackett,* and *Pfund series* were found in the infrared. The form of the equation describing each series is the same as that of the Balmer equation, the only difference being the value of the parameter, *a*, and the minimum value of the parameter, *m*, in Eq. (1–10). For *a* = 1, we have the Lyman series, and the Paschen, Brackett, and Pfund series arise from *a* = 3, 4, and 5, respectively.

Shortly after the discovery of the Balmer formula, Rydberg sought to find an equation of more general character. By 1890, he was able to show that a large number of the observed series could be represented by the formula

$$\bar{\nu}_n = \bar{\nu}_\infty - \frac{R}{(n + b)^2} \tag{1–11}$$

where b and $\bar{\nu}_\infty$ are constants depending on the particular series, and n is a parameter that can take on successive integral values. This means that the wave number of each line can be represented by the difference of two terms, one of which is constant. In this case $\bar{\nu}_\infty$ is the constant term. Following up the work of Liveing and Dewar, Rydberg was able to classify a large number of series in the spectra of the more complex elements such as the alkali metals. He found it possible to distinguish between certain of these series that had lines that were quite sharp and others that had lines that were more diffuse than ordinary, and he named them accordingly. In addition, he noted another type of series in which the lines tended to be brighter than in other cases, and he called this the *principal series*. All of these series were found to be related by a formula of the type

$$\bar{\nu} = \frac{R}{(m + a)^2} - \frac{R}{(n + b)^2} \tag{1–12}$$

Four of these series are of particular interest, mainly due to the continued use of the symbols S, P, D, and F in subsequent work. These are:

Principal series: $\qquad \bar{\nu} = \dfrac{R}{(1 + S)^2} - \dfrac{R}{(n + P)^2}$, $n = 2,3,4, \ldots,$

Sharp series:
$$\bar{\nu} = \frac{R}{(2+P)^2} - \frac{R}{(n+S)^2}, \; n = 2,3,4,\ldots,$$

Diffuse series:
$$\bar{\nu} = \frac{R}{(2+P)^2} - \frac{R}{(n+D)^2}, \; n = 3,4,5,\ldots,$$

Fundamental series:
$\bar{\nu} = \dfrac{R}{(3+D)^2} - \dfrac{R}{(n+F)^2}, \; n = 4,5,6,\ldots,$

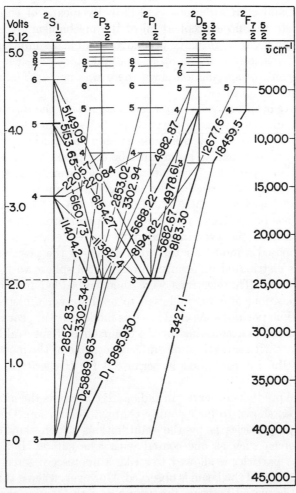

FIGURE 1–7. Energy Level Diagram of Sodium. Wave lengths of the various transitions are given in angstroms along the lines.

Here S, P, D, and F are constants that are characteristics of the particular series and R has its usual significance. An example of the sharp, principal, and diffuse series is seen in Figure 1–7, where a diagram of a portion of the spectrum of the sodium atom is shown.

ATOMIC MODELS

Although the early developments in atomic spectra were significant, they were nevertheless empirical. For the most part, they were restricted to classifying and correlating observed data by means of empirical relations, and there was no concept at all of the mechanism by which these spectral lines arose. It might have been a reasonable assumption that they came from atoms, but how the atom was able to emit such lines could hardly be a point of speculation since there was no satisfactory concept of the structure of an atom.

This situation, of course, did not last long. With the discovery of the emission of both positive and negative particles from an atom through radioactive decay along with other associations of the electron with the atom, it was realized that an atom must be composed in some manner of these newly found particles. The questions then naturally arise as to how many of each of these particles exist in a given atom and how they are arranged. The answers to these questions will depend on which of the proposed models best satisfies the observed experimental data.

On the basis of the experimental data available at that time, J. J. Thomson proposed a model for the atom in which the positive charge of the atom was distributed uniformly throughout a sphere with a diameter of about 10^{-8} cm. The electrons were then embedded in the sphere in equilibrium positions and were allowed to oscillate when disturbed about these equilibrium positions. As crude as this model may appear to us today, it had some merit in accounting for the occurrence of spectral lines. However, it also met with several serious difficulties. One of the most important of these was the interpretation it permitted for the scattering of alpha particles.

One of the products observed in radioactive decay is the *alpha particle*, which has been shown to be a doubly charged helium ion. One means of observing such particles is by the scintillations which they cause on a fluorescent screen such as one coated with zinc sulfide. If a collimated beam of alpha particles is allowed to strike a fluorescent screen, an image of the cross-section of the beam is observed. However, when a thin film such as a gold foil is placed between the source and the screen, the pattern is found to increase in size and become somewhat diffuse. This is due to the scattering of the incident particles by the atoms of the foil. Since the atoms that make up the foil are composed of electrical charges distributed in some manner, and the alpha particles are also charged, some change in the pattern would be expected. The question that immediately arises is how will a given distribution of charge in the atom affect the scatter pattern of the incident alpha particles. Using his model of the atom, Thomson calculated theoretically what the expression for the average deflection should be.[3] This calculation, coupled with calculations by Rutherford and experimentation by Geiger, showed that for the Thomson model of the atom, the probability of large-angle scattering of alpha particles was essentially zero. Yet, Geiger and Marsden noted experimentally that about 1 in 8000 alpha particles incident on a gold foil were deflected through an angle greater than 90°.[4] This, of course, was in complete disagreement with the predictions of the Thomson model, which predicted only small-angle scattering.

To resolve this problem, Rutherford proposed a new model of an atom[5] in which the positive charge was concentrated in a small volume at the center of the atom. The electrons were then assumed to move around this center of positive charge in various orbits as the planets in the solar system. This model was an improvement over the Thomson model, since it gave a distribution of positive and negative charge in the atom that was in agreement with the observed scattering of alpha particles. Nevertheless, it also met with some serious problems. To begin with, the electrons could not be considered to be stationary because the unlike charges of the electron and the nucleus would cause them to come together. On the other hand, if the electrons were considered to be moving around the nucleus, another problem arose. When an electric charge is accelerated it emits or absorbs radiation. If the electrons are pictured as moving around the nucleus, they are subject to centripetal accelerations. According to the principles of electromagnetic theory, the electrons, therefore, must radiate energy. The only place for this continuous supply of energy to come from is the atom itself, and eventually the electron should spiral into the nucleus and, in essence, run down. Since we have no evidence to indicate that atoms run down, we are forced to the conclusion that the Rutherford atom is not the final answer.

The problems existing in atomic structure at that time were not solely problems concerning the distribution of the electrons and the nucleus in the atom. Even with a given distribution, it had yet to be determined how an atom was able to give discrete spectral lines, if they came from atoms at all. Neither Thomson nor Rutherford had been able to satisfactorily solve this problem. An important contribution was made by Conway in 1907, when he made probably the first attempt to explain the phenomenon in terms of quantum ideas. Without the aid of an atomic model, Conway concluded that an atom produced spectral lines one at a time and that a complete spectrum resulted from an extremely large number of atoms, each of which had to be in an excited state involving one electron.

THE BOHR ATOM

As is the case in any phase of physics or chemistry, numerous theoretical models have also been proposed for the atom, and certainly there will be more. Each one is usually found to be superior to the previous ones in some manner or other. However, there have been few models in any field of physics or chemistry that have attracted such universal recognition as the one proposed in 1913 by Niels Bohr for the hydrogen-like atom.[6] Using the structural ideas of the Rutherford atom, Bohr was successful in applying the concepts of quantum theory quantitatively to explain the origin of line spectra as well as the stability of the atom.

It was seen that a major problem with the Rutherford atom was that of continual radiation of energy as the electron moved about the nucleus. Bohr was able to overcome this problem by applying the quantum concept of *discrete* energy states. He maintained that the electron in an atom is restricted to move in a particular stable orbit, and as long as it remains in this orbit it will not radiate energy. Then, using the quantum principle that an oscillator will not emit energy except as a result of a jump from one of these energy states to another, Bohr postulated that when the electron jumps from a stable energy state of energy W_1 to a state of lower energy, W_2, a quantum of radiation is emitted with an energy equal to the energy difference of the two states. Mathematically, this is given by

$$h\nu = W_1 - W_2 \qquad (1\text{--}13)$$

Once it is decided that the electron remains in some stable orbit around the nucleus, the question of the size and shape of this orbit arises. In the final form of his theory, Bohr assumed the orbits to be circular with a size such as to satisfy the quantum condition that the angular momentum, p, of the electron is an integral multiple of the quantity $h/2\pi$. Thus, we obtain

$$p = \frac{nh}{2\pi} = mvr \qquad (1\text{--}14)$$

where m and v are the mass and the velocity of the electron, r is the radius of the orbit, h is Planck's constant, and n is a positive integer known as a quantum number. This leads to the picture of an atom as shown in Figure 1–8. For different values of the quantum number we find different orbits available for the electron. The lowest orbit, for which $n = 1$, is the most stable orbit for a hydrogen-like atom; and an electron in this orbit is said to be in its *ground state*. The emission of radiation can then be seen to result when the electron is raised by some means to an excited state and then drops back to one of the available lower energy states.

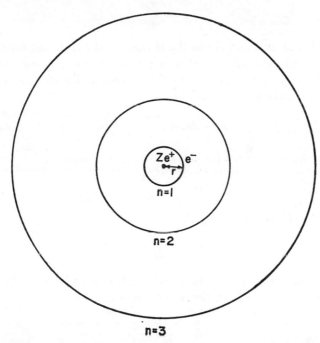

FIGURE 1–8. A Simple Representation of the Bohr Atom Showing the First Three Energy Levels.

The acceptance of the Bohr model resulted primarily from its success in quantitatively explaining the line spectra of the hydrogen-like atom. This success was necessary, for there were several facets of the Bohr model that made it difficult to accept. It is interesting to note that there is no mechanism provided for the electron to radiate energy in the Bohr model. When Bohr threw out the idea of continuous radiation by an accelerated charge, he threw out the only known means for a charged particle to radiate energy. According to the Bohr model, the radiation results from a change in energy state of the electron, but how this takes place is not answered. In addition, Bohr arbitrarily utilized both classical and quantum ideas as he found necessary in order to obtain his final result. Therefore, we see that the quite remarkable agreement between the theoretical calculations of the Bohr model and the experimentally determined data was the justification of the Bohr approach.

For a quantitative treatment of a one-electron system, the force of attraction between the electron and the nucleus is considered to arise from the electrostatic attraction between the positive charge of the nucleus and the negative charge of the electron. Thus,

$$F = \frac{Ze^2}{r^2} \tag{1-15}$$

where Z is the atomic number of the element and r is the distance between the electron and the nucleus. This electrostatic attractive force must equal the centripetal force resulting from the motion of the electron about the nucleus. This leads to the relations

$$F = ma = \frac{mv^2}{r} = \frac{Ze^2}{r^2} \tag{1-16}$$

If this expression is solved for the radius r, we obtain

$$r = \frac{Ze^2}{mv^2} \tag{1-17}$$

But from Eq. (1–14) it is seen that

$$v = \frac{nh}{2\pi mr} \tag{1-18}$$

If the value of v from Eq. (1–18) is now substituted into Eq. (1–17), it is found that the radius of the electron orbit is given by

$$r = \frac{n^2h^2}{4\pi^2mZe^2} \tag{1-19}$$

For the hydrogen atom, $Z = 1$, and if we consider the electron to be in its ground state ($n = 1$), the radius of the atom can readily be calculated to be $r = 0.529 \times 10^{-8}$ cm or 0.529 Å, which is of the correct order of magnitude as compared with r determined from other sources. Here, we see an early success of the Bohr atom.

The energy of the electron in the atom, however, is the problem of primary importance. The total energy of the electron is made up of its kinetic energy and its potential energy. If the zero of potential energy is defined as the energy of the electron when it is at rest at an infinite distance from the nucleus, its potential energy with respect to the nucleus at any distance r is found to be

$$V = \int_{\infty}^{r} F \cdot dr = \int_{\infty}^{r} \frac{Ze^2}{r^2}\, dr = -\frac{Ze^2}{r} \tag{1-20}$$

Using Eq. (1–16), it is seen that the kinetic energy is given by

$$T = \tfrac{1}{2}\, mv^2 = \frac{Ze^2}{2r} \tag{1-21}$$

Since the total energy of the electron is the sum of the kinetic and potential energy, we find that

$$W = T + V = \frac{Ze^2}{2r} - \frac{Ze^2}{r} = -\frac{Ze^2}{2r} \qquad (1\text{-}22)$$

Now, by substituting the value found for r in Eq. (1–19) into Eq. (1–22), the energy of the electron in the nth quantum state is found to be

$$W_n = -\frac{2\pi^2 m e^4 Z^2}{n^2 h^2} \qquad (1\text{-}23)$$

It is important to note that the quantum number n is, in a sense, a measure of the energy of the electron. When the electron is in the first shell ($n = 1$), it has a maximum stability but as n increases, the electron energy with respect to the nucleus decreases until it approaches zero energy as $n \to \infty$.

It was shown earlier that the energy of the radiation emitted by the atom was equal to the difference in energy of two given quantum states. Thus, for a transition between two quantum states of energy W_{n1} and W_{n2} the frequency of the emitted radiation is found to be

$$\nu = \frac{W_{n1} - W_{n2}}{h} \qquad (1\text{-}24)$$

Now, if the expression for W_n is substituted into Eq. (1–24), and the frequency is converted to wave number by the relation $\bar{\nu} = \nu/c$, it is found that the wave number is given by

$$\bar{\nu} = \frac{2\pi^2 m e^4}{ch^3} Z^2 \left(\frac{1}{n_2^2} - \frac{1}{n_1^2} \right) \qquad (1\text{-}25)$$

If the parameter n_2 is given the value of 2, it is seen that Eq. (1–25) is of exactly the same form as the Balmer equation, Eq. (1–9). This then offers a real challenge to the Bohr theory. The constant term in Eq. (1–25), $2\pi^2 m e^4/ch^3$, must give a reasonable value for the Rydberg constant in order to be in agreement with experiment. If the Bohr theory had failed in this test, it would have been necessary to start looking for a new atomic model. As it turned out, the agreement was found to be very good, and if further refinements are made, the calculated value of R can be brought into even better agreement.

The most significant improvement can be made by considering the finite mass of the nucleus and the electron. Thus far, it has been assumed that the mass of the nucleus is infinitely great with regard to that of the electron. With this assumption it was possible to neglect the motion of the nucleus and to consider it to exist at the exact center of the atom. However, for a nucleus of finite mass, it is necessary to consider both the motion of the nucleus and the electron around a common center of mass, as seen

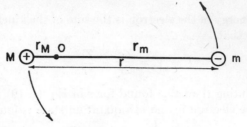

FIGURE 1–9. Motion Around the Center of Mass of a Hydrogen Atom.

in Figure 1–9. This leads to the following expression for R:

$$R = \frac{2\pi^2 m e^4}{c h^3} Z^2 \frac{1}{1 + \dfrac{m}{M}} \qquad (1\text{–}26)$$

Using the *reduced mass* and the best known values of c, h, m, and e, it is

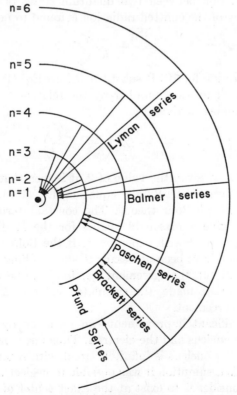

FIGURE 1–10. Transitions Leading to the Five Spectral Series of the Hydrogen Atom.

found that $R = 109,681$ cm^{-1} which is in excellent agreement with the experimentally determined value of 109,677.58 cm^{-1}.

Now that it has been shown that the equation for the wave number developed by Bohr is the same as that found by Balmer, it is possible to understand the origin of such series. For the Balmer series, the constant, a, in Eq. (1–10) was found to equal 2. From Figure 1–10, it is seen that the value of $a = 2$ arises from the fact that the electron transitions are to the second shell. In a similar manner, an analogous relation exists between $a = 1$ and the Lyman series, and $a = 3, 4,$ and 5 for the Paschen, Brackett, and Pfund series respectively. At the time the Bohr atom was developed, only the Balmer and the Paschen series were known. The completion of the five series, all of which could be predicted by the Bohr theory, came with the discovery of the Pfund series in 1924.

EXTENSIONS OF THE BOHR THEORY

It is certainly true that the Bohr theory met with many successes, such as the quantitative prediction of the energies of the line spectra of the hydrogen-like atom. Yet, it also met with some difficulties. One of the first of these was the problem of the *fine structure* in the line spectrum of the hydrogen-like atom. The Bohr theory had explained the existence of the various lines in the hydrogen spectrum, but it predicted that only a series of single lines exist. At that time, this is exactly what had been observed. However, as better instruments and techniques were developed, it was realized that what had been thought to be single lines were actually a collection of several lines very close together. This implies that there are several energy levels close together rather than a single level for each quantum number n. This would then require the existence of new quantum numbers, and there is no way to obtain them directly from the Bohr model.

This problem was solved to some extent by Sommerfeld when he considered in detail the effect of *elliptical* orbits for the electron. Bohr had admitted the possibility of elliptical orbits in his original work but had carried it no further. For the case of circular orbits for the electron, the only coordinate that varies is the angle of revolution, φ. However, for an elliptical orbit, it can be seen in Figure 1–11 that both the angle, φ, and the radius vector, r, can vary. With two degrees of freedom the possibility of two quantum conditions arises. In order to quantize both degrees of freedom, Sommerfeld generalized the quantum condition of Bohr that $p = h/2\,\pi$, to the condition

$$\oint p_i \, dq_i = n_i h \tag{1–27}$$

Here p_i is the momentum for the given coordinate, q_i. In terms of the two variables, φ and r, the following two integrals result:

$$\oint p_\varphi \, d\varphi = n_\varphi h$$

$$\oint p_r \, dr = n_r h$$

Since the angular momentum of an isolated system is a constant, the integral for the angular momentum gives the same result as obtained by Bohr,

$$p_\varphi = n_\varphi \frac{h}{2\pi} \qquad (1\text{--}28)$$

The quantum number n_φ is known as the *azimuthal* or *angular momentum* quantum number. The solution to the radial integral is not nearly so simple as that for the angular momentum. The solution contains a relation between the azimuthal quantum number, the radial quantum number, n_r, and the eccentricity of the ellipse.

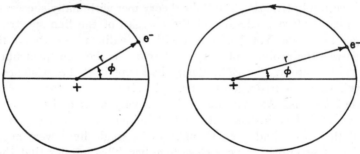

FIGURE 1–11. Effect of an Elliptical Orbit on the Variables r and φ.

In carrying out his treatment, Sommerfeld was then able to show that the energy of the electron depends on the principal quantum number which can be defined as $\qquad n = n_\varphi + n_r$

It turns out that by using the relation for the principal quantum number as defined here, the same expression for the energy is obtained as for a circular orbit with the Bohr quantum number n. Thus, we find that the introduction of the new quantum condition does not in itself give new energy terms. It only determines a greater number of possible orbits for a given value of n. For instance, as seen in Figure 1–12, when $n = 3$, there is the possibility of a circular orbit where $n_\varphi = 3$ and $n_r = 0$, or two different ellipses for $n_\varphi = 2$ and $n_r = 1$, and $n_\varphi = 1$ and $n_r = 2$.

When one quantum number is sufficient to determine the energy states of a system with two or more degrees of freedom, the system is said to be *degenerate*. In order to explain the fine structure in the hydrogen-like spectrum it was necessary to remove this degeneracy. This means that at

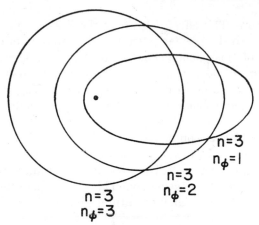

FIGURE 1–12. Possible Electron Orbits Arising from the Quantum Number $n = 3$.

least two quantum numbers will have to make a contribution to the energy of the system. Sommerfeld found that the degeneracy in his atomic model can be removed by considering the *relativistic* change in the mass of the electron during its motion around the nucleus. As the electron revolves around the nucleus, its velocity changes continuously, depending on its proximity to the nucleus. From the special theory of relativity it is known that the mass of a particle increases as its velocity increases. If this effect is taken into consideration, a small difference in energy is found to exist between a circular orbit and an elliptical orbit. This energy difference is a function of the azimuthal quantum number n_φ, and can be related to the physical picture of energy levels in the Bohr atom by considering each major energy level to be composed of several sub-levels lying very close together. With this picture, a rather reasonable agreement with the observed fine structure in the hydrogen spectrum was obtained.

In the presence of a magnetic field, it is found that the spectral lines

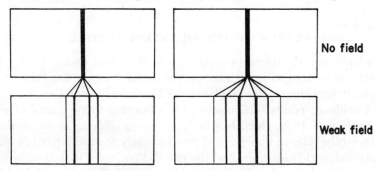

FIGURE 1–13. Zeeman Pattern for the Sodium Principal Doublet in the Presence of a Weak Magnetic Field.

are split even more. This effect, known as the *Zeeman effect*, is illustrated in Figure 1–13, with the Zeeman pattern for the sodium principal doublet. An explanation of this phenomenon requires the introduction of a third quantum number, m, the *magnetic* quantum number. An electron in space requires three coordinates to describe its position. This results in three degrees of freedom and should require three quantum numbers to describe its energy. Without a spatial reference, the arrangement of the orbital plane of the electron is completely arbitrary, and this third degree of freedom is degenerate. However, in the presence of an external field, the orbital plane of the electron will *precess* about the direction of the field and thereby remove the degeneracy. This third quantum condition is similar to that of the angular momentum, giving

$$p_z = m\frac{h}{2\pi} \qquad (1\text{–}29)$$

Thus, we now see the necessity of using three quantum numbers to describe the energy of the electron. Each new quantum number had to be introduced to meet the demands of experiment. Yet, even with three quantum numbers a complete explanation of the line spectra was not possible. For instance, the effect of a weak magnetic field gave the so-called *anomalous* Zeeman effect, and this could not be understood in terms of the Bohr-Sommerfeld model. In addition to this shortcoming, there were numerous other points where the Bohr atom and its modifications failed. Among the more important of these was the inability to apply the system to more complicated atoms. Application of the theory to the spectrum of an atom as simple as helium met with complete failure, and all attempts to understand the basis of the periodic system in terms of the Bohr model were unsuccessful. This indicated that the treatment was valid only for a one-electron system. Such a limitation is unreasonable, and we therefore see the need for something better.

STATUS OF THE QUANTUM THEORY

We have seen the concepts of the nature of radiant energy change from one extreme to another and then apparently back again since the time of Newton. Before the studies of Planck on black body radiation, all experimental evidence pointed unquestionably toward a wave theory of radiation. Yet, since 1900, there has been an overwhelming accumulation of experimental evidence that pointed just as surely toward a particle theory of electromagnetic radiation. And the end did not come with the particular cases considered thus far. Einstein, and later Debye, treated the problem of specific heats of solids in terms of quantum ideas, and Compton explained the scattering of X rays with electrons by treating the collisions as if they were between relativistic billiard balls.

With such a preponderance of evidence in favor of the quantum theory, one might be prone to feel that the cycle is complete and we are back again to the basic ideas of Newton. But this is not really true. For we cannot neglect the fact that electromagnetic radiation has been shown to have wave character just as surely as it has been shown to have particle character. This leaves us faced with a dilemma: Is a photon a wave or is it a particle? The problem is one that is not easily reconciled, and the answer does not lie in a simple chemical or physical approach. For here we see a new side to natural science. It must now take on a definite philosophical character.

Possibly the root of the problem lies in the nature of the macroscopic world in which we live. Here we observe only two types of motion, one of which is of a wave nature and the other of a particle nature. If a baseball is thrown, it appears to be a particle and its motion can be described by Newton's laws of motion. On the other hand, if a pebble is dropped into a pool of water we see a motion that must be described by a wave equation. Nowhere in our experience do we see a motion that is in between these two extremes. However, this does not mean that it does not exist. Nevertheless, it is extremely difficult to conceive of something that is foreign to our experience, and it is impossible to conceive of a type of motion that actually contradicts our experience. Yet, this is what we are faced with, and out of this dilemma must come our new approach to the problems of chemistry and physics.

BIBLIOGRAPHY

1. Planck, M., *Ann. d. Physik*, **4**, 553 (1901).
2. Einstein, A., *Ann. d. Physik*, **17**, 132 (1905).
3. Thomson, J. J., *Proc. Phil. Soc. (Cambridge)*, **15**, 465 (1910).
4. Geiger, H. and Marsden, E., *Proc. Roy. Soc. (London)*, **82A**, 495 (1909).
5. Rutherford, E., *Phil. Mag.*, **21**, 669 (1911).
6. Bohr, N., *Phil. Mag.*, **26**, 1 (1913).

SUGGESTED SUPPLEMENTARY READING

Richtmeyer, F. K. and Kennard, E. H., "Introduction to Modern Physics," 5th ed., McGraw-Hill Book Co., New York, N.Y., 1955.

Whittaker, Sir Edmund, "A History of the Theories of Aether and Electricity," Thomas Nelson and Sons, London, 1951.

Semat, H., "Introduction to Atomic Physics," 3rd ed., Longmans, Green & Co., Inc., New York, N.Y., 1949.

Herzberg, G., "Atomic Spectra and Atomic Structure," Dover Publications, Inc., New York, N.Y., 1946.

Born, M., "Atomic Physics," Hafner Publishing Co., Inc., New York, N.Y., 1946.

Kaplan, I., "Nuclear Physics," Addison-Wesley Publishing Co., Cambridge, 1956.

2 / *Wave Mechanics*

It was seen in the last chapter that electromagnetic radiation exhibits a duality in character. Under certain experimental conditions it is found to behave as a wave, and at other times it takes on the unmistakable nature of a particle. A behavior such as this is in complete contradiction to all physical experience. We have always observed a particle to be constrained within certain finite boundaries, whereas a wave tends to dissipate itself throughout space. Any attempt to construct an ordinary physical picture of such a system cannot help but fail, and we are forced to admit the existence of a situation which defies any understanding in terms of our classical ideas of nature.

MATTER WAVES

To add to the dilemma, Louis de Broglie proposed in 1924,[1] that this duality should apply not only to radiant energy but to matter itself, thereby leading to matter waves. The duality of radiant energy was a serious problem, but not nearly so difficult as the acceptance of matter waves. Our experience with radiant energy is only indirect, but we deal directly with matter and feel much more familiar with its properties. For instance, a rock is a particle, and we feel quite confident that it will remain as such. Yet, if it has wave characteristics, it should show the features of wave motion. This means that it must be dissipating itself throughout space if our common ideas of wave motion are to be retained. Obviously, such a classical approach to the problem is inadequate.

Of course, the mere proposal of the existence of wave character for a material particle would in itself be insignificant. Some demonstration of this existence must be found before so radical a view could be acceptable.

We have seen that a link does exist between the wave and particle character of a photon in the expression for its energy,

$$E = h\nu \tag{2-1}$$

The frequency is certainly a variable that is associated with wave motion, but the energy of a system can be expressed in terms of particle concepts such as mass and velocity. In terms of relativity theory, the energy of a particle of mass, m, is given by

$$E = mc^2 \tag{2-2}$$

where c is the velocity of light. By equating these two expressions, we obtain

$$h\nu = mc^2$$

or

$$\frac{h\nu}{c} = mc = p$$

where, in this case, p is the momentum of a photon. In terms of wave length, this becomes for a photon,

$$\lambda = \frac{h}{mc} = \frac{h}{p} \tag{2-3}$$

If we now consider a material particle of mass m and velocity v, the wave length is seen to be

$$\lambda = \frac{h}{mv} = \frac{h}{p} \tag{2-4}$$

Due to its origin, the wave length of a *particle* wave is often referred to as the *de Broglie* wave length. Thus, for any particle of mass m and a known velocity, the de Broglie wave length of the particle can be calculated. If we consider the case of an electron with an energy of about 1.6×10^{-10} erg, which is a rather low energy, the de Broglie wave length is found to be of the order of 1.2 Å. This distance is of the same order of magnitude as the spacings in a crystal lattice.

Taking advantage of the similarity in magnitude of crystal spacings and the de Broglie wave length of an electron with an energy of the order of 1.6×10^{-10} erg, Davisson and Germer[2] were able to show that the electron actually did possess a wave character. Using the crystal spacings in a nickel crystal as a diffraction grating, they were able to obtain diffraction patterns that could readily be understood in terms of wave motion of the electron. Although some question might arise as to the true particle character of an electron, wave properties have also been observed for such unquestionable material particles as the neutron and the helium atom.

The question of whether these waves are true waves in terms of our mechanical analogs such as water waves and vibrating strings is difficult to answer. It is possible that the only similarity is in their mathematical behavior. Throughout the nineteenth century the tendency was to reduce physical phenomenon to a mechanical picture in terms of our observable physical experience. However, the scientific advances of the twentieth century seem to make this no longer possible, and it may be that a mathematical understanding is the best for which we can hope. We may rationalize the difficulty to some extent by recalling the development of our ideas of atomic structure. Starting with the Thomson atom and proceeding on through the Bohr atom we see a consistent trend toward a superior model. In each of these models we may have felt that the approach to *true objective reality* had been attained. However, such an attitude is belief, not science. There is no scientific proof that further advancement will not be made, and from a scientific point of view it is necessary to keep an open mind to any such possible advancement. In fact, if an atomic model were proposed that happened to be identical with some sort of *true* atom, we could not be aware of this good fortune. The superiority of each of our models lies in its consistency with a greater number of experimental observations than the previous model. If this model defies description in terms of a reasonable physical picture, then we must be satisfied with a mathematical picture.

THE UNCERTAINTY PRINCIPLE

In the wave properties of the electron we find the first of the two underlying precepts of wave mechanics. The second of these is the *Heisenberg uncertainty principle*, which finds its expression in the statistical nature of scientific observation. We have seen that before the advent of wave mechanics, it was customary to construct a model of atomic-sized systems in terms of our familiar everyday concepts. With the wave-particle dilemma, the impossibility of constructing such a *deterministic* model was first realized. This might lead one to question the validity of even considering the wave character of a particle. However, we might, at the same time, question if it is really justifiable to feel that a strict *particle* treatment would allow the construction of such a model. It is certainly possible that in the domain of the atom the situation might be quite different from what it is in our macroscopic world.

If we are to maintain that a certain *thing* is a particle, we should be able to measure the particle properties of this *thing*, such as its momentum and position. This would not be a difficult problem if the *thing* were a baseball, but it might be worth considering in some detail the nature of such measurements on an electron. To carry out these measurements, the position of the electron could be determined by use of a microscope such

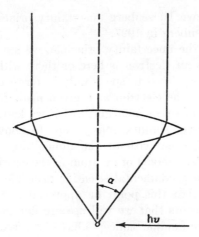

FIGURE 2-1. Diagramatic Operation
of a Gamma Ray Microscope.

as that shown schematically in **Figure 2-1**. It has been found that a limit
of accuracy in the position measured by a microscope exists, which is
dependent upon the resolving power of the instrument. The x-component
of this error is given by the expression $\Delta x \sim \lambda/\sin \alpha$. Since we are interested in determining the exact position of the electron, it is obvious that
the error in position Δx must be made as small as possible. From the expression for Δx it is readily seen that this can be accomplished merely by
using an illuminating light of very short wave length, λ. For this purpose
a gamma-ray source might be used. However, this offers a new problem.
When a high-energy photon such as a gamma ray collides with an electron,
there will be a resultant Compton recoil. The gamma ray will be scattered
by the electron, and its resultant momentum will be of the order of magnitude $p = h/\lambda$; but immediately we realize that there is a degree of
uncertainty in this momentum. In order for the electron to be observed, it
will be necessary for the scattered gamma ray to enter the microscope.
On reference to Figure 2-1, we see that there is a considerable x-component
in which the photon may enter the microscope and still be observed. This
leads to an uncertainty in the x-component of momentum of the electron
given by

$$\Delta p_x \sim \frac{h}{\lambda} \sin \alpha$$

If we now take the product of the error in position and the error in momentum, we obtain the approximate relation

$$\Delta x \Delta p \sim \left(\frac{\lambda}{\sin \alpha}\right) \left(\frac{h}{\lambda} \sin \alpha\right) \sim h \qquad (2\text{-}5)$$

This is the well-known Heisenberg uncertainty principle[3] which was first enunciated by Heisenberg in 1927.

On the basis of the uncertainty principle, we see that it is no longer possible to say that an electron is here or there with a known velocity; but rather, we are restricted to speak only in terms of probability. If we know the position of the electron at a given instant, we can only speak of a probable value of its momentum; and if we know the momentum of the electron, we cannot simultaneously hope to know its exact position. Thus, we find that even without the difficulties of the wave-particle dualism, a deterministic model of an atom in the classical sense is actually in contradiction to a fundamental scientific principle.

It is important that this point be appreciated in approaching wave mechanics. The concepts that we will use are not those of our everyday experience. For these familiar concepts have been seen to be inconsistent with our observations of nature in the realm of the atom. It is very possible that the wave-particle dilemma is completely illusionary. The difficulty may arise from the fact that in all of our previous experience only two types of motion have been observed, and it is only natural to attempt to explain the motion of an atom or electron in terms of this experience. The only thing we can really say is that the electron behavior can be described by an equation that is of the same general form as that found for wave motion. Nevertheless, regardless of what philosophical conclusion one might come to with regard to the characteristics of an atom, we must admit that it is no longer possible to construct a deterministic model in the classical sense, and whatever type of model we use, it must be consistent with our observations of nature. This means that we must recognize (1) the wave-like behavior of the system, and (2) the probability character of our observations.

THE WAVE NATURE OF THE ELECTRON

Since the electron is found to behave in the same manner as a wave, it will be necessary to describe its motion by a wave equation. Ordinarily, the mathematical treatment of wave motion involves a second-order differential equation. For instance, the transmission of a disturbance along a stretched string can be expressed by the equation

$$\frac{\partial^2 \Phi}{\partial x^2} = \frac{1}{c^2} \frac{\partial^2 \Phi}{\partial t^2} \tag{2-6}$$

where c is the velocity of propagation of the wave. The wave function, Φ, is seen to be the displacement of the string as a function of the variable, x, at any time, t, and is therefore an amplitude function. An equation of this form is found to be applicable to virtually all forms of wave motion from the vibration of a string to the transmission of electromagnetic radiation. In three-dimensional cartesian space, the wave equation becomes

$$\frac{\partial^2 \Phi}{\partial x^2} + \frac{\partial^2 \Phi}{\partial y^2} + \frac{\partial^2 \Phi}{\partial z^2} = \frac{1}{c^2} \frac{\partial^2 \Phi}{\partial t^2} \tag{2-7}$$

or more simply

$$\nabla^2 \Phi = \frac{1}{c^2} \frac{\partial^2 \Phi}{\partial t^2}$$

∇^2 is the *Laplacian operator*, which in cartesian coordinates is given by

$$\nabla^2 = \left(\frac{\partial^2}{\partial x^2} + \frac{\partial^2}{\partial y^2} + \frac{\partial^2}{\partial z^2} \right)$$

A typical example of such a wave function, Φ, is the familiar sine function

$$\Phi = A \sin \frac{2\pi}{\lambda} (x - ct) \tag{2-8}$$

This, of course, could just as readily be a cosine function or any other function that is still a solution to the differential equation of wave motion. This is a type of wave motion with which we are familiar. However, its extension to matter waves is not necessarily straightforward. We have never encountered the problem of matter waves before, and we can only guess at the type of equation that will successfully describe their properties. The validity of our ultimate choice can be known only by the results we obtain.

INTERPRETATION OF THE WAVE FUNCTION

Although we have not, as yet, decided the exact manner in which the wave character of the electron will be expressed, we are certain that it must be with a wave equation. This necessitates a wave function to describe something about the electron. For the familiar forms of wave motion, it has been possible to give a physical interpretation to the wave function that is both reasonable and useful. However, the question of what significance a wave function of a particle might have is not so readily answered. The success of wave mechanics was well demonstrated by Erwin Schroedinger before an acceptable interpretation of the wave function was known. This might indicate that the wave function has only a mathematical significance and no interpretation in a physical sense is really necessary. This would appear to be particularly true in the light of the conceptual difficulties of the wave-particle duality. Such a viewpoint should have appeal to those who feel any attempt to give a physical picture to all natural processes is a hindrance to scientific advancement. However, there is also much to be said for a description of natural processes in terms of concepts that maintain some link with our physical world.

Max Born utilized the probability concepts of the uncertainty principle to give us our presently accepted ideas of the wave function.[4] According to Born, the wave function of a particle is not an amplitude function in the common sense used for ordinary waves, but rather, it is a measure of the probability of a mechanical event. When the wave amplitude is large, the probability of the event is large, and when the amplitude is small, the probability of the event is correspondingly small. To some extent, we have lost sight of the physical world in this interpretation, for this wave motion is not the wave motion with which we are familiar. Yet, such a concept is consistent with reasonable interpretations of certain quantum considerations of electromagnetic wave motion.

If a beam of light is incident upon a cross-section perpendicular to its path, the intensity of the beam of light can be thought of as the number of photons that pass through a unit area, $dxdy$, of this cross-section per second. Since the velocity of the photon is a constant, in a given time it will have traveled a distance, dz, and therefore will have defined a volume element, $dxdydz$. The intensity, as defined by the number of photons passing through the unit cross-section, is proportional to the photon density, the number of photons in the volume element. Now, according to wave theory, the intensity, I, of a light beam has been shown to be proportional to the square of the amplitude of the electric vector, E,

$$I = \frac{c}{4\pi} E^2$$

This indicates that a link exists between the density of particles and the square of the wave function.

More correctly, the density can be considered to be a probability density. An appreciation of the probability character of such a system can readily be had by considering the diffraction of a light beam by a narrow slit. If a photographic plate is placed behind the slit, a diffraction pattern is observed on the plate after exposure in which there are alternate regions of dark and light corresponding to high and low intensities, respectively. Where the intensity of the incident photons is great, the film will be dark due to exposure, and where the intensity is small, there will be a light region. If we now consider a beam of very low intensity, it is seen that we cannot be certain exactly where the photons will strike the film. Where the film had been observed to be the darkest, we could say that the probability would be the greatest that it should strike in that region. However, each region is not sharply defined, and this leads to the possibility of an infinite number of positions at which the photon might strike the film. Thus, it is seen that our knowledge of the position of the photon can be expressed only in terms of probability, and we are led to the conclusion that the wave function squared expresses the probability of finding the photon in a given element of volume $dxdydz$.

There is certainly an analogy between the diffraction of a light beam and the diffraction of a beam of electrons. It might then be expected that a quantum interpretation that seems quite reasonable for a photon should also hold for an electron. This leads to the postulate that the square of the wave function of an electron is proportional to the probability of finding the electron in a given volume element, $dxdydz$. Such an interpretation is just a postulate and may or may not be legitimate. Thus far it appears to be consistent with experimental observation. One of the most significant indications of its validity lies in the treatment of directional bonding in molecules. The positions at which the electron density of the bonding electrons is calculated to be the greatest are where the bonded atoms are found to be located. For instance, in the molecule H_2S, the hydrogen atoms lie at an angle of about 92 degrees with respect to each other, and according to simple theoretical calculations the electron density is a maximum at an angle of 90 degrees.

The symbol ψ is usually used to denote the wave function of an electron, and very often ψ contains the imaginary quantity, i, the square root of -1. Since the probability that an electron is in a given volume element must be a real quantity, the product $\psi\psi^*$ is used rather than ψ^2, where ψ^* is the complex conjugate of ψ. The product $\psi\psi^*$ will always be real, whereas ψ^2 can possibly be imaginary. As an example, ψ can be considered to be the complex quantity $a \pm ib$. The complex conjugate of ψ can then be obtained by changing i to $-i$, giving $a \mp ib$. The product $\psi\psi^*$ will then be $a^2 + b^2$, which is a real quantity. If ψ turns out to be a real quantity initially, then ψ and its complex conjugate are the same.

NORMALIZED AND ORTHOGONAL WAVE FUNCTIONS

The square of the wave function is said to be proportional rather than equal to the probability that the electron is in a given volume element, $dxdydz$. This arises from the fact that if ψ is a solution to the wave equation, multiplication by any constant such as A will give a wave function $A\psi$, which is also a solution to the wave equation. This means that it is not possible to say in general that $\int \psi\psi^* dxdydz$ is equal to the probability, but only that it is proportional to the probability that the electron is in the given volume element. However, since multiplication by a constant is possible, it is usually convenient to multiply the wave function by a constant that will make the square of the resultant wave function equal to the probability.

The probability of a certainty is defined as unity. Thus, if it is a known fact that the electron is in a given volume element, *dxdydz*, then we can say that the probability that it is in this volume element is unity. This leads to the relation

$$\int \psi \psi^* dxdydz = 1 \tag{2-9}$$

If a wave function satisfies this relation, it is said to be *normalized*, and if the electron is in the volume element, *dxdydz*, then $\int \psi \psi^* dxdydz$ will be equal to the probability that the electron is in this volume element. Very often ψ is not a normalized wave function. However, we know that it is possible to multiply ψ by a constant, A, to give a new wave function, $A\psi$, which is also a solution to the wave equation. The problem is to choose the proper value of A to make the new wave function a normalized function. In order for the new wave function, $A\psi$, to be a normalized function, it must meet the requirement

$$\int A\psi \, A\psi^* \, dxdydz = 1$$

Since A is a constant, it can be removed from under the integral sign giving

$$A^2 \int \psi \psi^* \, dxdydz = 1$$

or

$$A^{-2} = \int \psi \psi^* \, dxdydz \tag{2-10}$$

A is known as a *normalizing constant* and can be determined from Eq. (2–10), and the new wave function, $A\psi$, will be a normalized wave function.

If we represent two different acceptable wave functions of a given system by ψ_i and ψ_j, the wave functions will be normalized if they meet the requirement that

$$\int \psi_i \psi_i^* \, dxdydz = 1 \quad \text{and} \quad \int \psi_j \psi_j^* \, dxdydz = 1$$

If, on the other hand, it is found that they behave such that

$$\int \psi_i \psi_j^* \, dxdydz = 0 \quad \text{or} \quad \int \psi_i^* \psi_j \, dxdydz = 0$$

they are said to be mutually *orthogonal*.

THE WAVE EQUATION

In the same sense that Newton's equations of motion have no derivation, the equation of motion of an electron should have no derivation. Both are consistent mathematical descriptions of certain processes of nature.

However, in the case of the electron we find that the final form of the equation is sufficiently complex to make it rather difficult to see directly. This difficulty probably arises because it is really a combination of observations. In our final equation, we find that it is necessary to incorporate two basic observations, (1) the wave character of the electron, and (2) the probability character of our measurements. These observations lead us to use a wave equation and attempt to introduce particle character through the de Broglie relation.

To introduce the wave character into our equation, the general partial differential equation of wave motion

$$\frac{\partial^2 \Phi}{\partial x^2} + \frac{\partial^2 \Phi}{\partial y^2} + \frac{\partial^2 \Phi}{\partial z^2} = \frac{1}{c^2} \frac{\partial^2 \Phi}{\partial t^2} \tag{2-7}$$

or more simply

$$\nabla^2 \Phi = \frac{1}{c^2} \frac{\partial^2 \Phi}{\partial t^2}$$

is used. Φ was seen to be the amplitude function of the wave and c is the velocity of light if the wave motion is that of an electromagnetic wave. Ordinarily the symbol Ψ is used for the wave function of an electron, and if the velocity of a particle, v, is substituted for c, the analogous equation for the wave motion of a particle of velocity v is obtained.

The wave function, Ψ, which has been used here is a function of both the space coordinates and the time. For the most part, we will find that an equation that gives *standing waves* will be of more interest to us. This requires an equation that does not contain the time as a variable. The *time-dependent* wave equation finds its application in the field of *radiation*, whereas the problems concerning the energy of the electron system utilize the *time-independent* equation.

In order to obtain the wave equation in a form that does not depend on the time, the assumption is made that the function, $\Psi_{(xyzt)}$, can be replaced by a product of functions such as $\Psi_{(xyzt)} = \psi_{(xyz)}g_{(t)}$, where $\psi_{(xyz)}$ is a function of the space coordinates only and $g_{(t)}$ is a function only of the time. The assumption that the variables are separable by means of such a substitution is a standard approach to the solution of a partial differential equation and will be used on numerous occasions. In order to successfully separate the time dependence from the wave equation, several possible wave functions may be chosen for $g_{(t)}$, such as exp $(2\pi i\nu t)$ or $\sin 2\pi\nu t$. In this particular case, it is not too difficult to find a function that will separate the time coordinate from the space coordinates. If the substitution $\Psi_{(xyzt)} = \psi_{(xyz)}\exp(2\pi i\nu t)$ is made, the equation

$$\nabla^2 \Psi = \frac{1}{v^2} \frac{\partial^2 \Psi}{\partial t^2}$$

becomes

$$\nabla^2 \, \psi_{(xyz)} \, e^{2\pi i\nu t} = \frac{1}{v^2} \, \frac{\partial^2}{\partial t^2} \, \psi_{(xyz)} \, e^{2\pi i\nu t}$$

Since the operator, ∇^2, contains only the space coordinates and not the time, the time function on the left side of the equation can be considered to be a constant. On the right side of the equation, $\psi_{(xyz)}$ can be considered as a constant with regard to the operator, $\partial^2/\partial t^2$. Rearranging the equation, we obtain

$$e^{2\pi i\nu t} \, \nabla^2 \, \psi_{(xyz)} = \frac{1}{v^2} \, \psi_{(xyz)} \, \frac{\partial^2}{\partial t^2} \, (e^{2\pi i\nu t})$$

which on two successive differentiations with respect to time gives

$$e^{2\pi i\nu t} \, \nabla^2 \, \psi_{(xyz)} = \frac{1}{v^2} \, \psi_{(xyz)} \, \frac{\partial}{\partial t} \, (2\pi i\nu e^{2\pi i\nu t})$$

$$e^{2\pi i\nu t} \, \nabla^2 \, \psi_{(xyz)} = \frac{1}{v^2} \, \psi_{(xyz)} \, (-4\pi^2\nu^2) \, e^{2\pi i\nu t}$$

$$\nabla^2 \, \psi_{(xyz)} = -\frac{4\pi^2\nu^2}{v^2} \, \psi_{(xyz)} \tag{2-11}$$

It is seen that the variable, t, cancels, and we have succeeded in separating out the time dependence thereby leaving a wave equation that depends only on the space coordinates of the system.

Now that the wave portion of the equation is in the proper form, the particle character must be introduced. If we take the particle analog of the expression $c = \lambda\nu$, we obtain $v = \lambda\nu = h\nu/p$. Making this substitution into Eq. (2–11) gives

$$\nabla^2 \, \psi_{(xyz)} = -\frac{4\pi^2 p^2}{h^2} \, \psi_{(xyz)} \tag{2-12}$$

The momentum, p, can be related to the kinetic energy, T, as follows:

$$T = \tfrac{1}{2} \, mv^2 = \frac{(mv)^2}{2m} = \frac{p^2}{2m}$$

Substituting for p^2, we obtain

$$\nabla^2 \, \psi_{(xyz)} = -\frac{4\pi^2(2Tm)}{h^2} \, \psi_{(xyz)}$$

Since the kinetic energy is equal to the difference of the total energy, E, and the potential energy, V, that is, $\mathrm{T} = E - V$, it is now possible to express the wave equation in the form

$$\nabla^2 \psi_{(xyz)} = -\frac{8\pi^2 m}{h^2} (E - V) \psi_{(xyz)}$$

or

$$\nabla^2 \psi_{(xyz)} + \frac{8\pi^2 m}{h^2} (E - V) \psi_{(xyz)} = 0 \qquad (2\text{--}13)$$

This is the well-known Schroedinger non-time-dependent wave equation[5] which we have obtained by taking the general differential equation for wave motion, separating out the space-dependent part, and using the de Broglie relation to introduce particle character.

THE PRINCIPLE OF SUPERPOSITION

If we return to an equation of the form of Eq. (2–11),

$$\nabla^2 \psi_{(xyz)} = -\frac{4\pi^2 \nu^2}{v^2} \psi_{(xyz)}$$

it is readily seen that in one dimension this equation will become

$$\frac{d^2 \psi_{(x)}}{dx^2} = -\frac{4\pi^2 \nu^2}{v^2} \psi_{(x)}$$

This may be expressed more simply by setting

$$\alpha^2 = \frac{4\pi^2 \nu^2}{v^2}$$

thereby giving

$$\frac{d^2 \psi_{(x)}}{dx^2} + \alpha^2 \psi_{(x)} = 0 \qquad (2\text{--}14)$$

One solution of this differential equation is

$$\psi_{(x)} = A \sin \alpha x + B \cos \alpha x \qquad (2\text{--}15)$$

This can easily be verified by carrying out the successive differentiations of the function, thus:

$$\psi_{(x)} = A \sin \alpha x + B \cos \alpha x$$

$$\frac{d\psi_{(x)}}{dx} = \alpha (A \cos \alpha x - B \sin \alpha x)$$

$$\frac{d^2 \psi_{(x)}}{dx^2} = -\alpha^2 (A \sin \alpha x + B \cos \alpha x) = -\alpha^2 \psi_{(x)}$$

or, on rearranging

$$\frac{d^2 \psi_{(x)}}{dx^2} + \alpha^2 \psi_{(x)} = 0$$

It is interesting to note that

as well as

$$\psi_{(x)} = A \sin \alpha\, x$$

$$\psi_{(x)} = B \cos \alpha\, x$$

and

$$\psi_{(x)} = C\, e^{i\alpha x}$$

are also solutions to Eq. (2–14). According to the principle of superposition, any linear combination of solutions is also a solution. For instance,

$$\psi_{(x)} = A \sin \alpha\, x \qquad \text{and} \qquad \psi_{(x)} = C\, e^{i\alpha x}$$

are both solutions to the differential equation

$$\frac{d^2\psi_{(x)}}{dx^2} + \alpha^2\, \psi_{(x)} = 0$$

Therefore,

$$\psi_{(x)} = A \sin \alpha\, x \pm C e^{i\alpha x}$$

is also a solution to the differential equation. The general solution as obtained here is of little value as such. However, we will see that a particular solution can be obtained by considering the boundary conditions of the given problem.

THE PARTICLE IN A ONE-DIMENSIONAL BOX

One of the simplest applications of wave mechanics is found in the treatment of a particle confined to move within a box. A rectangular box with dimensions *abc* lying along the *x,y*, and *z* axes, respectively, is chosen, and the particle is restricted so as to move only inside the box. That is, it has no existence outside the box. Such a restriction may be met by allowing the potential energy to go to infinity at the sides of the box. This results in a *reflection* of the particle as it comes in contact with a side of the box rather than a possible *penetration*. Anywhere inside of the box the particle sees a zero potential energy.

For the sake of simplicity, a one-dimensional box will first be considered. In the three-dimensional box, the wave function is represented by $\psi_{(xyz)}$ and in a one-dimensional box by $\psi_{(x)}$. Since the particle is to be some sort of realistic particle such as an electron, our wave function must be a function that does things a real particle will do. Such a function is known as a *well-behaved* function or one of class Q. In general, this requires that it be everywhere *continuous*, *finite*, and *single-valued*.

To solve a problem in wave mechanics, it is necessary to solve the wave equation

$$\nabla^2\, \psi_{(xyz)} + \frac{8\pi^2 m}{h^2}\, (E - V)\, \psi_{(xyz)} = 0$$

for the particular problem at hand. For the case of the one dimensional system, the wave equation reduces to

$$\frac{d^2\psi_{(x)}}{dx^2} + \frac{8\pi^2 m}{h^2} (E - V)\, \psi_{(x)} = 0$$

It was assumed that while the particle remained in the box, it had zero potential energy. Thus, as long as the particle remains in the box its potential energy will be zero and the wave equation will reduce further to

$$\frac{d^2\psi_{(x)}}{dx^2} + \frac{8\pi^2 m}{h^2} E\, \psi_{(x)} = 0 \qquad (2\text{--}16)$$

This can be simplified to

$$\frac{d^2\psi_{(x)}}{dx^2} + \alpha^2\, \psi_{(x)} = 0$$

by letting $\alpha^2 = 8\pi^2 mE/h^2$. We now have an equation that is identical to Eq. (2–14), and the solution was shown to be

$$\psi_{(x)} = A \sin \alpha x + B \cos \alpha x$$

This, then, is a solution to the wave equation for the particle in our one-dimensional box.

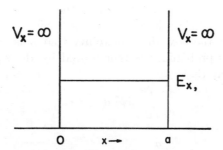

FIGURE 2–2. Particle of Energy E_x in a One-dimensional Box.

As such, the general solution to the differential equation gives very little information. However, we know certain restrictions that apply to this particular system. These are known as *boundary conditions*. For instance, since the particle must not exist outside the box, it is necessary for the wave function, $\psi_{(x)}$, to go to zero at the walls of the box. This means that for our one-dimensional box shown in Figure 2–2, $\psi_{(x)} = 0$ at the point $x = 0$.

Thus, we find that at the point $x = 0$,

$$0 = A \sin \alpha\, 0 + B \cos \alpha\, 0$$

$$0 = A\,(0) + B\,(1)$$

In order for the equality to hold, it is obvious that the constant, B, must equal zero. As a result of this boundary condition, the wave function reduces to

$$\psi_{(x)} = A \sin \alpha \, x$$

At the other wall, it is seen that the wave function must again go to zero, and therefore at the point $x = a$, it is again necessary that $\psi_{(x)} = 0$. This condition offers two possible solutions. For the point $x = a$, the wave function becomes

$$0 = A \sin \alpha \, a$$

The right side of the equation may be forced to equal zero by letting A equal zero. This would maintain the identity, but it would accomplish nothing towards a useful solution. Such a solution is a *trivial* solution. However, there is another way in which the identity may be maintained. The sine of an angle is zero at any integral multiple of π. Thus, if $\alpha = n\pi/a$, where n is an integer, the identity can still be satisfied. As a result of applying these boundary conditions, the wave equation for the particle now becomes

$$\psi_{(x)} = A \sin \frac{n\pi}{a} x \tag{2-17}$$

The only term yet to be determined is the coefficient, A. This can be determined by normalizing the wave function. Since it is known that the particle must be in the box, the probability that it is in the box is unity. Knowing that this probability is represented by the square of the wave function, we can say that

$$\int_0^a \psi\psi^* \, dx = 1$$

which leads to

$$\int_0^a A^2 \sin^2 \alpha \, dx = 1$$

or

$$\frac{1}{A^2} = \int_0^a \sin^2 \alpha \, dx$$

If this expression is solved for A and the results substituted into the wave equation, the complete normalized wave function for the particle in a one-dimensional box is found to be

$$\psi_{(x)} = \sqrt{\frac{2}{a}} \sin \frac{n\pi}{a} x \tag{2-18}$$

It is apparent that the wave function does not have to be determined in order to find the energy of the particle. This can be done once the value of α is known. The parameter can be removed from the expression $\alpha^2 = 8\pi^2 mE/h^2$ by noting also that $\alpha = n\pi/a$. By equating the two values of α, we obtain

$$\frac{8\pi^2 mE}{h^2} = \frac{n^2\pi^2}{a^2}$$

which can be solved for the energy, giving

$$E = \frac{n^2 h^2}{8ma^2} \tag{2-19}$$

There are two significant features to be noted with regard to the energy of the particle. To begin with, it is seen that the energy is quantized. Since the parameter, n, can have only integral values, the energy takes on the same type of discontinuous character that quantum theory has demanded since its rebirth with Max Planck in 1900. One of the beauties of wave mechanics is that this discontinuity results from a limited number of basic postulates rather than an *ad hoc* proposal as was necessary in the Bohr model of the atom. Secondly, a relation between the size of the box and the energy of the particle is seen to exist. The smaller the box becomes, the greater is the energy of the particle. This observation will later be used with regard to the question of the existence of electrons in the nucleus of an atom.

THE PARTICLE IN A THREE-DIMENSIONAL BOX

For the particle in a three-dimensional box, the wave function will be a function of all three space coordinates. The wave equation for such a particle moving in a region of zero potential energy is

$$\nabla^2 \psi_{(xyz)} + \frac{8\pi^2 m}{h^2} E \psi_{(xyz)} = 0 \tag{2-20}$$

This is a partial differential equation containing three variables, and the standard approach to the solution of such an equation is about the same as that used to separate the time and space parts of the time-dependent wave equation. The first step is to assume that the variables are separable into three individual equations, each containing only one variable. Each of these equations will then be a total differential equation since it will contain only one variable, and it is often possible to find some sort of solution to these final equations.

It is not always possible to find an expression that will allow the variables to be separated, but the assumption that the total wave function can be represented as a product of wave functions is the usual place to start. For the particle in a three-dimensional box, it is then assumed that

$$\psi_{(xyz)} = X_{(x)} \, Y_{(y)} \, Z_{(z)}$$

where $X_{(x)}$ represents a wave function which depends only on the variable, x; $Y_{(y)}$ represents a wave function that depends only on the variable, y; and so on. If this expression is now substituted for $\psi_{(xyz)}$ in the wave equation, we obtain

$$\left(\frac{\partial^2}{\partial x^2} + \frac{\partial^2}{\partial y^2} + \frac{\partial^2}{\partial z^2}\right) X_{(x)}Y_{(y)}Z_{(z)} + \frac{8\pi^2 m}{h^2} E \, X_{(x)} \, Y_{(y)} \, Z_{(z)} = 0$$

Since the operator, $\partial^2/\partial x^2$, has no effect on $Y_{(y)}$ and $Z_{(z)}$, and the operator, $\partial^2/\partial y^2$, has no effect on $X_{(x)}$ and $Z_{(z)}$, etc., the wave equation may be rearranged to give

$$Y_{(y)}Z_{(z)} \frac{\partial^2 X_{(x)}}{\partial x^2} + X_{(x)}Z_{(z)} \frac{\partial^2 Y_{(x)}}{\partial y^2} + X_{(x)}Y_{(y)} \frac{\partial^2 Z_{(z)}}{\partial z^2}$$

$$+ \frac{8\pi^2 mE}{h^2} X_{(x)}Y_{(y)}Z_{(z)} = 0 \qquad (2\text{--}21)$$

If we now divide Eq. (2–21) by $X_{(x)}Y_{(y)}Z_{(z)}$, it is found that

$$\frac{1}{X_{(x)}} \frac{\partial^2 X_{(x)}}{\partial x^2} + \frac{1}{Y_{(y)}} \frac{\partial^2 Y_{(y)}}{\partial y^2} + \frac{1}{Z_{(z)}} \frac{\partial^2 Z_{(z)}}{\partial z^2} = -\frac{8\pi^2 m}{h^2} E \qquad (2\text{--}22)$$

It is to be noted that each term on the left side of Eq. (2–22) is a function of only one variable, and the sum of these terms is the constant $-8\pi^2 mE/h^2$. If we now keep the variables, y and z, constant and allow x to vary, it is seen that the sum of the three terms is still the same constant. Such a situation can exist only if the term $\dfrac{1}{X_{(x)}} \dfrac{\partial^2 X_{(x)}}{\partial x^2}$ is independent of x, and is therefore itself a constant. The same argument will apply equally well to the y and the z terms. Thus, each variable is seen to be independent of the other variables, and we have succeeded in our separation. If the constants are represented by $-\alpha_x{}^2$ for the x term, $-\alpha_y{}^2$ for the y term, and $-\alpha_z{}^2$ for the z term, the following three total differential equations are obtained:

$$\frac{1}{X_{(x)}} \frac{d^2 X_{(x)}}{dx^2} = -\alpha_x{}^2 \qquad (2\text{--}23\text{a})$$

$$\frac{1}{Y_{(y)}} \frac{d^2 Y_{(y)}}{dy^2} = -\alpha_y{}^2 \qquad (2\text{--}23\text{b})$$

$$\frac{1}{Z_{(z)}} \frac{d^2 Z_{(z)}}{dz^2} = -\alpha_z{}^2 \qquad (2\text{--}23\text{c})$$

From the development of our equations, it is seen that

$$\alpha_x{}^2 + \alpha_y{}^2 + \alpha_z{}^2 = \frac{8\pi^2 m}{h^2} E \qquad (2\text{--}24)$$

Thus, each degree of freedom can make its own contribution, such that

$$\alpha_x{}^2 = \frac{8\pi^2 m}{h^2} E_x \qquad (2\text{--}25\text{a})$$

$$\alpha_y{}^2 = \frac{8\pi^2 m}{h^2} E_y \qquad (2\text{--}25\text{b})$$

$$\alpha_z{}^2 = \frac{8\pi^2 m}{h^2} E_z \qquad (2\text{--}25\text{c})$$

Now that the variables have been separated, it is necessary to solve each of the equations. In this particular problem, all three of the resulting equations are of the same form. Thus, the solution of one is sufficient to demonstrate the method. If the equation in x is used as an example, it is seen that on rearrangement it is of the exact form as the wave equation we have just solved for the one-dimensional box,

$$\frac{d^2 X_{(x)}}{dx^2} + \alpha_x{}^2 X_{(x)} = 0$$

The normalized solution then is

$$X_{(x)} = \sqrt{\frac{2}{a}} \sin \frac{n_x \pi}{a} x$$

and an analogous solution would be obtained for the y and z equations. Since $\psi_{(xyz)} = X_{(x)} Y_{(y)} Z_{(z)}$, the total wave function is given by

$$\psi_{(xyz)} = \sqrt{\frac{8}{abc}} \sin \frac{n_x \pi}{a} x \sin \frac{n_y \pi}{b} y \sin \frac{n_z \pi}{c} z \qquad (2\text{--}26)$$

It is significant to note that there is a quantum number for each degree of freedom. This same idea was emphasized in the Sommerfeld quantization of the hydrogen atom.

Now that it is seen that $\alpha_x{}^2 = n_x \pi / a$, $\alpha_y{}^2 = n_y \pi / b$, and $\alpha_z{}^2 = n_z \pi / c$, the total energy for the particle in the three-dimensional box can be expressed as

$$E = E_x + E_y + E_z = \frac{h^2}{8m} \left(\frac{n_x{}^2}{a^2} + \frac{n_y{}^2}{b^2} + \frac{n_z{}^2}{c^2} \right) \qquad (2\text{--}27)$$

Here, again, it is seen that the energy of the particle is quantized. This might lead one to wonder at the success of the classical approach to the mechanics of atoms and molecules as found in the kinetic theory of gases. Actually, no conflict exists between the two approaches. If quantum numbers and containers of reasonable size are chosen, it is found that the separation of energy levels is so small that the energy distribution will essentially be *continuous*.

DEGENERACY

For a complete description of the energy states of a particle in a three-dimensional box, we see that it is necessary to consider three quantum numbers. This, of course, is what one should expect. The idea of quantum numbers in atomic spectra, for instance, came from an attempt to understand the positions of the spectral lines, that is, the energies they represent. The observation of new lines necessarily led to a new quantum number which could be associated with the corresponding new energy levels. Thus, we are prone to conclude that each quantum number represents a contribution to the energy of the system. However, it is frequently found that for various reasons a particular set of the quantum numbers may not be unique in defining the energy of the particle. If, as an example, the particle in a three-dimensional box is considered, we can again say that the energy is given by

$$E = E_x + E_y + E_z = \frac{h^2}{8m}\left(\frac{n_x^2}{a^2} + \frac{n_y^2}{b^2} + \frac{n_z^2}{c^2}\right) \qquad (2\text{--}27)$$

But if we now choose a box that is cubical in shape such that $a = b = c$, the energy can be expressed by

$$E = \frac{h^2}{8ma^2}\left(n_x^2 + n_y^2 + n_z^2\right)$$

For the lowest quantum state, (111), in which n_x, n_y, and n_z, respectively, equal unity, it is seen that $E = 3h^2/8ma^2$. There is only one set of quantum numbers that gives this energy state, and this level is said to be *non-*

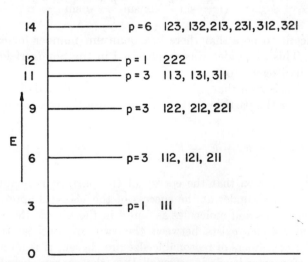

FIGURE 2–3. Degeneracy of the Energy Levels in a Three-dimensional Box. The energy scale is in units of $h^2/8ma^2$.

degenerate. If we now consider the second energy state as shown in Figure 2–3, it is seen that there are three sets (112), (121), and (211) of the quantum numbers n_x, n_y, and n_z that will give the same energy level, $E = 3h^2/4ma^2$. Such a level is said to be *degenerate*, and in this particular case, the level is *triply* degenerate. For a cubical box, it can be concluded from Figure 2–3, that virtually all of the energy levels are degenerate to some degree.

The mathematics of systems with degenerate energy states and the means of removing the degeneracy are often problems of considerable importance. For the particle in a three-dimensional box, the degeneracy can be removed by using a box of different dimensions. If no integral relationship exists between the sides of the box, a, b, and c, the energy levels will all be nondegenerate. Thus, it is a relatively simple problem to obtain nondegenerate energy states for the particle in a box. However, in the problems of atoms and molecules it is not always so simple.

THE HYDROGEN ATOM

One would like to think that wave mechanics can, in principle, offer a solution to all the theoretical problems of chemistry and physics. And this may be the case. However, from a practical standpoint this is not so. No matter how far quantum mechanics might go towards this end, a practical barrier always arises. It is usually possible to set up the differential equation for a particular problem, but it is then found that the resulting differential equation can rarely be solved without resorting to approximation methods. In fact, there are very few quantum mechanical problems that can be solved without some form of approximation, and the hydrogen-like atom is one of these. This fact alone is sufficient to emphasize the importance of the hydrogen atom problem. Yet, in addition to this, there are also numerous principles and concepts that carry over to any future wave mechanical treatment.

The problem, of course, is to solve the Schroedinger equation as set up for the hydrogen atom. Thus far, we have expressed the Schroedinger equation in the form

$$\nabla^2 \psi_{(xyz)} + \frac{8\pi^2 m}{h^2} (E - V) \psi_{(xyz)} = 0$$

which has proved satisfactory for the motion of a single particle of mass m. In the hydrogen atom there are two particles, the electron and the nucleus. For such a system, it will be found convenient to put the wave equation in the form

$$\frac{1}{m} \nabla^2 \psi_{(xyz)} + \frac{8\pi^2}{h^2} (E - V) \psi_{(xyz)} = 0 \qquad (2\text{–}28)$$

Now, when we consider the motion of the two particles in the hydrogen atom, the wave equation becomes

$$\frac{1}{m_1} \nabla_1{}^2 \psi_\tau + \frac{1}{m_2} \nabla_2{}^2 \psi_\tau + \frac{8\pi^2}{h^2} (E - V) \psi_\tau = 0 \qquad (2\text{--}29)$$

where m_1 is the mass of the electron and m_2 is the mass of the nucleus.

In order to evaluate the potential energy term, it is necessary to consider the coulombic attraction between the electron and the nucleus. In this case, the potential energy is defined as the work necessary to take the electron to infinity from its equilibrium distance, r, with respect to the nucleus. Since work is represented by the product of force times distance, the potential energy may be determined as follows:

$$V = \int F \cdot dr = \int_r^\infty \frac{q_1 q_2}{r^2} \, dr = - \frac{q_1 q_2}{r} \bigg]_r^\infty$$

$$V = \frac{Ze^2}{r} \qquad (2\text{--}30)$$

Ze is the nuclear charge and e is the charge on the electron. If the potential energy term is now introduced, the equation for the hydrogen atom becomes

$$\frac{1}{m_1} \nabla_1{}^2 \psi_\tau + \frac{1}{m_2} \nabla_2{}^2 \psi_\tau + \frac{8\pi^2}{h^2} \left(E - \frac{Ze^2}{r} \right) \psi_\tau = 0 \qquad (2\text{--}31)$$

Transformation of Coordinates

A new problem arises when we note that the total energy, E, in the wave equation is made up of two parts: (1) the translational motion of the atom as a whole, and (2) the energy of the electron with respect to the proton. It is this latter portion of the energy in which we are interested. This leads us again to the problem of separation of variables. In order to obtain the desired equation, it will be necessary to separate out and discard the translational portion of the total wave equation. To carry out this particular separation, it is necessary to introduce a new set of variables x, y, and z, which are cartesian coordinates of the *center of mass* of the hydrogen atom, and the variables r, θ, and φ, which are polar coordinates of the electron with respect to the nucleus. A coordinate of the center of mass of a system is, in general, given by

$$q = \frac{\sum\limits_i m_i q_i}{\sum\limits_i m_i} \qquad (2\text{--}32)$$

where m_i is the mass of the ith particle and q_i is the q coordinate of the

i^{th} particle. For the hydrogen atom, the cartesian coordinates of the center of mass will be given by

$$x = \frac{m_1x_1 + m_2x_2}{m_1 + m_2} \tag{2-33a}$$

$$y = \frac{m_1y_1 + m_2y_2}{m_1 + m_2} \tag{2-33b}$$

$$z = \frac{m_1z_1 + m_2z_2}{m_1 + m_2} \tag{2 33c}$$

and the transformation to spherical coordinates can be seen from Figure 2–4, to be

$$r \sin \theta \cos \varphi = x_2 - x_1 \tag{2-34a}$$

$$r \sin \theta \sin \varphi = y_2 - y_1 \tag{2-34b}$$

$$r \cos \theta = z_2 - z_1 \tag{2-34c}$$

By using these transformation equations, it is a straightforward procedure to obtain the wave equation in terms of the cartesian coordinates of the center of mass of the system and the polar coordinates r, θ, and φ. The x, y, z coordinates of the center of mass of the atom obviously relate to the translational motion of the atom as a whole, and the r, θ, φ coordinates

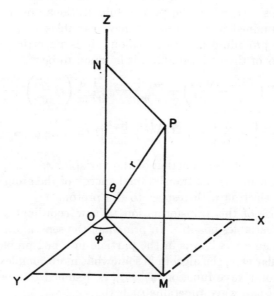

FIGURE 2–4.   Transformation   Diagram   for Spherical Coordinates.

are seen to relate the coordinates of the electron (x_1, y_1, z_1) to the coordinates of the nucleus (x_2, y_2, z_2).

As an example of the procedure, consider the z coordinate. Solving Eq. (2–33c) for z_2, it is seen that

$$z_2 = \left(\frac{m_1 + m_2}{m_2}\right) z - \frac{m_1}{m_2} z_1$$

If the value of z_2 is now substituted into Eq. (2–34c), it is found that

$$r \cos \theta = \frac{m_1 + m_2}{m_2} z - \frac{m_1}{m_2} z_1 - z_1$$

or

$$z_1 = z - \frac{m_2}{m_1 + m_2} r \cos \theta$$

If we now multiply through by the term m_1/m_1, we obtain the expression

$$z_1 = z - \frac{\mu}{m_1} r \cos \theta \qquad (2\text{–}35)$$

where μ is the reduced mass of the system and is given by

$$\mu = \frac{m_1 m_2}{m_1 + m_2} \qquad (2\text{–}36)$$

Using this procedure, a transformation equation can be found for each of the coordinates, and when the proper substitutions are made, the wave equation is obtained in terms of the new variables x, y, z, r, θ, and φ. Although the procedure is rather tedious, it is nevertheless straightforward. In terms of the new variables, it is found to be

$$\frac{1}{m_1 + m_2}\left(\frac{\partial^2 \psi_\tau}{\partial x^2} + \frac{\partial^2 \psi_\tau}{\partial y^2} + \frac{\partial^2 \psi_\tau}{\partial z^2}\right) + \frac{m_1 + m_2}{m_1 m_2}\left\{\frac{1}{r^2}\frac{\partial}{\partial r}\left(r^2 \frac{\partial \psi_\tau}{\partial r}\right) + \frac{1}{r^2 \sin^2 \theta}\frac{\partial^2 \psi_\tau}{\partial \varphi^2}\right.$$

$$\left. + \frac{1}{r^2 \sin \theta}\frac{\partial}{\partial \theta}\left(\sin \theta \frac{\partial \psi_\tau}{\partial \theta}\right)\right\} + \frac{8\pi^2}{h^2}[E - V_{(r)}]\psi_\tau = 0 \qquad (2\text{–}37)$$

The wave function ψ_τ is a function of the variables x, y, z, r, θ, and φ, and the energy, E, contains the translational energy of the atom as well as the energy of the electron with respect to the proton.

The purpose of this transformation to new coordinates is to make a separation of variables possible. In principle, the separation is carried out in the same manner as it was in the particle in a box problem. However, in this particular case, the algebra is somewhat more complex. In the usual manner, the total wave function, $\psi_{(xyzr\theta\varphi)}$, is assumed to be expressable as the product of two wave functions such that

$$\psi_{(xyzr\theta\varphi)} = F_{(xyz)} \, \psi_{(r\theta\varphi)}$$

When this expression is substituted into Eq. (2–37), it is found that the following two equations are obtained:

1) $$\frac{\partial^2 F_{(xyz)}}{\partial x^2} + \frac{\partial^2 F_{(xyz)}}{\partial y^2} + \frac{\partial^2 F_{(xyz)}}{\partial z^2} + \frac{8\pi^2(m_1 + m_2)}{h^2} E_{\text{trans}}\, F_{(xyz)} = 0 \qquad (2\text{–}38)$$

2) $$\frac{1}{r^2}\frac{\partial}{\partial r}\left(r^2\frac{\partial \psi_{(r\theta\varphi)}}{\partial r}\right) + \frac{1}{r^2 \sin^2\theta}\frac{\partial^2 \psi_{(r\theta\varphi)}}{\partial \varphi^2} + \frac{1}{r^2 \sin\theta}\frac{\partial}{\partial\theta}\left(\sin\theta\,\frac{\partial \psi_{(r\theta\varphi)}}{\partial\theta}\right)$$

$$+ \frac{8\pi^2\mu}{h^2}\,[E - V_{(r)}]\,\psi_{(r\theta\varphi)} = 0 \qquad (2\text{–}39)$$

The first of these equations contains only the variables x, y, and z, with no potential energy term. This is identical to the wave equation for a free particle, and therefore represents the translational energy of the atom as a whole. The second equation, which relates the electron to the proton, is the equation of particular interest to us.

Separation of Variables

Since it is the second part of the total wave equation that is of interest, the translational part will be discarded. We now have the desired wave equation for the electron with respect to the nucleus. This equation is a second-order partial differential equation, and the standard methods already used must again be employed to obtain its solution. This will require that the variables be separated such that three independent equations are obtained, each containing only one of the three variables.

In order to separate the variables, it is necessary to assume that the wave function $\psi_{(r\theta\varphi)}$ may be represented by the product of three wave functions, each containing one and only one of the three variables r, θ, and φ. If we let

$$\psi_{(r\theta\varphi)} = R_{(r)}\,\Theta_{(\theta)}\,\Phi_{(\varphi)}$$

and make this substitution into Eq. (2–39), we obtain

$$\frac{1}{r^2}\frac{\partial}{\partial r}\left(r^2\frac{\partial}{\partial r}R_{(r)}\,\Theta_{(\theta)}\,\Phi_{(\varphi)}\right) + \frac{1}{r^2 \sin^2\theta}\frac{\partial^2}{\partial\varphi^2}R_{(r)}\,\Theta_{(\theta)}\,\Phi_{(\varphi)}$$

$$+ \frac{1}{r^2 \sin\theta}\frac{\partial}{\partial\theta}(\sin\theta R_{(r)}\,\Theta_{(\theta)}\,\Phi_{(\varphi)}) + \frac{8\pi^2\mu}{h^2}\,[E - V_{(r)}]\,R_{(r)}\,\Theta_{(\theta)}\,\Phi_{(\varphi)} = 0$$

which, on dividing by $R_{(r)}\,\Theta_{(\theta)}\,\Phi_{\varphi}$ gives

$$\frac{1}{r^2 R_{(r)}}\frac{\partial}{\partial r}\left(r^2\frac{\partial R_{(r)}}{\partial r}\right) + \frac{1}{\Phi_{(\varphi)}\,r^2 \sin^2\theta}\frac{\partial^2 \Phi_{(\varphi)}}{\partial\varphi^2} + \frac{1}{\Theta_{(\theta)}\,r^2 \sin\theta}\frac{\partial}{\partial\theta}\left(\sin\theta\,\frac{\partial\Theta_{(\theta)}}{\partial\theta}\right)$$

$$+ \frac{8\pi^2\mu}{h^2}\,[E - V_{(r)}] = 0$$

If we multiply by $r^2 \sin^2 \theta$, we obtain

$$\frac{\sin^2 \theta}{R_{(r)}} \frac{\partial}{\partial r} \left(r^2 \frac{\partial R_{(r)}}{\partial r} \right) + \frac{1}{\Phi_{(\varphi)}} \frac{\partial^2 \Phi_{(\varphi)}}{\partial \varphi^2} + \frac{\sin \theta}{\Theta_{(\theta)}} \frac{\partial}{\partial \theta} \left(\sin \theta \frac{\partial \Theta_{(\theta)}}{\partial \theta} \right)$$

$$+ \frac{8\pi^2 \mu r^2 \sin^2 \theta}{h^2} [E - V_{(r)}] = 0$$

or

$$\frac{\sin^2 \theta}{R_{(r)}} \frac{\partial}{\partial r} \left(r^2 \frac{\partial R_{(r)}}{\partial r} \right) + \frac{\sin \theta}{\Theta_{(\theta)}} \frac{\partial}{\partial \theta} \left(\sin \theta \frac{\partial \Theta_{(\theta)}}{\partial \theta} \right)$$

$$+ \frac{8\pi^2 \mu r^2 \sin^2 \theta}{h^2} [E - V_{(r)}] = - \frac{1}{\Phi_{(\varphi)}} \frac{\partial^2 \Phi_{(\varphi)}}{\partial \varphi^2} \quad (2\text{-}40)$$

This leads to a situation that is analogous to that which arose for the particle in a three-dimensional box. The left side of Eq. (2–40) contains only the variables r and θ, whereas the right side of the equation contains only the variable φ. No matter what values r, θ, or φ might independently take, the sum of the terms on the left must always equal the term on the right. This can be true only if each side of the equation is equal to the same constant. If we let this constant be m^2, it is seen that the variable φ can immediately be separated from Eq. (2–40), giving

$$\frac{1}{\Phi_{(\varphi)}} \frac{d^2 \Phi_{(\varphi)}}{d\varphi^2} = -m^2 \quad (2\text{-}41)$$

Thus, we find that the first of the three variables has been successfully separated from the original wave equation. The problem now is to carry out the separation of the remaining two variables r and θ. By equating the equation containing $R_{(r)}$ and $\Theta_{(\theta)}$ to the constant m^2, it is seen that

$$\frac{\sin^2 \theta}{R_{(r)}} \frac{\partial}{\partial r} \left(r^2 \frac{\partial R_{(r)}}{\partial r} \right) + \frac{\sin \theta}{\Theta_{(\theta)}} \frac{\partial}{\partial \theta} \left(\sin \theta \frac{\partial \Theta_{(\theta)}}{\partial \theta} \right) + \frac{8\pi^2 \mu r^2 \sin^2 \theta}{h^2} [E - V_{(r)}] = m^2$$

On division by $\sin^2 \theta$, this becomes

$$\frac{1}{R_{(r)}} \frac{\partial}{\partial r} \left(r^2 \frac{\partial R_{(r)}}{\partial r} \right) + \frac{1}{\Theta_{(\theta)} \sin \theta} \frac{\partial}{\partial \theta} \left(\sin \theta \frac{\partial \Theta_{(\theta)}}{\partial \theta} \right)$$

$$- \frac{m^2}{\sin^2 \theta} + \frac{8\pi^2 \mu r^2}{h^2} [E - V_{(r)}] = 0$$

or, on rearranging

$$\frac{1}{R_{(r)}} \frac{\partial}{\partial r} \left(r^2 \frac{\partial R_{(r)}}{\partial r} \right) + \frac{8\pi^2 \mu r^2}{h^2} [E - V_{(r)}] = \frac{m^2}{\sin^2 \theta} - \frac{1}{\Theta_{(\theta)} \sin \theta} \frac{\partial}{\partial \theta} \left(\sin \theta \frac{\partial \Theta_{(\theta)}}{\partial \theta} \right)$$

This identity can hold only if m is zero or has a positive or negative integral value. Such characteristics are those that would be expected of a quantum number, and the particular restrictions on m indicate that it is the analog of the magnetic quantum number of the Bohr-Sommerfeld model.

Very often, in the treatment of the hydrogen atom, the exponential solution to the Φ equation,

$$\Phi_m(\varphi) = C \, e^{\pm im\varphi} \tag{2-45}$$

is used. In order to evaluate the constant, C, it would be most convenient to choose C in such a manner that the wave function, $\Phi(\varphi)$, will be a normalized wave function. This requires that

$$\int_0^{2\pi} \Phi\Phi^* \, d\varphi = 1$$

which leads to

$$\int_0^{2\pi} C^2 e^{\mp im\varphi} \, e^{\pm im\varphi} \, d\varphi = 1$$

or

$$C^2 \int_0^{2\pi} d\varphi = 2\,\pi\,C^2 = 1$$

The value of the constant, C, that gives a normalized wave function is seen to be $C = 1/\sqrt{2\pi}$, and the final normalized wave function is

$$\Phi_m(\varphi) = \frac{1}{\sqrt{2\pi}} \, e^{\pm im\varphi}, \; m = 0, \, \pm 1, \, \pm 2, \, \cdots . \tag{2-46}$$

The Θ Equation

The solutions to the Θ equation and the radial equation, unfortunately, are not quite so simple as the solution to the Φ equation. However, it happens that the Θ equation can be put into a form that was known by the mathematicians many years before the advent of quantum mechanics. This particular equation is known as *Legendre's equation* and has the normalized solution

$$\Theta_{l,\,m}(\theta) = \sqrt{\frac{(2l+1)\,(l-|m|)\,!}{2(l+|m|)\,!}} \; P_l^{|m|}\,(\cos\theta) \tag{2-47}$$

where $P_l^{|m|}$ is the associated Legendre function of degree l and order $|m|$. The form of the solution is obviously quite complicated. However, as can be seen in Table 2-3, for particular values of the parameters l and m the solution reduces to much simpler forms.

Again, since each side of the equation contains only one variable, they both must be equal to the same constant. If the right side of the equation is set equal to the constant β, this gives on multiplication by $\Theta_{(\theta)}$,

$$\frac{m^2 \, \Theta_{(\theta)}}{\sin^2 \theta} - \frac{1}{\sin \theta} \frac{d}{d\theta} \left(\sin \theta \, \frac{d\Theta_{(\theta)}}{d\theta} \right) - \beta \, \Theta_{(\theta)} = 0 \qquad (2\text{-}42)$$

This is the desired form of the Θ equation. The remaining part of the original equation is the R equation,

$$\frac{1}{r^2} \frac{d}{dr} \left(r^2 \frac{dR_{(r)}}{dr} \right) - \frac{\beta}{r^2} R_{(r)} + \frac{8\pi^2 \mu}{h^2} [E - V_{(r)}] R_{(r)} = 0 \qquad (2\text{-}43)$$

Thus, the three variables have been successfully separated, and the three independent total differential equations that result are

1) $\dfrac{d^2 \, \Phi_{(\varphi)}}{d\varphi^2} + m^2 \, \Phi_{(\varphi)} = 0$ \hfill $(2\text{-}41)$

2) $\dfrac{1}{\sin \theta} \dfrac{d}{d\theta} \left(\sin \theta \, \dfrac{d \, \Theta_{(\theta)}}{d\theta} \right) - \dfrac{m^2 \, \Theta_{(\theta)}}{\sin^2 \theta} + \beta \, \Theta_{(\theta)} = 0$ \hfill $(2\text{-}42)$

3) $\dfrac{1}{r^2} \dfrac{d}{dr} \left(r^2 \dfrac{dR_{(r)}}{dr} \right) - \dfrac{\beta}{r^2} R_{(r)} + \dfrac{8\pi^2 \mu}{h^2} [E - V_{(r)}] R_{(r)} = 0$ \hfill $(2\text{-}43)$

The Φ Equation

The first of these equations is the Φ equation, and it is seen to be of the same form as the wave equation for the particle in a box. In terms of sine and cosine, the solution is

$$\Phi_m(\varphi) = A \sin m\varphi + B \cos m\varphi \qquad (2\text{-}44)$$

In order for a wave function to be acceptable, it must be of the well-behaved class. One of the requirements of such a function is that it be *single valued*. To meet this restriction, the function $\Phi_m(\varphi)$ must have the same value for $\varphi = 0$ as it does for $\varphi = 2\pi$. For the case of $\varphi = 0$, it is seen that

$$\Phi_m(0) = A \sin (0) + B \cos (0) = B$$

and when $\varphi = 2\pi$, we have

$$\Phi_m(2\pi) = A \sin m2\pi + B \cos m2\pi$$

Since the value of $\Phi_m(\varphi)$ must be the same under both of these conditions, it is necessary that

$$B = A \sin m2\pi + B \cos m2\pi$$

In spite of the complicated nature of the solution, several important features can be observed. Although the mathematics is far too complex to be considered here, it can be shown that in Eq. (2–42), $\beta = l(l+1)$, where the allowed values of l are 0, 1, 2, 3, $\cdot \cdot \cdot \cdot$. This is the source of the new parameter found in Eq. (2–47), and its properties appear to be similar in many ways to those of the azimuthal quantum number of the Bohr-Sommerfeld atom. It can also be seen that there is now a new restriction on the quantum number m. In the normalizing factor of the solution to the Θ equation, the term $(l - |m|)!$ occurs. If $|m|$ is allowed to be greater than l, the factorial of a negative number results. Since a negative factorial is undefined, the maximum value of m must be l.* Thus, the restrictions on the quantum number m now become $m = 0, \pm1, \pm2, \pm3, \ldots, \pm l$. These are the same restrictions that were found to be necessary for the magnetic quantum number in the Bohr-Sommerfeld theory.

Spherical Harmonics

Both the solution to the Θ equation and the solution to the Φ equation contain trigonometric functions and therefore determine the angular character of the electron wave function. Very often it is found that the total wave function can most conveniently be used if it is separated into a *radial* portion and an *angular* portion such that

$$\psi_{(r\theta\varphi)} = R_{n,l}(r) \; Y_{l,m}(\theta, \varphi)$$

The term $Y_{l,m}(\theta,\varphi)$ is referred to as the spherical harmonics, and is given by

$$Y_{l,m}(\theta, \varphi) = \Theta_{l,m}(\theta) \; \Phi_m(\varphi) \tag{2–48}$$

It is this portion of the total wave function that will be of primary concern in the treatment of directional bonding.

The Radial Equation

The remaining equation to be solved is the radial equation

$$\frac{1}{r^2} \frac{d}{dr} \left(r^2 \frac{dR_{(r)}}{dr} \right) - \frac{\beta R_{(r)}}{r^2} + \frac{8\pi^2 \mu}{h^2} \left[E - \frac{Ze^2}{r} \right] R_{(r)} = 0 \tag{2–43}$$

This, like the Θ equation, can be put into a form that has long been known to the mathematicians. This particular equation is the *Laguerre equation*, and its normalized solution is

$$R_{n,l}(r) = \sqrt{\left(\frac{2Z}{na_0} \right)^3 \frac{(n-l-1)!}{2n\,[(n+l)!]^3}} \; e^{-\rho/2} \; \rho^l \; L_{n+l}^{2l+1} \tag{2–49}$$

---

* It should be mentioned that the method used here to determine the restrictions on the m quantum number is not the ordinary method used to determine these restrictions.

where $\rho = (2Z/na_0)r$, $a_0 = h^2/4\pi^2\mu e^2$, and $L_{n+l}^{2l+1}(\rho)$ represents the associated Laguerre polynomial. As was the case with the Θ equation, the solution to the radial equation is also rather complex in form. However, again it is possible to make some pertinent observations from the solution. It is to be noted that a new parameter, the quantum number n, has been added. Due to the complexity of the mathematics, it is possible to say here only that n is restricted to take on the integral values 1, 2, 3, $\cdots$. Both the relation of n to the radial wave function, which is a measure of the position of the electron with respect to the nucleus, and its similar restrictions, indicate that n is the quantum mechanical analog of the principal quantum number of the Bohr theory.

Using the same approach as that applied to the magnetic quantum number, a new restriction can be seen for the quantum number l. It is apparent from the normalizing factor of the solution to the radial equation, that the term $(n - l - 1)$ requires that the maximum value of l be $(n - 1)$. If l is allowed a value greater than this, the factorial of a negative number would result. Thus, the quantum number is restricted to the values $l = 0, 1, 2, \cdots, (n - 1)$.

Quantum States

From the solution of the total wave equation, we have arrived at three quantum numbers. These had been postulated out of necessity in the Bohr-Sommerfeld theory, and this was a fundamental weakness of the theory. It is, therefore, gratifying to see that they occur as the result of a few basic postulates in the wave mechanical treatment. However, it might be considered unfortunate that they can no longer be thought of in the pictorial manner of the Bohr theory. We have one quantum number for each degree of freedom, but the idea of precessing orbits is no longer valid.

The quantum numbers with their allowed values may be summarized as follows:

Radial quantum number: $\quad n = 1, 2, 3, \ldots,$

Azimuthal quantum number: $\quad l = 0, 1, 2, \ldots, n - 1$ (inclusive)

Magnetic quantum number: $\quad m = 0, \pm 1, \pm 2, \ldots, \pm l$ (inclusive)

According to these restrictions, there are only certain values of the quantum number, l, that are permissible for a given value of n. The maximum value of l is seen always to be $(n - 1)$. For example, when $n = 4$, l can be any integer up to and including $l = 3$, but no greater. This is illustrated in Table 2–1, where the allowed values of l are shown for the first four radial shells.

TABLE 2–1. / **Quantum Numbers With Allowed Values for First Four Radial Shells.**

Value of n:	1	2	3	4
Allowed values of l:	0	0,1	0,1,2	0,1,2,3

It should be noted that $l = 0$ occurs for every value of n, $l = 1$ occurs for every value of n greater than $n = 1$, and so on. These values of the quantum number, l, play a rather important role in both the geometry and the energy states of the atom. Because of this importance, they are given the following special designations:

$$l = 0 \qquad s \text{ state}$$
$$l = 1 \qquad p \text{ state}$$
$$l = 2 \qquad d \text{ state}$$
$$l = 3 \qquad f \text{ state}$$

It is much more common to speak in terms of the electron state than the particular value of the l quantum number.

For the first radial shell, the value of the radial quantum number is $n = 1$, and the l quantum number can only have the value $l = 0$. This state is usually represented by $(1s)$ where the 1 represents the value of the n quantum number and s represents $l = 0$. For $n = 2$, the azimuthal quantum number can have the values $l = 0$ and $l = 1$. This gives the two states $(2s)$ and $(2p)$, respectively. For the case of $n = 3$, it can be seen from the allowed values of the l quantum number that there can be the three states $(3s)$, $(3p)$, and $(3d)$ for $l = 0$, $l = 1$, and $l = 2$, respectively. Finally, for the fourth shell for which $n = 4$, it is seen that there can be the four states $(4s)$, $(4p)$, $(4d)$, and $(4f)$. These states determine the energies of the electrons, and if the l quantum number contributes to the energy as does the n quantum number, each state will represent a different energy.

The Electron Spin

In addition to the orbital fine structure which could be explained in terms of the l quantum number, it was experimentally observed that a doublet structure existed in the spectra of the alkali metals. Spectral lines that had once been thought to be single lines, actually turned out to be two lines very close together. An understanding of this doublet character could not be found in the Bohr-Sommerfeld model. In 1925, Uhlenbeck and Goudsmit[6] offered an explanation in which they proposed that the electron has, in addition to its orbital motion, an angular momentum of rotation about its own axis and a corresponding *magnetic moment*. This leads to a new quantum number known as the *spin* quantum number.

The magnitude of this spin angular momentum is found to be $\pm\frac{1}{2}$ in units of $h/2\pi$. The plus or minus values of the spin can be thought of as arising from the direction of the spin. For instance, if the electron spin is considered to be clockwise it interacts with the orbital magnetic moment of the electron to give a different energy than if it is spinning in a counter-clockwise manner. The energy difference resulting from these opposite spins is small, but it is sufficient to lead to the observed doublet structure. Actually, there are several serious difficulties that arise from the concept of a physically spinning electron. However, the agreement between theory and experiment is sufficiently good to retain the theory.

In 1928, a quantum mechanical answer was found to the problem of electron spin. The wave equation as developed by Schroedinger was non-relativistic. In an attempt to bring the wave mechanics into harmony with relativity theory, Dirac succeeded in developing a wave equation that led naturally to the proper spin angular momentum for the electron. According to the Dirac theory, the electron has the same angular momentum and magnetic moment as the spinning electron of Uhlenbeck and Goudsmit. Yet, as was the case for the other three quantum numbers, the quantum mechanical properties of the electron spin are the result of a consistent mathematical treatment and do not offer the problems that result from the physical picture of an electron spinning on its own axis.

Energy States of the Hydrogen Atom

In the wave equation of the hydrogen-like atom, the energy term occurs only in the radial equation; and it is from its solution that the energy states of the hydrogen atom are obtained. Since the potential energy of the electron with respect to the nucleus is defined as zero when the two particles are infinitely far apart, the potential energy becomes increasingly negative as the electron approaches the nucleus. Consequently, the energy of the electron is defined in such a manner that it is negative, and it is therefore the negative energy states that will be of primary interest. If only these negative states are considered, it can be shown that the allowed values of the energy of the electron are given by

$$E_n = -\frac{2\pi^2 \mu Z^2 e^4}{n^2 h^2}, \; n = 1, 2, 3, \ldots. \tag{2-50}$$

Here we see that the expression for the energy of the electron as determined by wave mechanics is identical with that of the Bohr theory.

The quantum number, n, that appears in the wave mechanical treatment is related to the principal quantum number of the Bohr theory and can therefore be associated with the electron shell. In the pictorial sense of an electron revolving in a prescribed orbit, this analogy is invalid. However, from the standpoint of an energy state of the electron they can be thought of in much the same manner. Thus, $n = 1$ corresponds to the first or K shell, and for $n = 2$ we have the L shell, etc.

It is very interesting to note that since the energy of the electron in the hydrogen-like atom is determined only by the n quantum number according to our wave equation, the resulting energy levels must be degenerate. The ground state of the hydrogen atom will be the ($1s$) state, and the subsequent order of energy levels will be

$$1s < 2s = 2p < 3s = 3p = 3d < 4s = 4p = 4d = 4f < 5s \cdots .$$

Since the l, m, and m_s quantum numbers contribute nothing to the energy of the electron state, all of the possible energy states in a given radial shell are of equal energy. This means that only single spectral lines such as those predicted by Bohr will be observed. Yet, it is well known that a fine structure exists in the hydrogen spectrum. This was the incentive for the development of the Bohr-Sommerfeld theory of the hydrogen atom. Obviously, our simple form of the wave equation is inadequate for a completely satisfactory treatment of the hydrogen atom, and thus we are little better off than we were with the Bohr model.

Actually, the sequence of levels obtained is the result of calculations based upon a nonrelativistic hydrogen-like atom in the absence of external electric or magnetic fields. By using a relativistic form of the wave equation, the orbital degeneracy can be removed, thereby leading to the experimentally observed fine structure. Unfortunately, due to the extreme complexity of the mathematics, a relativistic treatment is not practical. For more complex atoms we will see that the orbital degeneracy can be removed by considering the effect of the electron-electron repulsion.

THE SELF-CONSISTENT FIELD METHOD

It has been noted that an exact solution to a quantum mechanical problem can be obtained in only a very few instances. The hydrogen-like

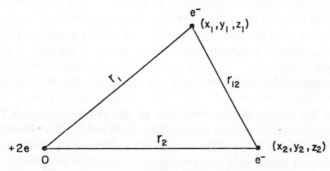

FIGURE 2-5.   Coordinates of the Helium Atom.

atom is one of these. For any atomic system with more than one electron, it is found that various approximation methods must be used in order to obtain a solution. This difficulty arises from the coulombic repulsion between electrons. As an example, if we consider the helium atom with two electrons, the potential energy term will contain not only the effect of the nucleus on each of the electrons, but also the coulombic repulsion between the two electrons. The relations between the electrons and the nucleus of the helium atom can be seen in Figure 2–5, where the nucleus is placed at the origin of the coordinate system and the coordinates of the two electrons are (x_1, y_1, z_1) and (x_2, y_2, z_2). The potential energy term is

$$V = \frac{2e^2}{r_1} + \frac{2e^2}{r_2} - \frac{e^2}{r_{12}}$$

and the resulting wave equation for the helium atom is then

$$\nabla_1{}^2 \, \psi_\tau + \nabla_2{}^2 \, \psi_\tau + \frac{8\pi^2 m}{h^2} \left(E - \frac{2e^2}{r_1} - \frac{2e^2}{r_2} + \frac{e^2}{r_{12}} \right) \psi_\tau = 0 \qquad (2\text{--}51)$$

where $\nabla_1{}^2$ is the Laplacian operator for electron 1 and $\nabla_2{}^2$ is the Laplacian operator for electron 2. Thus, it is seen that for the helium atom, the motion of one electron is dependent on the motion of the other electron, and as we go to more complex atoms the wave equation must contain the coulombic repulsion between all electrons.

The difficulty in the solution arises from the inseparability of the various electron wave functions. This problem can, however, be solved by a method developed by Hartree[7], in which a single electron is treated as if it were moving in the presence of a central electric field resulting from the average charge distribution of the nucleus and the remaining electrons. The general approach is to estimate a potential energy function due to the nucleus and all of the electrons. The wave function of one particular electron is then estimated by considering the chosen electron to be moving in the presence of the average field of the remaining electrons and the nucleus. The solution to the wave equation for the first electron will give a better estimate of the average central field which can then be used for the wave equation of a second electron, and so on. This general procedure is continued to give successively improved wave functions for the electrons until no appreciable change is noted. At this point the field is said to be *self-consistent*.

One of the important consequences of the electron-electron repulsion is the removal of the orbital degeneracy observed in the solution of the hydrogenic wave equation. Whereas all of the levels in a given radial shell in the hydrogen atom were observed to be degenerate and therefore of the same energy, these levels are found to separate in the more complex atoms.

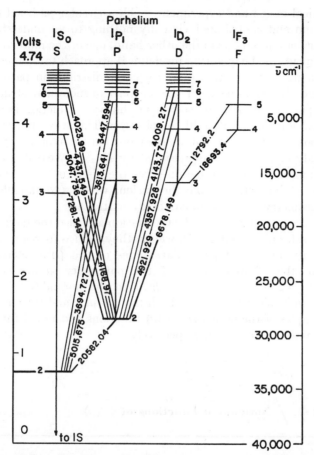

FIGURE 2–6. Energy Level Diagram for Parhelium. Wave lengths of the various transitions are given along the lines in angstroms.

This separation is illustrated in the level scheme for parhelium shown in Figure 2–6, where it is seen that the order of levels becomes

$$1s < 2s < 2p < 3s < 3p \sim 3d < 4s \cdots .$$

On going to yet heavier elements, the order of levels will be altered further, and we find the ns states to be at lower energies than the $(n-1)d$ states.

WAVE FUNCTIONS OF THE HYDROGEN ATOM

In the Bohr atom, it was postulated that the electron followed a particular circular path in its motion about the nucleus. This particular path was chosen because it was the simplest path that gave agreement between the theoretical model and experiment. Such a circular path led to a symmetrical atom and contributed virtually nothing to an understanding of the geometry of molecules. On the other hand, one of the more outstanding accomplishments of the quantum mechanical approach to atomic structure has been in its determination of the general distribution pattern of the electron, and the relationship of this pattern to molecular structure.

It was postulated that the square of the wave function is a measure of the probability distribution of the electron. This wave function is seen to be composed of two parts, an angular portion represented by $Y_{l,m}(\theta,\varphi)$ and a radial portion that is represented by $R_{n,l}(r)$. We will see that the radial portion of the wave function gives the distribution of the electron with respect to its distance from the nucleus whereas the angular portion gives the geometry of the various energy states.

The normalized solutions of the Θ equation and also the radial equation are, in general, quite complex. However, they reduce to relatively simple forms on introduction of particular values of the parameters. For the Φ equation, the allowed values of the parameter m are seen to be $m = 0, \pm 1, \pm 2, \cdots, \pm l$. These lead to the normalized functions of $\Phi(\varphi)$ shown in Table 2-2, in which both the complex and the real forms are given. Examples of the normalized $\Theta(\theta)$ functions and radial functions are given in Tables 2-3 and 2-4, respectively.

TABLE 2-2. / **Normalized Functions of $\Phi_m(\varphi)$.**

$$\Phi_m(\varphi) = \frac{1}{\sqrt{2\pi}} e^{\pm im\varphi}$$

$$\Phi_0(\varphi) = \frac{1}{\sqrt{2\pi}} \qquad \text{or} \qquad \Phi_0(\varphi) = \frac{1}{\sqrt{2}}$$

$$\Phi_1(\varphi) = \frac{1}{\sqrt{2\pi}} e^{i\varphi} \qquad \text{or} \qquad \Phi_1(\varphi) = \frac{1}{\sqrt{\pi}} \cos\varphi$$

$$\Phi_{-1}(\varphi) = \frac{1}{\sqrt{2\pi}} e^{-i\varphi} \qquad \text{or} \qquad \Phi_{-1}(\varphi) = \frac{1}{\sqrt{\pi}} \sin\varphi$$

TABLE 2–3. / **Normalized Functions of $\Theta_{l,m}(\theta)$.**

$$\Theta_{l,m}(\theta) = \sqrt{\frac{(2l+1)\,(l-|m|)!}{2(l+|m|)!}}\; P_l^{|m|}(\cos\theta)$$

$$l = 0:\qquad \Theta_{0,0}(\theta) = \frac{\sqrt{2}}{2}$$

$$l = 1:\qquad \Theta_{1,0}(\theta) = \frac{\sqrt{6}}{2}\cos\theta$$

$$\Theta_{1,\pm1}(\theta) = \frac{\sqrt{3}}{2}\sin\theta$$

TABLE 2–4. / **Normalized Functions of $R_{n,l}(r)$.**

$$R_{n,l}(r) = \sqrt{\left(\frac{2Z}{na_0}\right)^3 \frac{(n-l-1)!}{2n\,[(n+l)!]^3}}\; e^{-\rho/2}\, \rho^l\, L_{n+l}^{2l+1}(\rho)$$

$n = 1$, K shell:

$\qquad l = 0:\quad R_{1,0}(r) = (Z/a_0)^{3/2}\, 2e^{-\rho/2}$

$n = 2$, L shell:

$\qquad l = 0:\quad R_{2,0}(r) = \dfrac{(Z/a_0)^{3/2}}{2\sqrt{2}}\, (2-\rho)\, e^{-\rho/2}$

$\qquad l = 1:\quad R_{2,1}(r) = \dfrac{(Z/a_0)^{3/2}}{2\sqrt{6}}\, \rho\, e^{-\rho/2}$

The normalized total wave function for the hydrogen atom is obtained from the relation

$$\psi_{(r\theta\varphi)} = R_{n,l}(r)\; Y_{l,m}(\theta,\varphi)$$

As we have seen, the particular choice of functions of $R_{n,l}(r)$, $\Theta_{l,m}(\theta)$, and $\Phi_m(\varphi)$ are not arbitrary. They are limited by the allowed values of the quantum numbers. By using all possible arrangements of these functions within the limitations of the quantum numbers, we obtain the normalized total wave functions listed in Table 2–5.

TABLE 2-5. / Normalized Hydrogen-like Wave Functions.

K Shell:

$n = 1, l = 0, m = 0$: $\quad \psi_{1s} = \dfrac{1}{\sqrt{\pi}} (Z/a_0)^{3/2} e^{-\rho}$

L Shell:

$n = 2, l = 0, m = 0$: $\quad \psi_{2s} = \dfrac{1}{4\sqrt{2\pi}} (Z/a_0)^{3/2} (2 - \rho) e^{-\rho/2}$

$n = 2, l = 1, m = 0$: $\quad \psi_{2p_z} = \dfrac{1}{4\sqrt{2\pi}} (Z/a_0)^{3/2} \rho\, e^{-\rho/2} \cos\theta$

$n = 2, l = 1, m = \pm 1$:
$$
\begin{cases}
\psi_{2p_x} = \dfrac{1}{4\sqrt{2\pi}} (Z/a_0)^{3/2} \rho\, e^{-\rho/2} \sin\theta \cos\varphi \\[2ex]
\psi_{2p_y} = \dfrac{1}{4\sqrt{2\pi}} (Z/a_0)^{3/2} \rho\, e^{-\rho/2} \sin\theta \sin\varphi
\end{cases}
$$

M Shell:

$n = 3, l = 0, m = 0$: $\quad \psi_{3s} = \dfrac{2}{81\sqrt{3\pi}} (Z/a_0)^{3/2} (27 - 18\rho + 2\rho^2) e^{-\rho/3}$.

RADIAL DISTRIBUTION CURVES

In its ground state, the wave function for the hydrogen atom is

$$\psi_{1s} = \dfrac{1}{\sqrt{\pi a_0}} e^{-r/a_0}$$

The square of this function should give the probability distribution for the electron with respect to the nucleus. The fact that a probability distribution exists at all is in conflict with the ideas of the Bohr theory where the electron was confined to a prescribed orbit at a given distance from the nucleus. Quantum mechanically, however, we see from the distribution curves in Figure 2–7, that there is a finite probability for the electron to exist even at very great distances from the nucleus. This probability, of course, is exceedingly small, and we note that it is most probable that the electron is less than 1 or 2Å from the nucleus.

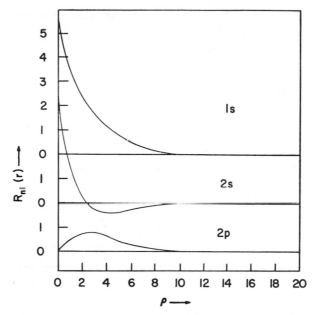

FIGURE 2–7. Radial Wave Functions for the 1s, 2s, and
2p States of the Hydrogen Atom.

A more indicative means for expressing the electron distribution is in
terms of the radial distribution function. This is a measure of the probability of finding the electron in a spherical shell between the distances
r and $r + dr$ from the nucleus. The volume lying between two spheres at
a distance of r to $r + dr$ from the origin is given by $4\pi r^2 dr$ and the probability that the electron is in this volume element should be given by

$$D_{(r)}dr = 4\pi r^2\ \psi\psi^*\ dr$$

or

$$D_{(r)}dr = \frac{4}{a_0{}^3}\ r^2 e^{-2r/a_0}\ dr \qquad\qquad (2\text{--}52)$$

A plot of the radial distribution function in units of a_0 is shown in Figure
2–8. It is interesting to note that, although the electron has a finite probability of existence at great distances from the nucleus, its maximum probability is at a_0, exactly the distance calculated by Bohr for the first electron
orbit in the Bohr atom.

In addition to the ground state, various excited states of the hydrogen
atom also exist. The radial distribution functions for these states can be
plotted in the same manner as the ground state function. Examples of a
few of these functions are also plotted in Figure 2–8.

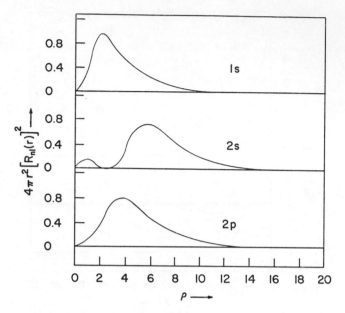

FIGURE 2–8. Radial Distribution Functions for the 1*s*, 2*s*, and 2*p* States of the Hydrogen Atom.

ANGULAR DEPENDENCE OF THE WAVE FUNCTION

The one-electron wave functions of the type we have obtained for the hydrogen atom are often referred to as *atomic orbitals*. The most characteristic feature of these atomic orbitals is their dependence on the angles θ and φ which determine the geometry of the atom. It is generally true that the radial dependence of the wave function is approximately the same for the various l states in a given major shell, n. Thus, to a good approximation, an s state and a p state in the same shell can be considered on the basis of their angular dependence alone. This angular dependence is represented by the spherical harmonics

$$Y_{l,m}(\theta,\varphi) = \Theta_{l,m}(\theta)\ \Phi_m(\varphi)$$

In Table 2–6, we see the spherical harmonics for the s state and the three p states for the hydrogen atom, along with their determining l and m quantum numbers.

If we consider the s orbital, the spherical harmonics is seen from Table 2–6 to be

$$Y_{0,0}\ (\theta,\varphi) = \frac{1}{\sqrt{4\pi}}$$

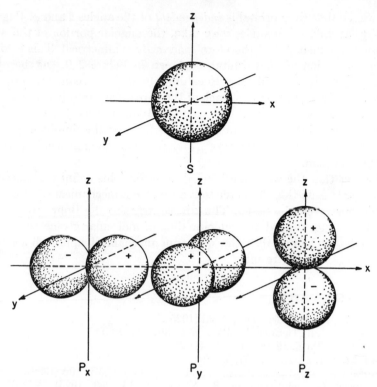

FIGURE 2–9. Angular Dependence of the s and p Orbitals.

TABLE 2–6. / **Spherical Harmonics for the s State and Three p States of the Hydrogen Atom, with Determining l and m Quantum Numbers.**

$$Y_{l,m}(\theta,\varphi) = \Theta_{l,m}(\theta)\,\Phi_m(\varphi)$$

$l = 0,\, m = 0$: $\quad Y_{0,0}(\theta,\varphi) = \dfrac{1}{\sqrt{4\pi}}$

$l = 1,\, m = 0$: $\quad Y_{1,0}(\theta,\varphi) = \sqrt{\dfrac{3}{4\pi}}\,\cos\theta$

$l = 1,\, m = 1$: $\quad Y_{1,1}(\theta,\varphi) = \sqrt{\dfrac{3}{4\pi}}\,\sin\theta\cos\varphi$

$l = 1,\, m = -1$: $Y_{1,-1}(\theta,\varphi) = \sqrt{\dfrac{3}{4\pi}}\,\sin\theta\sin\varphi$

Here we see that the *s* orbital is *independent* of the angles θ and φ. Regardless of what values the angles may take, the angular portion of the wave function is a constant and therefore *spherically* symmetrical. This leads to the representation of an *s* orbital as shown in Figure 2–9. On the other hand, the *p* orbitals are all seen to exhibit the definite geometry shown in Figure 2–9. If a plot is made of each of the three *p* orbitals, it is found that they form identical *dumbbell*-like patterns lying mutually perpendicular to each other. Thus, we find one *p* orbital forming the dumbbell pattern along the *x* axis, one along the *y* axis, and one along the *z* axis of a cartesian coordinate system.

The fact that the wave mechanical atom has this definite geometry is significant. It is on this character that a quantum mechanical treatment of stereochemistry can be based. Thus, in contrast to the Bohr atom which had little to offer toward an understanding of molecular geometry, we will see in a later chapter that the quantum mechanical approach leads to some quite satisfying results.

BIBLIOGRAPHY

1. de Broglie, L., *Ann. de. Phys.*, **3**, 22 (1925).
2. Davisson, C. and Germer, L., *Phys. Rev.*, **30**, 705 (1927).
3. Heisenberg, W., *Z. Physik*, **43**, 172 (1927).
4. Born, M., *Z.f. Phys.*, **37**, 863; **38**, 803 (1926).
5. Schroedinger, E., *Ann. d. Phys.*, **79**, 361, 489; **80**, 437; **81**, 109 (1926).
6. Uhlenbeck, G. and Goudsmit, S., *Naturwiss.*, **13**, 953 (1925); *Nature*, **117**, 264 (1926).
7. Hartree, D., *Proc. Cambridge Phil. Soc.*, **24**, 89 (1928).

SUGGESTED SUPPLEMENTARY READING

Glasstone, S., "Theoretical Chemistry," D. Van Nostrand Co., Inc., New York, N.Y., 1944.
Heitler, W., "Elementary Wave Mechanics," Clarendon Press, Oxford, 1945.
Pauling, L. and Wilson, E., "Introduction to Quantum Mechanics," McGraw-Hill Book Co., New York, N.Y., 1935.

3 / *The Periodic Table*

The periodic classification of the elements must be listed among the more outstanding contributions to the development of chemistry. Certainly, the importance of such a systemization cannot be questioned, but at times we are prone to forget the difficulties that faced those who were instrumental in the early development of the periodic system. In the light of our present understanding of the relation of electron configurations to the properties of the elements, the correlations seem rather obvious. However, it is necessary to realize that at the time of the development of the periodic system, the quantity and very often the quality of experimental data on which to base such a classification was lacking.

THE DEVELOPMENT OF THE PERIODIC LAW

At the beginning of the nineteenth century not only was there an insufficient number of elements known on which to base a periodic classification, but equally important, the distinction between atomic weight and equivalent weight had not yet been made. Until this problem was resolved, no significant contribution could be possible. In addition to these difficulties, the accepted values for the atomic weights of many of the elements were questionable. Starting shortly after 1800, this problem was attacked, principally by Berzelius and later by Stas. The accuracy of their atomic weight determinations left little to be desired, and as a result, one of the major barriers to a periodic classification was removed. However, the formulation of a satisfactory periodic law had to wait until after 1860.

An understanding of the relation of atomic weight to equivalent weight did not come until the middle of the nineteenth century. When John Dalton applied the atomic theory to chemistry in 1807, he proposed that when two elements combined to form a compound, one atom of the first element combined with only one atom of the second element. Thus, if hydrogen and oxygen combined to form water, the resultant molecule of water would have the formula HO, rather than H_2O as we know it today. If the atomic weight of hydrogen is taken to be 1, this leads to an atomic weight of 8 for oxygen. This idea was attacked as early as 1809 by Gay-Lussac, but the key to the problem lay in the hypothesis of the physicist Amadeo Avogadro. It was in 1811 that Avogadro published in the *Journal de Physique* the article that contained the basic ideas for what we now refer to as *Avogadro's hypothesis*. In his publication, Avogadro made clear the distinction between atoms (*molecules elementaires*) and molecules (*molecules integrantes*). He pointed out that with the assumption that the elementary gases are actually made up of two or more *molecules elementaires*, the problem of combining volumes with regard to atomic weights could be resolved. Unfortunately, Avogadro's work achieved little recognition at the time of its publication. However, in 1843, it was revived when Gerhardt used Avogadro's hypothesis as a basis for determining molecular weights and volumes. At that time, he came to the conclusion that the water molecule should be written as H_2O.

In spite of a steady realization of a difference in the atomic weight and the combining weight of an element, it was not until the first International Chemical Congress held at Karlsruhe in 1860, where Cannizzaro presented a paper based on the hypothesis of Avogadro, that his ideas began to receive the recognition that they deserved. As a result, during the next few years some general agreement on the molecular weights of the more important compounds was possible.

Dobereiner's Triads

Although, a set of atomic weights was not available for all elements, very definite similarities in both chemical and physical properties between a few groups of elements were observed quite early in the nineteenth century. In 1829, Johann Wolfgang Dobereiner made the first truly significant attempt to show a relation between the chemical properties of the elements and their atomic weights. He noted that certain similar elements occurred in groups of three which he called *triads*. A particularly interesting feature of these triads was that the atomic weight of the middle member of the triad was very nearly equal to the arithmetic mean of the weights of the other two members of the triad. For instance, such a triad was observed for chlorine, bromine, and iodine where the mean of the atomic weights of chlorine and iodine is 81, which is very nearly the atomic weight of bromine. Other such triads are sulfur, selenium, and tellurium; and lithium, sodium, and potassium. In each of these cases it is seen that the mathematical relationship of the atomic weights holds quite well.

In the years that followed, numerous attempts were made at a more comprehensive classification in which the ideas of Dobereiner were extended and various group similarities were noted. For instance, Dumas noted some analogous trends in the successive molecular weights of a series of hydro-carbon radicals such as shown in Table 3–1.

TABLE 3–1. / **Weight-Formula Trends of a Series of Hydrocarbon Radicals.**

Radical	Formula	Molecular Weight
Hydrogen	II	1
Methyl	CH_3	15
Ethyl	C_2H_5	29
Propyl	C_3H_7	43
Butyl	C_4H_9	57
Amyl	C_5H_{11}	71

It may be noted that as we pass from one radical to the next, the molecular weight increases by 14 units. If the value of the first term is designated by a and the difference by d, the value of any given radical may be represented by the expression $a + nd$. It is also seen that the triad relation of Dobereiner again holds. If any three successive terms are considered, the molecular weight of the middle member is then found to be the arithmetic mean of the other two members. Observations such as these point to the existence of some sort of relation between chemical properties and molecular weight, but in themselves are of little value.

The Telluric Helix

It was in 1862, that a periodic classification of the elements was devel-oped that approached the ideas we have today. At that time, A. E. de Chancourtois, a professor of geology at the Ecole des Mines in Paris, presented an account of his telluric helix in a series of papers before the French Academie des Sciences, in which he indicated a relation between the properties of the elements and their atomic weights. De Chancourtois used a vertical cylinder with 16 equidistant lines on its surface, the lines lying parallel to its axis. He then drew a helix at 45 degrees to the axis and arranged the elements on the spiral in the order of their increasing atomic weights. In this manner, elements that differed from each other in atomic weight by 16 or multiples of 16 fell very nearly on the same vertical line. As can be seen in Figure 3–1, it turns out that in some cases the elements lying directly under each other show a definite similarity. In addition to the 16 vertical lines, de Chancourtois felt that other con-necting lines could be drawn, and that all elements lying on such lines

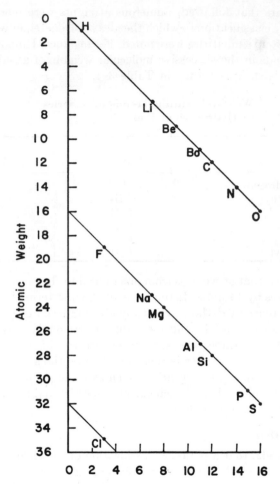

FIGURE 3–1. The Telluric Helix of de Chancourtois.

were related in some manner. His arrangement resulted in the proposal by de Chancourtois that *the properties of the elements are the properties of numbers.* This was a rather close approach to the basic ideas of the later periodic classifications, but it left much to be desired in the light of the subsequent contributions by Mendeléev and Meyer. Nevertheless, an effort was made by two of his fellow countrymen, de Boisbaudran and Lapparent, to obtain some credit for de Chancourtois for his contributions to the periodic law. However, their opinions were not generally shared. Commenting on the *telluric screw,* around 1900, the British chemist, Dr. W. A. Tilden stated,[1] *"the author seems to have had a dim idea that properties*

	No.		No.		No.		No.		No.		No.		No.		No.		No.
H	1	F	8	Cl	15	Co&Ni	22	Br	29	Pd	36	I	42	Pt&Ir	50
Li	2	Na	9	K	16	Cu	23	Rb	30	Ag	37	Cs	44	Tl	53
G	3	Mg	10	Ca	17	Zn	25	Sr	31	Cd	38	Ba&V	45	Pb	54
Bo	4	Al	11	Cr	19	Y	24	Ce&La	33	U	40	Ta	46	Th	56
C	5	Si	12	Ti	18	In	26	Zr	32	Sn	39	W	47	Hg	52
N	6	P	13	Mn	20	As	27	Di&Mo	34	Sb	41	Nb	48	Bi	55
O	7	S	14	Fe	21	Se	28	Ro&Ru	35	Te	43	Au	49	Os	51

FIGURE 3–2. Periodic Table Proposed by Newlands.

were in some way related to atomic weight, but this idea is so confused by fantastic notions of his own, that it is impossible to be sure that he really recognized anything like periodicity in this relation."

The Law of Octaves

Very shortly after the telluric screw of de Chancourtois, John Alexander Reina Newlands in England made the first attempt to correlate the chemical properties of the elements with their atomic weights. This, of course, had not been possible until the difference in atomic weight and equivalent weight was appreciated. In 1864, the first of several papers by Newlands on the subject of periodicity of properties of the elements was published in *Chemical News*. In listing the elements in the consecutive order of their increasing atomic weights, Newlands noted a striking similarity between every eighth element. In the summer of the next year, Newlands published another paper in the *Chemical News*, in which he again listed the elements in groups of seven, but found that with a few changes in the order of certain elements, the elements that appeared to belong to the same group would appear on the same horizontal line. This improved table of Newlands is seen in Figure 3–2.

Newlands made the unfortunate mistake of naming his generalization the *law of octaves*, due to its similarity to the musical scale. On the presentation of his periodic system before the Chemical Society in London in 1866, he was met with ridicule to the extent that one chemist asked sarcastically if he had tried arranging the elements in alphabetical order. Nevertheless, there can be little question that Newlands was the first to publish a list of the elements in the order of their increasing atomic weights and to realize that a systematic relationship existed between this order and their chemical and physical properties. In 1887 Newlands finally received the Davy Medal in recognition of his contribution, but even today he is probably given far less credit than he deserves in the development of the periodic law[2].

			Mo 96	W 184
			—	Au 196.5
			Pd 106.5	Pt 197
L 7	Na 23	—	Ag 108	—
G 9	Mg 24	Zn 65	Cd 112	Hg 200
B 11	Al 27.5	—	—	Tl 203
C 12	Si 28	—	Sn 118	Pb 207
N 14	P 31	As 75	Sb 122	Bi 210
O 16	S 32	Se 79.5	Te 129	—
F 19	Cl 35.5	Br 80	I 127	—
	K 39	Rb 85	Cs 133	
	Ca 40	Sr 87.5	Ba 137	
	Ti 48	Zr 89.5	—	Th 231
	Cr 52.5	—	V 138	
	Mn 55	—	—	

FIGURE 3–3. Classification of the Elements According to Odling.

Only a very few months after the first paper of Newlands, what would appear to be a somewhat superior relation was published in the *Quarterly Journal of Science* by Odling. He pointed out that a purely arithmetical listing of the elements was in very close agreement with their recognized chemical similarities. Odling chose to represent his classification in the form shown in Figure 3–3. It is quite remarkable how similar it is to the table

			Ti = 50	Zr = 90	? = 180
			V = 51	Nb = 94	Ta = 182
			Cr = 52	Mo = 96	W = 186
			Mn = 55	Rh = 104.4	Pt = 197.4
			Fe = 56	Ru = 104.4	Ir = 198
		Ni =	Co = 59	Pd = 106.6	Os = 199
H = 1			Cu = 63.4	Ag = 108	Hg = 200
	Be = 9.4	Mg = 24	Zn = 65.2	Cd = 112	
	B = 11	Al = 27.4	? = 68	Ur = 116	Au = 197?
	C = 12	Si = 28	? = 70	Sn = 118	
	N = 14	P = 31	As = 75	Sb = 122	Bi = 210
	O = 16	S = 32	Se = 79.4	Te = 128?	
	F = 19	Cl = 35.5	Br = 80	I = 127	
Li = 7	Na = 23	K = 39	Rb = 85.4	Cs = 133	Tl = 204
		Ca = 40	Sr = 87.6	Ba = 137	Pb = 207
		? = 45	Ce = 92		
		?Er = 56	La = 94		
		?Yt = 60	Di = 95		
		?In = 75.6	Th = 118?		

FIGURE 3–4. Mendeléev's Original Table of the Elements.

shown in Figure 3–4, which was proposed by Mendeléev in 1869. Nevertheless, it appears that Odling failed to realize the implications of his table and as a result received virtually no part of the credit for the development of the periodic system of the elements.

THE PERIODIC LAW

In spite of the importance of the earlier contributions, the major portion of the credit for the development of the periodic system must go to the Russian, Dmitrii Ivanovich Mendeléev, and to the German, Julius Lothar Meyer. Their independent realization that *the properties of the elements can be represented as periodic functions of their atomic weights* made possible a periodic classification that has suffered few significant changes in the subsequent years. Mendeléev published the first account of his periodic system in 1869, a few months before the publication of the table by Meyer. However, there can be no doubt that both men deserve equal credit for the development of the periodic law, regardless of the difference in the publication dates. This fact was recognized by the Royal Society in 1882 by the presentation of the Davy Medal to both Mendeléev and Meyer.

It was in March of 1869 that Mendeléev communicated the first of a series of papers to the Russian Chemical Society in which he set forth the arrangement of the elements in terms of their increasing atomic weights as shown in Figure 3–4. It might be noted that in many respects the Mendeléev arrangement differed little from that proposed five years earlier by Odling. However, Mendeléev appeared to be the first to fully appreciate the significance of this periodicity. In his first paper, Mendeléev emphasized the group similarities of the elements to the extent that he reversed the order of atomic weights where necessary in order to maintain this group similarity. He pointed out that this might be an indication of the correctness of the then accepted value for a given atomic weight and specifically mentioned the relative atomic weights of tellurium and iodine. Of considerable interest and importance is the fact that Mendeléev left vacant positions in his proposed table for yet undiscovered elements and went so far as to express the opinion that the chemical and physical properties of these elements might well be predicted from their positions in the table.

In the summer of 1871, Mendeléev published a much more comprehensive treatment of what he chose to call the *periodic law*. At this time he presented the more familiar form of the periodic table shown in Figure 3–5. Although this particular form of the table differs somewhat from the *short form* that is sometimes used today, it is substantially the same.

It was in his publication of 1871, that Mendeléev utilized the periodic character to predict the properties of the unknown elements lying directly

Series	Group I R$_2$O	Group II RO	Group III R$_2$O$_3$	Group IV RH$_4$ RO$_2$	Group V RH$_3$ R$_2$O$_5$	Group VI RH$_2$ RO$_3$	Group VII RH R$_2$O$_7$	Group VIII — RO$_4$
1	H = 1							
2	Li = 7	Be = 9.4	B = 11	C = 12	N = 14	O = 16	F = 19	
3	Na = 23	Mg = 24	Al = 27.3	Si = 28	P = 31	S = 32	Cl = 35.5	
4	K = 39	Ca = 40	— = 44	Ti = 48	V = 51	Cr = 52	Mn = 55	Fe = 56 Co = 59 Ni = 59 Cu = 63
5	(Cu = 63)	Zn = 65	— = 68	— = 72	As = 75	Se = 78	Br = 80	
6	Rb = 85	Sr = 87	?Yt = 88	Zr = 90	Nb = 94	Mo = 96	— = 100	Ru = 104 Rh = 104 Pd = 106 Ag = 108
7	(Ag = 108)	Cd = 112	In = 113	Sn = 118	Sb = 122	Te = 125	I = 127	— —
8	Cs = 133	Ba = 137	?Di = 138	?Ce = 140	—	—	—	— —
9	(—)	—	—	—	—			
10	—	—	?Er = 178	?La = 180	Ta = 182	W = 184	—	Os = 195 Ir = 197 Pt = 198 Au = 199
11	(Au = 199)	Hg = 200	Tl = 204	Pb = 207	Bi = 208	—	—	— —
12	—	—	—	Th = 231	—	U = 240	—	— —

Figure 3–5. Mendeléev's Periodic Table of 1871.

below boron, aluminum, and silicon. These he named *eka-boron, eka-aluminum,* and *eka-silicon,* respectively. Starting in 1875 with the discovery of gallium by Lecog de Boisbaudran, the three blank positions were soon filled. Eka-boron became scandium, eka-aluminum became gallium, and eka-silicon became germanium. In Table 3–2, we see a comparison of the predictions for the element eka-silicon made by Mendeléev and the observed properties of germanium. The remarkable agreement is certainly a complete justification of Mendeléev's faith in his periodic law.

TABLE 3–2. / **Comparison of Eka-silicon and Germanium.**

Property	Eka-silicon (1871)	Germanium (1886)
Atomic weight	72	72.32
Specific gravity	5.5	5.47
Specific heat	0.073	0.076
Atomic volume	13 cc	13.22 cc
Color	dark gray	grayish white
Sp. gr. of dioxide	4.7	4.703
B.p. of tetrachloride	100° C	86° C
Sp. gr. of tetrachloride	1.9	1.887
B.p. of tetraethyl derivative	160° C	160° C

In December, 1869, a paper was submitted by Lothar Meyer to *Liebig's Annalen* with the title "The Nature of the Chemical Elements as Functions

I	II	III	IV	V	VI	VII	VIII	IX
	B 11	Al 27·3	—	—		?In 113·4	—	Tl 202·7
	C 12	Si 28		—		Sn 117·8		Pb 2064
			Ti 48		Zr 89·7			—
	N 14	P 30·9		As 74·9		Sb 122·1		Bi 207·5
			V 51·2		Nb 93·7		Ta 182·2	
	O 16	S 32		Se 78		Te 128?		
			Cr 52·4		Mo 95·6		W 183·5	
	F 19·1	Cl 35·4		Br 79·75		I 126·5		
			Mn 54·8		Ru 103·5		Os 1986?	
			Fe 55·9		Rh 104·1		Ir 196·7	
		Co=	Ni 58·6		Rb 106·2		Pt 196·7	
Li 7·0	Na 22·9	K 39		Rb 85·2		Cs 132·7		
			Cu 63·3		Ag 107·7		Au 192·2	
?Be 9·3	Mg 23·9	Ca 39·9		Sr 87		Ba 136·8		Hg 199·3
			Zn 64·9		Cd 111·6			

FIGURE 3–6. Periodic Table According to Lothar Meyer.

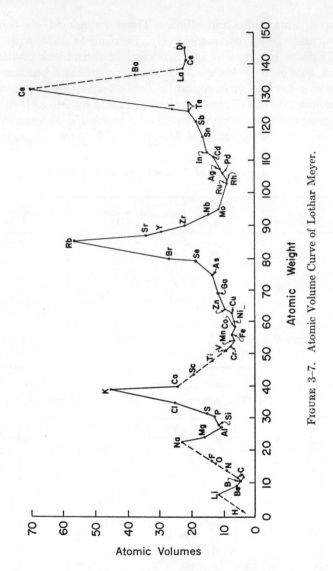

FIGURE 3–7. Atomic Volume Curve of Lothar Meyer.

of Their Atomic Weight." This was very shortly after the publication of Mendeléev's first paper on the periodic classification of the elements. In this publication, Meyer proposed the periodic table as seen in Figure 3–6, which is very similar to the one published by Mendeléev. Emphasizing the physical properties of the elements, Meyer pointed out that, in general, *the properties of the elements are periodic functions of their atomic weights.* This periodicity was very clearly shown by Meyer by means of the *atomic volume curve.* If the atomic weight of a substance is divided by its density, a quantity known as the atomic volume is obtained. Meyer plotted this quantity against the atomic weight, giving the curve shown in Figure 3–7. In spite of several shortcomings of the concept of atomic volumes as used by Meyer, there can be no question of a general periodic trend. The maximum position in any period is seen to be always occupied by an alkali metal, and each member of a given family consistently holds a given position in its respective period.

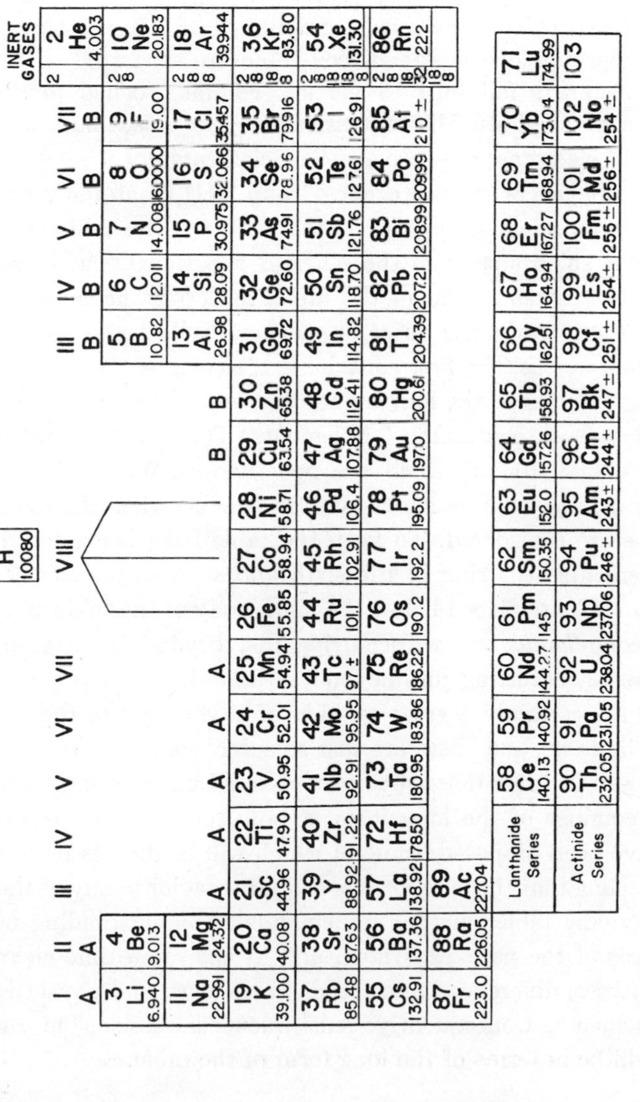

FIGURE 3–8. The Long Form of the Periodic Table.

THE LONG FORM OF THE PERIODIC TABLE

Many different forms of a periodic classification of the elements have appeared since the 1871 periodic table by Mendeléev. Each table was designed to point up the various trends and relationships which its author considered most significant. From the literally hundreds of tables which have been proposed, perhaps the most popular and easily reproduced periodic table is the conventional *extended* or *long form*, which is shown in Figure 3–8. First used in a simpler form, by Rang in 1893, it was developed further by Werner in 1905 and evolved into its present form due to the strong support which it received from Bury and many others.

The subgroups of the Mendeléev table are separated with the result that the elements fall into 18 vertical columns, called *families*, representing, as we shall see, the successive filling of s, p, and d orbitals with 2, 6, and 10 electrons, respectively. The elements in each column are true analogs or congeners of each other. Group VIII, containing the iron and platinum group metals, appears at the center of the table and separates the seven A subgroups from the seven B subgroups. The inert gases are placed at the extreme right of the table, reflecting the completion of the s and p sublevels of their outer or valency shell. There are 7 horizontal rows, called *periods*, the first containing 2 elements, the second and third containing 8 elements, the fourth and fifth containing 18 elements, and the sixth and seventh containing 32 elements. This gives a total of 118 elements, the first 103 of which are now known. We shall see that this particular arrangement becomes quite reasonable when the electronic configurations are considered. To keep the table from being too drawn out, the 14 elements occurring in the sixth and seventh periods belonging in the group IIIA are placed below the main body of the table and are designated the *lanthanide series* (occurring just beyond lanthanum) and the *actinide series* (occurring just beyond actinium).

There are certainly a great number of advantages to the long form of the periodic table, and there are just as surely some disadvantages. These are discussed in some detail by Foster[3] and Luder[4], respectively. Due to the shortcomings of the long form, a multitude of more recent periodic tables have been proposed, some of which will be discussed. Nevertheless, it is our feeling that the long form is still far superior to any of the presently known periodic tables in that it demands an understanding of the electronic basis of the periodic system and at the same time clearly reflects the similarities, differences, and trends in chemical and physical properties of the elements. Consequently, subsequent discussions on the periodic system will be in terms of the long form of the table.

BASIS OF A PERIODIC CLASSIFICATION

Although the periodic law of Mendeléev met with considerable success, there were several glaring anomalies. According to the periodic law, the properties of the elements are periodic functions of their atomic weight. If this were strictly true, it would not be possible to have two elements with the same atomic weight and different chemical and physical properties. Yet, this is observed to be very nearly true for the case of cobalt and nickel. It would also be difficult to understand the relation of tellurium to iodine, where the order of increasing atomic weights is reversed. Mendeléev felt that the atomic weight of tellurium must be in error. However, this was shown not to be the case, and we find that tellurium must be placed ahead of iodine in the periodic table even though it has a larger atomic weight. In addition to these problems, there was the questionable location of such groupings of elements as the group VIII elements, what we now call the rare earth elements, and, by 1900, the inert gases. It was apparent that there was something in the fundamental structure of the elements that brought about this periodicity, but the atomic weight did not appear to be the final answer.

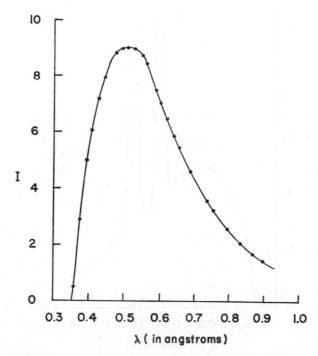

FIGURE 3-9. Continuous X-ray Spectrum of Tungsten as a Result of a 35,000-Volt Potential.

The first major step toward a solution to the problem came with the observation of the characteristic radiation of X rays. If a target is bombarded by high-energy electrons, two different types of X rays are usually observed. One type results in a continuous spectrum similar to that shown in Figure 3–9, in which we see a continuous distribution of wave lengths. The high-energy end of the spectrum is determined by the potential difference through which the electron falls. Superimposed on the continuous spectrum is often found a characteristic spectrum. The wave lengths of the characteristic X rays are found to be a function of the target material but independent of the exciting potential so long as the energy of the incident electrons is greater than some minimum value. In Figure 3–10, the X-ray spectrum for a molybdenum sample is reproduced in which two characteristic lines are seen to be superimposed on the continuous spectrum.

The first serious studies of the characteristic radiation were conducted by Barkla and Sadler, starting around 1908. By studying the absorption properties of these radiations, they were led to the conclusion that the

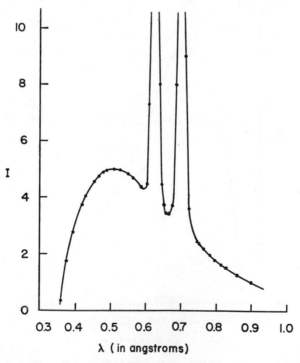

FIGURE 3–10. Characteristic X-ray Spectrum of Molybdenum Superimposed on the Continuous Spectrum.

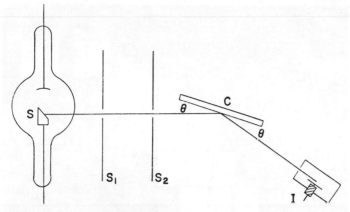

FIGURE 3–11. Schematic Diagram of the Crystal Spectrometer
Developed by Bragg and Adapted by Moseley for his Study of
the Characteristic X-ray Spectra.

characteristic radiation could be separated into two types, one of which
was more penetrating than the other. The most penetrating of the two
was called the K radiation and the less penetrating was called the L radiation. Although absorption measurements are not particularly accurate,
Barkla and Sadler were able to determine that the energy of either the K
or the L radiation increased with an increase in atomic number of the
target element.

In 1913, H. G. J. Moseley made the first detailed study of the characteristic X-ray spectra emitted by different elements[5]. Using the adapta-
tion of the crystal spectrometer developed by Bragg (Figure 3–11), Moseley
studied the spectra of 38 elements. On analysis of the characteristic lines,
Moseley was able to show that they could be separated into two distinct
series which then could be related to the K and L radiations observed earlier
by Barkla and Sadler. In Figure 3–12 is seen a reproduction of a photograph of the K series of the elements from calcium to copper. The elements
are here arranged in terms of increasing atomic number. It can be seen that
for each element, the K radiation consists of two lines, a K_α and a K_β line.
The apparent discrepancy in the case of cobalt, where four lines are
observed, can be attributed to impurities of iron and nickel in the cobalt
sample.

It is readily seen that the wave length of the characteristic K radiation
decreases in a regular manner with an increase in atomic number. The only
irregularity is observed between calcium and titanium, thereby indicating
that an element has been omitted. This position, of course, belongs to the
element scandium. A technique so powerful as this immediately found
application to several then pertinent problems in the periodic system. By

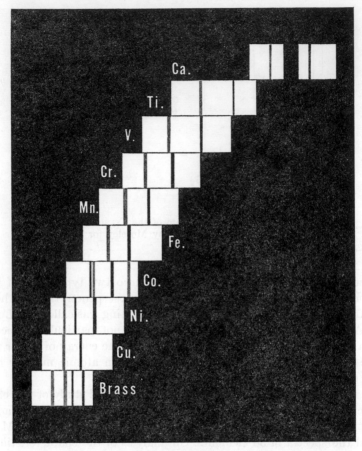

FIGURE 3–12. K_α and K_β X-ray Lines as Observed by Moseley.

1913, there were three pairs of elements that, due to their chemical and physical properties, could not be placed in the order of their increasing atomic weights. These were argon and potassium, cobalt and nickel, and tellurium and iodine. By means of the X-ray spectrum, it was found that although their order was inverted in terms of atomic weight, it was in the proper sequence with regard to atomic number. This then would indicate that the atomic number is a more fundamental quantity than the atomic weight, and is possibly the key to an understanding of the periodic system of the elements.

Empirically, Moseley found that the frequency, ν, of the characteristic X-ray line could be related to the atomic number by means of the relation

$$\sqrt{\nu} = K(Z - k) \tag{3-1}$$

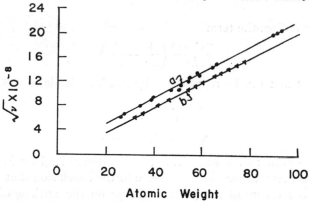

FIGURE 3–13. Relationship Between the Frequencies of the Characteristic X-ray Lines and (•) Atomic weights and (▾) Atomic numbers as Observed by Moseley.

where K and k are both constants, and Z is the atomic number of the element. The accuracy of this relation is readily determined by plotting $\sqrt{\nu}$ against the atomic number. As can be seen in Figure 3–13, an excellent straight line is obtained. For comparison, a plot of $\sqrt{\nu}$ against the atomic weight is shown on the same graph.

In an attempt to explain the relation between the frequency and the atomic number, Moseley utilized the treatment developed by Bohr for the hydrogen atom. From the Bohr model, it appeared reasonable that an X ray resulted from an electron transition in the K or L shell. Bohr had shown that the frequency, ν, in the emission spectrum of the hydrogen atom could be represented by the formula

$$\nu = \frac{2\pi^2 \mu e^4}{h^3} Z^2 \left(\frac{1}{n_f^2} - \frac{1}{n_i^2} \right) \tag{3–2}$$

where μ is the reduced mass, h is Planck's constant, Z is the atomic number, and n_f and n_i are the quantum numbers of the final and initial states, respectively. If this basic formula is applied to a heavy atom in which there are a large number of electrons, it would be expected that the effective nuclear charge seen by a given electron would be less than the nuclear charge, Ze, due to the shielding effect of the electrons lying between the nucleus and the given electron. It should more accurately be represented by $(Z - S)$ where S is a constant known as the screening constant and measures the degree to which other electrons in the atom are able to screen or shield the nucleus from a given electron. If we now use this effective nuclear charge in the Bohr equation we obtain the expression

$$\nu = \frac{2\pi^2 \mu e^4}{h^3} (Z - S)^2 \left(\frac{1}{n_f^2} - \frac{1}{n_i^2} \right) \tag{3–3}$$

For a given K line, the term

$$\frac{2\pi^2 \, \mu e^4}{h^3} \left(\frac{1}{n_f{}^2} - \frac{1}{n_i{}^2} \right)$$

is a constant and can be represented by K^2. This leads to the expression

$$\nu = K^2(Z - S)^2$$

or

$$\sqrt{\nu} = K(Z - S)$$

which is the same as the empirical equation determined by Moseley.

From his observations, Moseley came to the conclusion that the atomic number is a measure of the positive charge on the nucleus of an atom. This property, for some reason, appeared to be a more fundamental quantity than the atomic weight. The positions in the periodic table of unknown elements could be predicted with a much greater degree of certainty than was possible in terms of atomic weights, and the atomic weight anomalies such as the reversed order of iodine and tellurium could be reconciled. Thus, we are led to a new statement of the periodic law: *The properties of the elements are periodic functions of their atomic numbers*. The realization that the properties of the elements are periodic with respect to the atomic numbers, of course, leads to a much deeper understanding of the basis of this periodicity. We now recognize that the periodic character of the elements is actually due to the number and arrangement of the electrons which, in turn, are dependent upon the atomic number. Thus, in the light of our present understanding, a more appropriate statement of the periodic law might be expressed in terms of electron configurations.

ELECTRONIC BASIS FOR THE PERIODIC CLASSIFICATION

With a better understanding of the part that the electron plays in the properties of the elements, a corresponding understanding of the periodic system came about. By 1923, it had been realized that an explanation of the line spectra of an atom demanded the use of four quantum numbers to determine the various energy states in the atom. Of these various states, one might expect that the electrons would exist in the lowest possible energy states available. Thus, if at all possible, an electron should try to be in the state where $n = 1$, $l = 0$, $m = 0$, and $m_s = 1/2$. However, it is quite obvious from atomic spectra that it is not reasonable that all of the electrons in a heavy atom are in this particular state. Therefore, before any real advance could be made, it was necessary to find a rule by which the electrons can be fed into these possible energy states. Such a rule came in 1925 in the form of the *Pauli Exclusion Principle* which states that in a given atom, no two electrons can have the same values for all four quantum numbers.

TABLE 3–3. / **Possible Arrangements of the Electrons.**

n	l	m	m_s	Number of Electrons in a Subgroup	Electron State
2	0	0	$\pm 1/2$	2	s
	1	+1	$\pm 1/2$		
		0	$\pm 1/2$	6	p
		−1	$\pm 1/2$		
3	0	0	$\pm 1/2$	2	s
	1	+1	$\pm 1/2$		
		0	$\pm 1/2$	6	p
		−1	$\pm 1/2$		
	2	+2	$\pm 1/2$		
		+1	$\pm 1/2$		
		0	$\pm 1/2$	10	d
		−1	$\pm 1/2$		
		−2	$\pm 1/2$		
4	0	0	$\pm 1/2$	2	s
	1	+1	$\pm 1/2$		
		0	$\pm 1/2$	6	p
		−1	$\pm 1/2$		
	2	+2	$\pm 1/2$		
		+1	$\pm 1/2$		
		0	$\pm 1/2$	10	d
		−1	$\pm 1/2$		
		−2	$\pm 1/2$		
	3	+3	$\pm 1/2$		
		+2	$\pm 1/2$		
		+1	$\pm 1/2$		
		0	$\pm 1/2$	14	f
		−1	$\pm 1/2$		
		−2	$\pm 1/2$		
		−3	$\pm 1/2$		

In essence, the Pauli Exclusion Principle states that there can be only one electron in each possible energy state of the atom. If all four of the quantum numbers are nondegenerate, every possible different arrangement of the four quantum numbers will define a new energy state, and in each of these states it will be possible to place only one electron. Thus, the key to the electronic structure of the elements and therefore the properties of the elements is found in the four quantum numbers with their restrictions along with the Pauli Exclusion Principle.

If we consider the four quantum numbers with their restrictions,

$$n = 1, 2, 3, 4, \cdots,$$
$$l = 0, 1, 2, 3, \cdots, (n-1) \text{ inclusive,}$$
$$m = 0, \pm1, \pm2, \pm3, \cdots, \pm l, \text{ inclusive,}$$
$$m_s = \pm1/2$$

we find that only certain combinations are possible. If, for instance, we consider the first or K shell, the principal quantum number equals 1. If $n = 1$, it is seen that the angular momentum quantum number, l, can be only zero since its maximum value is $(n-1)$. It is also found that if $l = 0$, the magnetic quantum number, m, can be only zero. However, the spin quantum number, m_s, can be either $+1/2$ or $-1/2$. Thus, we find that in the first shell there are only two possible arrangements of the four quantum numbers within the given restrictions. This means that in the first shell there can be only two electrons, and since $l = 0$, the electrons must be in an s state. For the second, third, and fourth shells, all of the possible arrangements of the four quantum numbers are shown in Table 3-3. It should be noted that the s state occurs in every shell, and it is seen to always contain two electrons. In the second shell there is the possibility of both an s and a p state, and the p state is seen to occur in all subsequent shells. The d state occurs first in the third shell and the f state first occurs in the fourth shell.

Since the lower the value of the quantum number, the lower the energy of an electron state, assuming the quantum states are nondegenerate, we should expect the order of increasing energy states to be

$$1s < 2s < 2p < 3s < 3p < 3d < 4s < 4p < 4d < 4f < 5s \ldots.$$

According to the Pauli Exclusion Principle, we should expect to fill in the $1s$ state first, then proceed to the $2s$, then to the $2p$, and so on. Thus, for hydrogen, which has one electron, we should expect the electron to go into the s state of the first shell giving the electron configuration $1s^1$. For helium, with two electrons, the electron configuration would be expected to be $1s^2$, and for lithium, the electron configuration would be $1s^2 2s^1$. In a like manner, it should be possible to write the electron configuration for each of the known elements.

In an attempt to relate the electron configuration of the elements to the periodic table, it is seen that the long form of the table can be divided into the four general sections shown in Figure 3-14. The region represented by s is found to contain a block of two elements in each period, whereas the p block contains six elements, the d block contains 10 elements, and

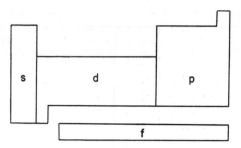

FIGURE 3–14. Division of the Long Form of
the Periodic Table in Terms of Blocks of s, p,
d, and f Electrons.

the f block contains 14 elements. This, of course, leads one to suspect a
link between the periodic table and the s, p, d, and f electron states since
they contain 2, 6, 10, and 14 electrons, respectively. In fact, since the
periodic table is based on experiment, it should be a guide to the order in
which the electrons fill in the successive elements.

If we assume that these blocks are more than coincidence, we can begin
to construct the electron configuration for each of the elements. In Table
3–4, the presently accepted electron configurations for the elements are

TABLE 3–4. / **Electron Configurations and Term Symbols of Atoms
in Their Normal States.**

Atomic Number	Element	Electronic Configuration	Ground State	Atomic Number	Element	Electronic Configuration	Ground State
1	H	$1s$	$^2S_{1/2}$	16	S	— $3s^23p^4$	$^3P_2$
2	He	$1s^2$	$^1S_0$	17	Cl	— $3s^23p^5$	$^2P_{3/2}$
3	Li	[He] $2s$	$^2S_{1/2}$	18	Ar	— $3s^23p^6$	$^1S_0$
4	Be	— $2s^2$	$^1S_0$	19	K	[Ar] $4s$	$^2S_{1/2}$
5	B	— $2s^22p$	$^2P_{1/2}$	20	Ca	— $4s^2$	$^1S_0$
6	C	— $2s^22p^2$	$^3P_0$	21	Sc	— $3d4s^2$	$^2D_{3/2}$
7	N	— $2s^22p^3$	$^4S_{3/2}$	22	Ti	— $3d^24s^2$	$^3F_2$
8	O	— $2s^22p^4$	$^3P_2$	23	V	— $3d^34s^2$	$^4F_{3/2}$
9	F	— $2s^22p^5$	$^2P_{3/2}$	24	Cr	— $3d^54s$	$^7S_3$
10	Ne	— $2s^22p^6$	$^1S_0$	25	Mn	— $3d^54s^2$	$^6S_{5/2}$
11	Na	[Ne] $3s$	$^2S_{1/2}$	26	Fe	— $3d^64s^2$	$^5D_4$
12	Mg	— $3s^2$	$^1S_0$	27	Co	— $3d^74s^2$	$^4F_{9/2}$
13	Al	— $3s^23p$	$^2P_{1/2}$	28	Ni	— $3d^84s^2$	$^3F_4$
14	Si	— $3s^23p^2$	$^3P_0$	29	Cu	— $3d^{10}4s$	$^2S_{1/2}$
15	P	— $3s^23p^3$	$^4S_{3/2}$	30	Zn	— $3d^{10}3s^2$	$^1S_0$

(TABLE 3–4 continued on p. 88)

TABLE 3–4 (Continued)

Atomic Number	Element	Electronic Configuration	Ground State	Atomic Number	Element	Electronic Configuration	Ground State
31	Ga	— $3d^{10}4s^24p$	$^2P_{1/2}$	69	Tm	— $4f^{13}6s^2$	$^2F_{7/2}$
32	Ge	— $3d^{10}4s^24p^2$	$^3P_0$	70	Yb	— $4f^{14}6s^2$	$^1S_0$
33	As	— $3d^{10}4s^24p^3$	$^4S_{3/2}$	71	Lu	— $4f^{14}5d6s^2$	$^2D_{3/2}$
34	Se	— $3d^{10}4s^24p^4$	$^3P_2$	72	Hf	— $4f^{14}5d^26s^2$	$^3F_2$
35	Br	— $3d^{10}4s^24p^5$	$^2P_{3/2}$	73	Ta	— $4f^{14}5d^36s^2$	$^4F_{3/2}$
36	Kr	— $3d^{10}4s^24p^6$	$^1S_0$	74	W	— $4f^{14}5d^46s^2$	$^5D_0$
37	Rb	[Kr] $5s$	$^2S_{1/2}$	75	Re	— $4f^{14}5d^56s^2$	$^6S_{5/2}$
38	Sr	— $5s^2$	$^1S_0$	76	Os	— $4f^{14}5d^66s^2$	$^5D_4$
39	Y	— $4d5s^2$	$^2D_{3/2}$	77	Ir	— $4f^{14}5d^76s^2$	$^4F_{9/2}$
40	Zr	— $4d^25s^2$	$^3F_2$	78	Pt	— $4f^{14}5d^96s$	$^3D_3$
41	Nb	— $4d^45s$	$^6D_{1/2}$	79	Au	[ ] $6s$	$^2S_{1/2}$
42	Mo	— $4d^55s$	$^7S_3$	80	Hg	— $6s^2$	$^1S_0$
43	Tc	— $4d^55s^2$	$^6S_{5/2}$	81	Tl	— $6s^26p$	$^2P_{1/2}$
44	Ru	— $4d^75s$	$^5F_5$	82	Pb	— $6s^26p^2$	$^3P_0$
45	Rh	— $4d^85s$	$^4F_{9/2}$	83	Bi	— $6s^26p^3$	$^4S_{3/2}$
46	Pd	— $4d^{10}$	$^1S_0$	84	Po	— $6s^26p^4$	$^3P_2$
47	Ag	— $4d^{10}5s$	$^2S_{1/2}$	85	At	— $6s^26p^5$	$^2P_{3/2}$
48	Cd	— $4d^{10}5s^2$	$^1S_0$	86	Rn	— $6s^26p^6$	$^1S_0$
49	In	— $4d^{10}5s^25p$	$^2P_{1/2}$	87	Fr	[Rn] $7s$	$^2S_{1/2}$
50	Sn	— $4d^{10}5s^25p^2$	$^3P_0$	88	Ra	— $7s^2$	$^1S_0$
51	Sb	— $4d^{10}5s^25p^3$	$^4S_{3/2}$	89	Ac	— $6d7s^2$	$^2D_{3/2}$
52	Te	— $4d^{10}5s^25p^4$	$^3P_2$	90	Th	— $6d^27s^2$	$^3F_2$
53	I	— $4d^{10}5s^25p^5$	$^2P_{3/2}$	91	Pa	— $5f^26d7s^2$	$^4K_{11/2}$
54	Xe	— $4d^{10}5s^25p^6$	$^1S_0$	92	U	— $5f^36d7s^2$	$^5L_6$
55	Cs	[Xe] $6s$	$^2S_{1/2}$	93	Np	— $5f^46d7s^2$	$^6L_{11/2}$
56	Ba	— $6s^2$	$^1S_0$	94	Pu	— $5f^67s^2$	$^7F_0$
57	La	— $5d6s^2$	$^2D_{3/2}$	95	Am	— $5f^77s^2$	$^8S_{7/2}$
58	Ce	— $4f^26s^2$	$^3H_4$	96	Cm	— $5f^76d7s^2$	$^9D_2$
59	Pr	— $4f^36s^2$	$^4I_{9/2}$	97	Bk	— $5f^86d7s^2$	$^8H_{17/2}$
60	Nd	— $4f^46s^2$	$^5I_4$			or	
61	Pm	— $4f^56s^2$	$^6H_{5/2}$			$5f^97s^2$	$^6H_{15/2}$
62	Sm	— $4f^66s^2$	$^7F_0$	98	Cf	— $5f^{10}7s^2$	$^5I_8$
63	Eu	— $4f^76s^2$	$^8S_{7/2}$	99	Es	— $5f^{11}7s^2$	$^4I_{15/2}$
64	Gd	— $4f^75d6s^2$	$^9D_2$	100	Fm	— $5f^{12}7s^2$	$^3H_6$
65	Tb	— $4f^96s^2$	$^6H_{15/2}$	101	Md	— $5f^{13}7s^2$	$^2F_{7/2}$
66	Dy	— $4f^{10}6s^2$	$^5I_8$	102	No	— $5f^{14}7s^2$	$^1S_0$
67	Ho	— $4f^{11}6s^2$	$^4I_{15/2}$	103		— $5f^{14}6d7s^2$	$^2D_{5/2}$
68	Er	— $4f^{12}6s^2$	$^3H_6$				

listed in terms of the s, p, d, and f states. It is interesting to note that the order of filling is not exactly that which one might expect. The order appears to be normal as far as element 18, where it is seen to be $1s^2\ 2s^2\ 2p^6\ 3s^2\ 3p^6$. We note that the s state in the first shell and the s and p states of the second shell are completely filled. In the third shell, the s and p states are completed giving a total of 18 electrons. The next state that would be expected to fill is the $3d$ state. However, element number 19 is potassium and lies in the block of 2, which means that the next electron must be an s electron rather than a d electron. This may not be what we would like to see, but it is what nature demands. Thus, the electron configuration for potassium is $1s^2\ 2s^2\ 2p^6\ 3s^2\ 3p^6\ 4s^1$. Element number 20 is calcium and also lies in the s block. Therefore, calcium will complete the $4s$ state giving the configuration - - - $4s^2$. At this point we find that the next element is the first in a block of 10. This, of course, would indicate the beginning of a d group of electrons. Since the d electrons occur first in the third shell, this must be a $3d$ electron, and the electron configuration for scandium will be

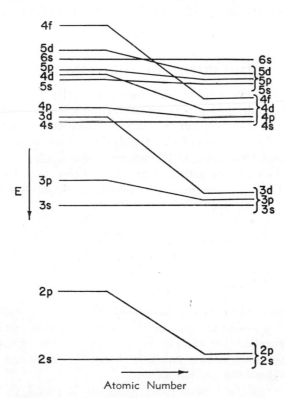

FIGURE 3–15. Energy Dependence of Atomic Orbitals as a Function of Atomic Number.

$1s^2\ 2s^2\ 2p^6\ 3s^2\ 3p^6\ 4s^2\ 3d^1$. Thus, it is seen that the simple order of filling does not hold and the $4s$ state fills before the $3d$ state. It is found that the three transition series are always one shell behind. For the rare earth series, it is found that an even greater overlap exists. The third transition series actually is observed to start with lanthanum which has an electron configuration - - - $6s^2\ 5d^1$. After lanthanum, element 58, cerium, is the first of a group of 14 elements, which indicates that it is the first member of a group of elements filling the f state. Since the f electrons occur first in the fourth shell, the $4f$ state obviously has been skipped until this point. Thus, the electron configuration for cerium would then be expected to be - - - $6s^2\ 5d^1\ 4f^1$. Actually, the $5d$ electron is found to drop down to the f state giving the configuration - - - $6s^2\ 4f^2$. Nevertheless, the f state is found to be two shells behind before it begins to fill.

The explanation of this unexpected order of filling of the electron states lies in the splitting of the energy levels as more and more electrons are fed into the atom. This splitting is indicated in Figure 3–15, where it is seen that the ns state overlaps the $(n-1)d$ state, and the $4f$ state is overlapped to an even greater extent.

SIMILARITIES OF THE ELEMENTS

The original periodic tables were based upon the observed similarities in chemical and physical properties of certain groups of elements. The alkali metals, for instance, were listed in a single column because it was observed that the members of this family had quite surprisingly similar properties. An understanding of the source of this similarity in properties, however, had to wait for a satisfactory model of the atom. In terms of our present model, we can see from the electron configurations of the alkali metals,

Li	$1s^2$	$2s^1$					
Na	- -	$2s^2$	$2p^6$	$3s^1$			
K	- - - - - -	$3s^2$	$3p^6$	$4s^1$			
Rb	- - - - - - - - - -	$4s^2$	$3d^{10}$	$4p^6$	$5s^1$		
Cs	- - - - - - - - - - - - - - - - -	$5s^2$	$4d^{10}$	$5p^6$	$6s^1$		

that each member of the family has one electron in the s state of the outside shell, with a similar internal electron structure. It is this similarity in electron configuration that leads to the similarities in chemical and physical properties of the alkali metals. Needless to say, this same sort of similarity is found throughout the periodic table.

In addition to the vertical similarities, it is found that horizontal similarities exist for certain groups of elements. This is particularly pronounced for the lanthanide elements, but it is also quite important in the transition elements. For the lanthanides, we note that the electron configuration between the fourteen members differs almost exclusively in the $4f$ subshell. If, for example, we consider the following four members with their electron configurations

Ce	$1s^2$	$2s^2$	$2p^6$	$3s^2$	$3p^6$	$4s^2$	$3d^{10}$	$4p^6$	$5s^2$	$4d^{10}$	$5p^6$	$6s^2$	$4f^2$	
Pr	-	-	-	-	-	-	-	-	-	-	-	$6s^2$	$4f^3$	
Nd	-	-	-	-	-	-	-	-	-	-	-	$6s^2$	$4f^4$	
Gd	-	-	-	-	-	-	-	-	-	-	-	$6s^2$	$4f^7$	$5d^1$

the only variation that is noted is the successive increase in the occupancy of the $4f$ orbital and the one electron in the $5d$ state in the case of gadolinium. Inasmuch as these shells are buried somewhat below the valence shell, their contribution to the properties of the elements is quite small, and a strong horizontal similarity results.

MODERN TRENDS IN PERIODIC TABLES

Realizing that the basis of the periodic system lies in the electron configurations of the elements, many authors have attempted to classify the elements in a manner that better emphasizes this fact.[6] Typical of this modern approach is the table proposed by Longuet-Higgins[7] shown in Figure 3–16. The important feature of the Longuet-Higgins table is the emphasis on the order of filling of electron states in relation to the order of increasing energy states. Visually this is convenient. However, it might be mentioned that, if the s, p, d, f blocks are recognized, the long form of the periodic table tells essentially the same thing. Nevertheless, there are some desirable features in the Longuet-Higgins table just as there are desirable features in most of the hundreds of other tables that have been proposed. The very fact that so many tables have been proposed points out the variety of opinions that exist and at the same time indicates how difficult it would be to prescribe a best periodic table.

THE TYPES OF ELEMENTS

Using electron configurations as the criterion, we ordinarily recognize four general types of elements; the *inert gas elements*, the *representative elements*, the *transition elements*, and the *inner transition elements*. The classification of the elements into these groups is dependent on the extent to which the s, p, d, and f orbitals are filled. That is, it is dependent on whether the particular orbitals are complete or incomplete. By a completed subshell, we refer to the agreement between the number of electrons

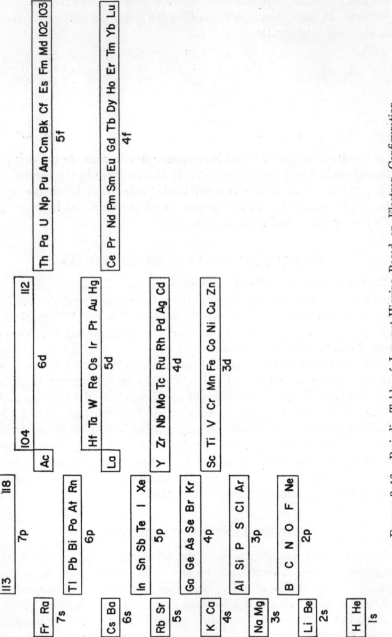

FIGURE 3–16. Periodic Table of Longuet-Higgins Based on Electron Configuration.

in the various shells of a given atom and the number in the corresponding shells of the inert gas of next higher or lower atomic number.

Inert Gas Elements

With the exception of helium which has the configuration $1s^2$, all of the members of this group of elements have completed s and p orbitals. Thus, in general, they may be characterized by the configuration $ns^2\,np^6$. This is the smallest class of elements, having but six members, all of which are chemically inert because of the high stability associated with the completed s and p orbitals.

Representative Elements

The members of this group of elements have all but their outer electron shell complete. Thus, any atom with an outer electron configuration from ns^1 to $ns^2\,np^5$ belongs in this class. There will be 44 members in this group if strict adherence to the above electronic arrangement is maintained. This includes the copper and zinc families. Some authors prefer to consider these latter six metals as transition elements because of their physical and chemical resemblance to that class. There are certainly some valid arguments for such a stand, particularly in light of the chemistry of the members of the copper family in their higher oxidation states.

The chemical behavior of the members of this class will be determined to a large extent by the tendency for these atoms to gain, lose, or share electrons in such a manner as to attain the electronic configuration of the inert gas of next higher or lower atomic number, or the so-called *pseudo-inert gas* configuration $(n-1)s^2p^6d^{10}$. Many of the metals, and all of the nonmetals and metalloids make up the group of representative elements.

Transition Elements

The transition elements have their two outer principal quantum shells incomplete and are characterized specifically by their incomplete $(n-1)d$ subshell. Because of the extra stability which is associated with empty, half-filled, and filled subshells, there are some apparent anomalies in electronic arrangements in the transition series. This empirical rule is illustrated by the chromium and copper configurations in the first d series of elements:

	Sc	Ti	V	Cr	Mn	Fe	Co	Ni	Cu	Zn
$3d$	1	2	3	5	5	6	7	8	10	10
$4s$	2	2	2	1	2	2	2	2	1	2

There are four transition series corresponding to unfilled $3d$, $4d$, $5d$, and $6d$ orbitals. The series begin with the group IIIA elements Sc, Y, La, and Ac, and the first three series end, by definition, with Ni, Pd, and Pt, respectively. The elements in this class show striking resemblances to each other, particularly in their physical properties. The oxidation states are very numerous, compounds are highly colored, and coordination compounds are the rule whereas simple compounds are the exception.

Inner Transition Elements

By definition, these elements are transition series elements, but they have an additional feature in their electronic arrangement which justifies setting them apart from the other transition elements. In this group, it is found that the outer three principal quantum levels are incomplete due to incomplete $(n-2)f$ orbitals. In general, the configuration for this class may be given as $(n-2)f^{1-14}$ $(n-1)s^2p^6d^{1 \text{ or } 0}ns^2$. The empty, half-filled, and filled sublevel stability rule holds here also, and indeed this is invoked to explain the oxidation states other than 3 among the lanthanides. The outstanding feature of these elements is the great similarity in chemical and physical properties which they display.

There can be no question that a second inner transition series exists in which $5f$ orbitals are being occupied. However, there is some question as to where this series actually begins, i.e., where $5f$ type electrons first appear. The primary difficulty in attempting to assign electrons to specific orbitals in the elements just beyond actinium lies in the closeness in energy between the $5f$ and $6d$ orbitals. The energy released in chemical bond formation is sufficient to transfer electrons between these high levels. By analogy with the $4f$ series, the first $5f$ electron should appear in thorium. However, many properties of this element indicate that it should be placed in family IVA, below hafnium, rather than below cerium in family IIIA. Likewise, on the basis of many of their properties, protactinium and uranium would appear to fit better into families VA and VIA respectively, rather than below praeseodymium and neodymium. Yet there is now substantial spectral and chemical evidence which supports the contention that the elements beyond actinium do form a second rare-earth series, and that the first appearance of $5f$ electrons is in protactinium.

One fact seems certain with regard to the second inner transition series and that is that, as in the other transition series, the relative energy position of the level which is being filled becomes lower as the successive electrons are added. By the time neptunium, plutonium and the subsequent members of the series are reached, the $5f$ shell seems clearly to be of lower energy than the $6d$ shell.

BIBLIOGRAPHY

1. Tilden, W., "A Short History of the Progress of Scientific Chemistry," Longmans, Green & Co., Inc., New York, N.Y., 1899.
2. Taylor, W., *J. Chem. Ed.*, **26,** 491 (1949).
3. Foster, L., *J. Chem. Ed.*, **16,** 409 (1939).
4. Luder, W., *J. Chem. Ed.*, **20,** 21 (1943).
5. Moseley, H., *Phil. Mag.*, **26,** 1024 (1913); **27,** 703 (1914).
6. Quam, G. and Quam, M., *J. Chem. Ed.*, **11,** 27, 217, 288 (1934).
7. Longuet-Higgins, H., *J. Chem. Ed.*, **34,** 30 (1957).

SUGGESTED SUPPLEMENTARY READING

Moeller, T., "Inorganic Chemistry," John Wiley & Sons, Inc., New York, N.Y., 1952.

Main Smith, J., "Chemistry and Atomic Structure," Ernest Benn Ltd., London, 1924.

Tilden, W., "A Short History of the Progress of Scientific Chemistry," Longmans, Green & Co., Inc., New York, N.Y., 1899.

4 / *Periodic Properties*

From the discussion of the periodic table, it is evident that those properties which depend upon the electron configuration of an atom will vary periodically with atomic number. On the other hand, those properties which depend upon the total number of electrons will show no such variations. Some of the more common properties which depend upon electron configuration are listed in Table 4–1. Not only are these properties periodic

TABLE 4–1. / **Properties Dependant Upon Electronic Configuration.**

Atomic radius (and volume)	Heat of solvation of ions
Ionic radius	Hardness
Density	Malleability
Ionization potential	Coefficient of expansion
Electron affinity	Optical spectrum
Electronegativity	Magnetic behavior
Melting point	Thermal conductivity
Boiling point	Electrical resistance
Standard redox potential	Ion mobility
Valence (and oxidation number)	Parachor
Compressibility	Refractive Index
Heats of fusion, vaporization and sublimation	Heat of formation of a given compound type

for the elements, but they are also periodic for the analogous compounds of the elements. It should be realized that, although the properties observed for one member within a family reappear in other members of the family, there is also a more or less regular change in these similar properties in going from the lightest to the heaviest member of the family. This can be seen in Table 4–2 in which are listed some trends in selected physical properties for several families.

TABLE 4–2. / **Trends of Physical Properties of Elements Within a Family.**

Boiling Points of the Inert Gases (°K)		Metallic Radii of Alkali Metal Atoms (Å)		Melting Points of Halogens (°K)		Densities of IIIB Elements (g/cc)	
He	4.2	Li	1.55	F	50	B	2.5
Ne	27.2	Na	1.90	Cl	171	Al	2.70
Ar	87.4	K	2.35	Br	266	Ga	5.91
Kr	121	Rb	2.48	I	386	In	7.3
Xe	164	Cs	2.67	At	—	Tl	11.85
Rn	211	Fr	—				

As aids in predicting and explaining chemical properties of the elements, some of the periodic properties are of much greater importance than others. These are the *ionization potential, electron affinity, electronegativity, valence* or *oxidation number,* and size properties such as *atomic* and *ionic radii.*

ATOMIC AND IONIC RADII[*]

Of the various properties of the atoms that affect their chemical character, the atomic and ionic size are among the most important. This has been emphasized in the periodic table shown in Figure 4–1, which was devised by Campbell and shows the variations of atomic and ionic radii. The Campbell table maintains the general arrangement of the long form of the periodic table, but the atoms and their ions are indicated as circles of varying sizes. The radii of the circles illustrate the relative sizes of the atoms and ions as determined from X-ray data. The actual radii in angstroms, appear below the circles.

The first attempt to correlate atomic sizes was in terms of the atomic volume. It was the atomic volume curve of Lothar Meyer shown in Figure 3–7, that brought him more fame than his periodic table based on the physical properties of the elements. It was seen that the atomic volume is determined by dividing the atomic weight of the element by its density, and consequently it is only as reliable as the density determination. Now, the density of an element is obviously going to depend to a great degree upon such factors as its physical state, its allotropic modification, the tem-

[*] We are actually dealing here with apparent radii since the various radii calculated from the measured dimensions of crystals do not represent the actual extension of atoms or ions, but rather are a measure of the distances to which the centers of the atoms or ions can approach one another in the crystal.

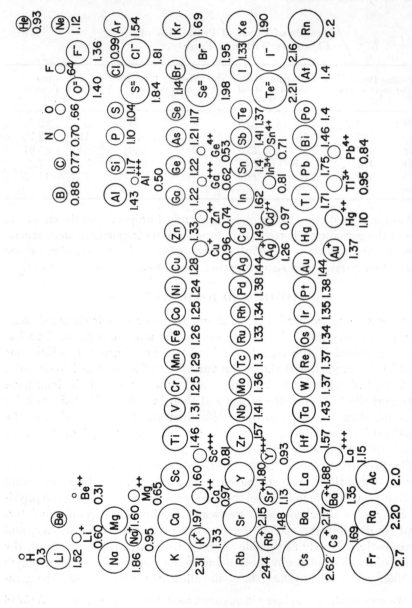

FIGURE 4–1.   Periodic Table According to Campbell Showing Atomic and Ionic Sizes.

perature at which the density was determined, and the crystal structure. Variations in any of these factors can lead to anomalous results. For instance, the white form of tin has a density of 7.31 whereas the gray form has a density of 5.75. With all of the possible variations that can affect the reliability of the atomic volume, it is rather surprising that the atomic volume curve is quite accurate in its representation of periodicity of properties depending on size.

Since it is obviously impossible to isolate an individual atom or ion and determine its radius, we must rely upon measurements made on bulk materials and assume that our atomic models are correct in their description of the ways in which atoms and ions occur in the whole structure. Here, it is soon realized that many factors will affect our calculations, among which may be mentioned the bond order, that is, whether the bonds are single or multiple bonds, the degree of ionic or covalent character in the bonds, the oxidation number of the atoms concerned, the crystal structure, and the bond type. Because of the many variables, it is found that no single type of atomic radius is completely satisfactory, and we must speak of such radii as *tetrahedral* radii, *ionic* radii, *van der Waals* radii, and so on.[1,2]

Covalent Radii

The covalent radius of an atom is taken as one half the distance between the nuclei of two like atoms forming a single covalent bond. From this we can infer that the bond distance between two atoms $A—B$ should be the arithmetic mean of the bond lengths $A—A$ and $B—B$. As an example, consider $A—A$ to represent the normal carbon-carbon bond distance and the $B—B$ to represent the normal silicon-silicon bond distance. We can now assign a covalent radius to carbon that is one half the experimentally determined distance between the carbon nuclei in the $C—C$ single bond. This leads to a value of 0.77 Å. The same treatment gives a value of 1.17 Å for the covalent radius of silicon. Now, if we consider the bond distance between carbon and silicon, we would expect a bond length of 1.94 Å. This is in very good agreement with the experimentally determined C-Si distance of 1.93 Å in carborundum (silicon carbide).

Although the results are extremely satisfying for the C-Si bond distance, this is not generally the case. Very often there is considerable deviation from the expected results, and a great amount of work has been devoted to this problem. These deviations from the ideal behavior are usually attributed to multiple bonds, ionic character, and the various possible hybridized orbitals that determine the geometry of covalently bonded molecules.

Due to different geometry of the orbitals in the covalently bonded atoms, it is necessary to speak of the covalent radii in terms of this geometry. For instance, many of the elements form structures in which there are four bonded atoms, each at the corner of a tetrahedron around the central atom. Such a structure is a tetrahedral structure, and the covalent radii for these structures are said to be *tetrahedral* radii. On the other hand, some elements have a coordination number of 6, and therefore have six atoms arranged around the central atom at the corners of an octahedron. Such a structure is an octahedral structure, and the covalent radii are here referred to as *octahedral* radii. The covalent radii are usually classified as either normal radii, tetrahedral radii, octahedral radii, square radii, or metallic radii. In general, there is little difference between the various types of covalent radii for a given atom, and they can often be used inter-changeably. The Campbell periodic table shown in Figure 4–1 gives values for atomic radii which are, in general, the same as single-bond covalent radii for elements whose atoms form single covalent bonds in the solid state. However, most elements are metals, and the metallic bond uniting their respective atoms affords a metallic radius which is invariably larger than the single-bond covalent radius for the same atoms. This is apparent from the comparison of the radii of the group of metals and nonmetals shown in Table 4–3.

TABLE 4–3. / **Comparison of Atomic Radii and Single-Bond Covalent Radii for Some Metals and Nonmetals.**

Metals	Atomic Radius	Single Bond Covalent Radius	Nonmetals	Atomic Radius	Single Bond Covalent Radius
K	2.31	2.025	C	0.77	0.771
Ba	2.17	1.981	P	1.10	1.10
La	1.88	1.690	S	1.04	1.04
Zr	1.57	1.454	Br	1.14	1.142
Pd	1.38	1.278			
In	1.62	1.497			

The simple additivity principle appears to work quite well for many elements, but it is particularly bad when the bonds involve elements with large differences in *electronegativity*. Since the ionic character of a bond increases with an increase in electronegativity difference between the bonded atoms, it would appear that the discrepancies are due to ionic character in the bond. To compensate for this ionic character, Schomaker and Stevenson[3] proposed the empirical relation

$$r_{AB} = r_A + r_B - 0.09 \, (x_A - x_B) \qquad (4-1)$$

where x_A and x_B are the Pauling electronegativity coefficients for elements A and B, respectively. Although, it appears that the Schomaker and Stevenson equation is not theoretically sound, the Schomaker and Stevenson correction is an improvement over the simple additivity of pure covalent radii. In 1953, M. L. Huggins[4] suggested a simple relationship between bond energies and bond lengths. He found that for a great many covalent bonds, there is a number, r^*_{AB}, called the *covalent energy distance* which is related to the actual bond length, r_{AB}, and the bond energy, E_{AB}, as follows:

$$r^*_{AB} = r_{AB} + \frac{1}{2} \log_{10} E_{AB} \qquad (4\text{-}2)$$

The constant energy distances are about 0.8 Å greater than ordinary covalent bond lengths. These are found to be separable into independent contributions from each of the bonded atoms. These separate contributing parts are termed *constant energy radii* and they may then be used to calculate bond lengths according to the relation

$$r_{AB} = r^*_A + r^*_B - \frac{1}{2} \log_{10} E_{AB} \qquad (4\text{-}3)$$

Except for hydrogen, the agreement with experiment is excellent.

Ionic Radii

When neutral atoms gain or lose electrons completely, ions are obtained. Positive ions will be smaller than their parent atoms and negative ions will be larger. This is readily understood in terms of the number of electrons the nuclear charge must hold. For a positive ion, the nuclear charge is acting on fewer electrons and hence pulls them all in closer, whereas in the case of a negative ion the nuclear charge must act upon more electrons so that each is held less tightly, and the electron cloud expands. As would be expected, the radius of the ion decreases with an increase in the number of electrons lost. This is illustrated in Tables 4–4 and 4–5.

TABLE 4–4. / **Radii of Ions With Inert Gas Configurations.**

	H^- 1.54	Li^+ 0.60	Be^{2+} 0.31	B^{3+} 0.20	C^{4+} 0.15			
$O^=$ 1.40	F^- 1.36	Na^+ 0.95	Mg^{2+} 0.65	Al^{3+} 0.50	Si^{4+} 0.41	P^{5+} 0.34	S^{6+} 0.29	Cl^{7+} 0.26
$S^=$ 1.84	Cl^- 1.81	K^+ 1.33	Ca^{2+} 0.99	Sc^{3+} 0.81	Ti^{4+} 0.68	V^{5+} 0.59	Cr^{6+} 0.52	Mn^{7+} 0.46
$Se^=$ 1.98	Br^- 1.95	Rb^+ 1.48	Sr^{2+} 1.13	Y^{3+} 0.93	Zr^{4+} 0.80	Nb^{5+} 0.70	Mo^{6+} 0.62	Tc^{7+} —
$Te^=$ 2.21	I^- 2.16	Cs^+ 1.69	Ba^{2+} 1.35	La^{3+} 1.15	Hf^{4+} 0.79	Ta^{5+} 0.71	W^{6+} 0.65	Re^{7+} 0.50

The problem of determining ionic radii is very different from that of obtaining covalent radii. Since like atoms do not form ionic bonds with each other, the measured distance between nuclei held by ionic bonds

TABLE 4–5. / **Comparison of Sizes of Atoms and Their Ions With Increasing Charge.***

Ti 1.46	V 1.31	Cr 1.25	Mn 1.29	Fe 1.26	Co 1.25	Ni 1.24	Pb 1.75
Ti^{2+} 0.90	V^{2+} 0.88	Cr^{2+} 0.84	Mn^{2+} 0.80	Fe^{2+} 0.76	Co^{2+} 0.74	Ni^{2+} 0.72	Pb^{2+} 1.20
Ti^{3+} 0.76	V^{3+} 0.74	Cr^{3+} 0.69	Mn^{3+} 0.66	Fe^{3+} 0.64	Co^{3+} 0.63	Ni^{3+} 0.62	
	V^{4+} 0.60	Cr^{4+} 0.56	Mn^{4+} 0.54				Pb^{4+} 0.84

* Values of the ions are empirical.

cannot be halved to give the desired ionic radii. The measurement of interionic distances can be readily made, but it is not a simple problem to determine that portion of the internuclear distance contributed by the cation and that portion contributed by the anion.

In order for the concept of ionic radii to be of use, it is necessary that the sum of two such radii be equal to the equilibrium distance between the corresponding ions in a crystal. For two oppositely charged ions, this distance will be dependent on the electron distributions and charges on the ions, the crystal structure, and the cation to anion radius ratio. A semiempirical method for obtaining a set of ionic radii which involves, first of all, a set of experimental values of interionic distances for the five ionic compounds NaF, KCl, RbBr, CsI, and Li_2O, has been devised by Pauling.[5] For the first four, most of the factors affecting ionic size are held constant since the ions in each are isoelectronic and univalent, and the radius ratios are all roughly 0.75. Now, the size of an ion is assumed by Pauling to be inversely proportional to the effective nuclear charge operative on these electrons. The *effective nuclear charge*, Z_{eff}, is equal to the actual nuclear charge minus the screening effect, S, of the other electrons in the ion. Therefore, we may write the equation for the radii of a sequence of isoelectronic ions as

$$r_{ion} = \frac{C_n}{Z - S} \qquad (4\text{--}4)$$

in which C_n is a constant depending only upon the principal quantum number of the outermost electrons.

For each of the five crystals chosen by Pauling we have two equations with two unknowns, the cation radius and the anion radius. The first of these,

$$r_c + r_a = \text{measured internuclear distance} \qquad (4\text{-}5)$$

is an experimental expression, and the second,

$$\frac{r_c}{r_a} = \frac{Z_a - S}{Z_c - S} \qquad (4\text{-}6)$$

is derived in terms of our semitheoretical considerations. Solving these equations simultaneously, the ionic radii in angstroms are found to be

Na^+	K^+	Rb^+	Cs^+
0.95	1.33	1.48	1.69

F^-	Cl^-	Br^-	I^-
1.36	1.81	1.95	2.16

A value of 0.60 Å was selected for Li^+ to agree with the observed $Li^+ - O^{2-}$ distance of 2.00 Å in Li_2O and the best empirical value for oxygen of 1.40 Å.

Using Eq. (4-4) and the values for C_n determined for the alkali halides, it is possible to obtain radii for all ions having the inert gas electron configurations. It should be pointed out, however, that the radii determined in this way for all polyvalent ions represent correctly only their sizes relative to those for the alkali and halide ions, and are not absolute values whose sums would yield equilibrium interionic distances. These relative radii are called *univalent radii*, and represent the radii that polyvalent ions would possess if they were to retain their electron distributions but enter into ionic interactions as if they were univalent. Fortunately it is possible to obtain the physically significant crystal radii for polyvalent ions from the univalent radii by multiplying the univalent radii by a factor derivable from the Born equation.[6]

PERIODIC TRENDS OF ATOMIC AND IONIC SIZE

Reference to Campbell's periodic table will show that in a given period of the periodic table there is a gradual decrease in atomic radius with increasing atomic number. While there is a progressive addition of electrons as we proceed across the table, these electrons are being added to orbitals having very nearly the same energy. The result is that the increased nuclear charge pulls in the entire electron cloud to an increasingly greater extent. In general, the decrease in size is most pronounced as a second s electron is added to the valence shell, and the relative decrease in size becomes progressively smaller for p, d, and f electrons.[7] Moving to the next period corresponds to addition of electrons to the next higher quantum level. Thus, the size goes up for the first member of each period and the gradual decrease is observed again proceeding across the table.

For ions of the representative elements, the contraction in size in going from left to right in the table is even more marked than is observed for the parent atoms. This is illustrated in Table 4–6, for the isoelectronic series C^{4-}, N^{3-}, O^{2-}, F^-, Na^+, Mg^{2+}, Al^{3+}, and Si^{4+}. The larger percentage

TABLE 4–6. / **Contraction in Size of an Isoelectronic Series of Ions.**

C	N	O	F	Na	Mg	Al	Si
0.77	0.70	0.66	0.64	1.51	1.36	1.25	1.17
C^{4-}	N^{3-}	O^{2-}	F^-	Na^+	Mg^{2+}	Al^{3+}	Si^{4+}
2.60	1.71	1.40	1.36	0.95	0.65	0.50	0.41

decrease in the size of the ions as compared to the sizes of the parent atoms is, of course, due to the increasing nuclear charge on the ions which is acting always on the same number of electrons. The negative ions are larger than their parent atoms, but will show the same trends.

For the transition elements, the variations in the atomic and ionic radii are not quite so simple as for the representative elements. Proceeding horizontally across the transition series of elements, it can be seen in Table 4–5, as well as from the Campbell Table, that a general decrease in atomic and ionic radii occurs. However, the decrease, which is not uniform, is slight when compared to the decrease observed with a given period of representative elements. This is undoubtedly a result of the fact that the differentiating electrons in the transition elements are entering an inner shell, the $(n - 1)d$ subshell. The additional electrons effectively screen much of the added nuclear charge from the outer ns electrons, and the size of the atom remains almost constant.

An increase in both atomic and ionic radii with atomic number occurs in a given transition family, but again, to a lesser extent than found in the representative element families. For example, the increase in size from germanium with a radius of 1.22 Å to lead with a radius of 1.75 Å is an increase of 43.5 per cent, but the increase from vanadium with a radius of 1.3 Å to tantalum with a radius of 1.43 Å is only 9.2 per cent. Furthermore, the major portion of this increase for a transition family occurs between the first and second member. This might seem somewhat surprising since each element in the second transition series is just 18 elements removed from its congener in the first transition series, whereas each element of the third transition series is 32 elements removed from its congener in the second series. However, the additional 14 intervening elements are members of the inner transition series of elements in which electrons are entering the $4f$ orbitals. Since the $4f$ subshell lies two quantum levels lower than the valence shell, there occurs a gradual contraction in size from lanthanum through lutetium. The regular decrease in size of the lanthanide atoms and trivalent ions has been termed the *lanthanide contraction*, and its effects upon the atomic and ionic sizes of postlanthanide elements is quite pronounced. The near identical sizes of both atoms and ions of zirconium and its congener hafnium, 32 atomic numbers later, gives rise to a chemical similarity between these elements almost unparalleled in the periodic table. Likewise, the elements niobium and tantalum are very similar to each other as are the other second and third transition series elements of a given family.

The great importance of size effects on the properties of the elements cannot be overemphasized. This is most evident to the chemist trying to affect the chemical separation of the lanthanide elements or of the pairs zirconium and hafnium or niobium and tantalum.

As expected, an analogous decrease in atom and ion size occurs in the second inner transition series and has been termed the *actinide contraction*. This, as well as the lanthanide contraction, is illustrated in Table 4–7. Because of the several oxidation states which these elements display, chemical separation is considerably easier than it is in the lanthanide series.

TABLE 4–7. / **Ionic Radii of the Actinide and the Lanthanide Elements.***

LANTHANIDE SERIES				ACTINIDE SERIES			
Element	Radius (Å)	Element	Radius (Å)	Element	Radius (Å)	Element	Radius (Å)
La^{3+}	1.061			Ac^{3+}	1.11		
Ce^{3+}	1.034	Ce^{4+}	0.92	(Th^{3+})	(1.08)	Th^{4+}	0.99
Pr^{3+}	1.013	Pr^{4+}	0.90	(Pa^{3+})	(1.05)	Pa^{4+}	0.96
Nd^{3+}	0.995			U^{3+}	1.03	U^{4+}	0.93
Pm^{3+}	(0.979)			Np^{3+}	1.01	Np^{4+}	0.92
Sm^{3+}	0.964			Pu^{3+}	1.00	Pu^{4+}	0.90
Eu^{3+}	0.950			Am^{3+}	0.99	Am^{4+}	0.89
Gd^{3+}	0.938						
Tb^{3+}	0.923	Tb^{4+}	0.84				
Dy^{3+}	0.908						
Ho^{3+}	0.894						
Er^{3+}	0.881						
Tm^{3+}	0.869						
Yb^{3+}	0.858						
Lu^{3+}	0.848						

* From Seaborg, G. T., "The Transuranium Elements," Yale University Press, New Haven, Conn., 1958.

IONIZATION POTENTIAL

The *ionization potential* of an element is defined as the work necessary to completely remove the most loosely bound electron from the ground state of a neutral gaseous atom of that element. More precisely, we have defined the *first* ionization potential. The *second, third*, etc., ionization potentials would arise from the removal of electrons from singly positive, doubly positive, etc., ions, respectively.

The ionization potential is one of the few fundamental properties of the atom which we are able to measure directly. For this reason, it is of more than usual importance that we recognize the major factors that influence its magnitude.[8] It is in terms of such factors as these that we attempt to understand many of the general trends in periodic properties. For the ionization potential, the most important factors will be (1) the magnitude of the nuclear charge, (2) the distance of the outermost electron from the nucleus, that is, the atomic radius, (3) the shielding effect of the underlying shells of electrons, and (4) the extent to which the outer electron penetrates the charge cloud set up by the lower-lying electrons. With regard to the latter effect, it is found that the degree of penetration of electrons in a given principal quantum level decreases in the order $s > p > d > f$. This corresponds to the extent of binding of the various electrons. An ns electron is more tightly bound than an np electron, which, in turn, is more tightly bound than an nd electron, etc.

Due to its greater extent of penetration, it can be concluded that an s electron more effectively screens the nucleus than a p electron, and a p electron more effectively screens the nucleus than a d electron, and so on. For example, the $3s^2$, $3p^6$, and $3d^{10}$ electrons do not screen the nucleus of the copper atom nearly as well as the $3s^2$ and $3p^6$ electrons of the potassium atom screen its nucleus. That is, the less penetrating d electrons do not screen as effectively as the s and p electrons.

Utilizing this basic idea, it is possible to evaluate a *screening constant* for a particular electron. This constant is a measure of the extent to which the other electrons in an atom are able to screen the nucleus from the chosen electron. To determine the constant, the electrons are divided into the groups, $1s$, $2sp$, $3sp$, $3d$, $4sp$, $4d$, $4f$, $5sp$, etc., and each group is assigned a contribution per electron. The summation of all such contributions that effect a given electron determine its screening constant. In determining the screening constant for a chosen electron, the assigned contributions are: (1) nothing for any electrons outside or farther removed from the nucleus than the one considered, (2) an amount of 0.35 for each additional electron in the group considered (except in the $1s$ group, where 0.30 is used), (3) an amount of 0.85 for each electron in the next inner shell, (4) an amount of 1.00 for each electron closer to the nucleus than the $(n - 1)$

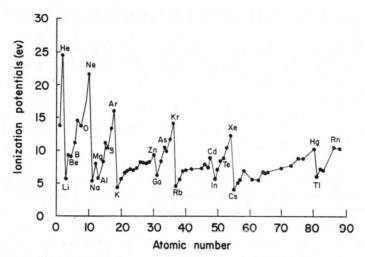

FIGURE 4–2. First Ionization Potentials of the Elements as a Function of Atomic Number.

shell, and (5) if the chosen electron is in a d or f shell, an amount of 1.00 contributed by each electron in a lower shell. As an example, the effective nuclear charge on an electron in the valence shell of nitrogen is

$$Z_{eff} = Z - S = 7 - (4 \times 0.35) - (2 \times 0.85) = 7 - 1.40 - 1.70 = 3.90$$

while the effective nuclear charge for an outer electron in gadolinium, $1s^2 \text{- - -} 4f^75s^25p^65d^16s^2$, is

$$Z_{eff} = 64 - (1 \times 0.35) - (9 \times 0.85) - (53 \times 1.00) = 64 - 61 = 3.0$$

The periodicity of the ionization potential can readily be appreciated from the plot of the first ionization potential *versus* atomic number shown in Figure 4–2. Consideration of the above factors permits an understanding of the general variations and trends in ionization potentials, provided the atomic radii and electronic configurations are known. The minima occupied by the I*A* elements on the curve are consistent with the lone valence electron being at a relatively large distance from the nucleus in addition to being well-shielded from it by the underlying inert gas configuration. Gradual increases occur as we proceed across any given period in the periodic table until maximums are reached at the inert gases on the extreme right, corresponding to the peaks in the curve. Minor irregularities which appear in the general trend are associated with the peculiar stability of filled, half-filled, and empty orbitals and are most pronounced among the representative elements. This may be illustrated with the third-period elements:

Element:	Na	Mg	Al	Si	P	S	Cl	Ar
IP (ev):	5.14	7.64	6.00	8.15	11.0	10.36	13.01	15.80

Magnesium has a filled 3s sublevel and phosphorus has a half-filled 3p sublevel.

Very little change in the ionization potential (IP) occurs across a given transition series. For that matter, very little change occurs among all of the transition elements, where numerical values range between 6 and 9 electron volts (ev). This would appear to be the result of the interplay of several factors. While the size is remaining relatively constant, the increased nuclear charge is offset by increased screening by the additional electrons entering lower-lying d sublevels.

As expected, the increase in atomic weight in a given family produces a decrease in ionization potential. This is to be associated with an increase in size while the same type of electron arrangement is maintained. This indicates that the effect of increased nuclear charge is more than counterbalanced by the size increase and the presence of more shielding electrons. There is, however, an exception to this vertical trend, and it occurs with the elements just following the lanthanides. The fact that these elements have higher ionization potentials than their congeners in the preceding period is another effect of the lanthanide contraction which results from the relatively large increase in nuclear charge without expansion to higher electron shells.

Finally, the peaks which occur at zinc, cadmium, and mercury, and the minima which occur at gallium, indium, and thallium are, most likely, the result of filled s sublevel stability and the very effective screening of the s pair.

A list of the ionization potentials of most of the elements is given in Table 4–8. The increased energy required to remove a second electron, the second ionization potential, or a third electron, the third ionization

TABLE 4–8. / **Ionization Potentials of the Elements.**

Atomic Number	Symbol	Ionization Potentials (ev)							
		I	II	III	IV	V	VI	VII	VIII
1	H	13.595							
2	He	24.580	54.403						
3	Li	5.390	75.619	122.420					
4	Be	9.320	18.206	153.850	217.657				
5	B	8.296	25.149	37.920	259.298	340.127			
6	C	11.264	24.376	47.864	64.476	391.986	489.84		
7	N	14.54	29.605	47.426	77.450	97.863	551.925	666.83	
8	O	13.614	35.146	54.934	77.394	113.873	138.080	739.114	871.12
9	F	17.418	34.98	62.646	87.23	114.214	157.117	185.139	953.60
10	Ne	21.559	41.07	64	97.16	126.4	157.91		

TABLE 4–8 (Continued)

Atomic No.	Symbol	Ionization Potentials		Atomic No.	Symbol	Ionization Potentials	
		I	II			I	II
11	Na	5.138	47.29	52	Te	9.01	21.5
12	Mg	7.644	15.03	53	I	10.44	19.0
13	Al	5.984	18.823	54	Xe	12.127	21.21
14	Si	8.149	16.34	55	Cs	3.893	25.1
15	P	10.55	19.65	56	Ba	5.210	10.001
16	S	10.357	23.4	57	La	5.61	11.43
17	Cl	13.01	23.80	58	Ce	(6.91)	14.8
18	Ar	15.755	27.62	59	Pr	(5.76)	
19	K	4.339	31.81	60	Nd	6.3	
20	Ca	6.111	11.87	61	Pm		
21	Sc	6.56	12.80	62	Sm	5.6	11.2
22	Ti	6.83	13.57	63	Eu	5.67	11.24
23	V	6.74	14.65	64	Gd	6.16	12.0
24	Cr	6.764	16.49	65	Tb	(6.74)	
25	Mn	7.432	15.64	66	Dy	(6.82)	
26	Fe	7.90	16.18	67	Ho		
27	Co	7.86	17.05	68	Er		
28	Ni	7.633	18.15	69	Tm		
29	Cu	7.724	20.29	70	Yb	6.22	12.10
30	Zn	9.391	17.96	71	Lu	6.15	14.7
31	Ga	6.00	20.51	72	Hf	7.5	14.9
32	Ge	7.88	15.93	73	Ta	7.7	
33	As	9.81	20.2	74	W	7.98	
34	Se	9.75	21.5	75	Re	7.87	
35	Br	11.84	21.6	76	Os	8.7	
36	Kr	13.996	24.56	77	Ir	9.2	
37	Rb	4.176	27.5	78	Pt	9.0	18.56
38	Sr	5.692	11.027	79	Au	9.22	20.5
39	Y	6.377	12.233	80	Hg	10.434	18.751
40	Zr	6.835	12.916	81	Tl	6.106	20.42
41	Nb	6.881	13.895	82	Pb	7.415	15.028
42	Mo	7.131	15.72	83	Bi	7.287	19.3
43	Tc	7.23	14.87	84	Po	8.43	
44	Ru	7.365	16.597	85	At		
45	Rh	7.461	15.92	86	Rn	10.745	
46	Pd	8.33	19.42	87	Fr		
47	Ag	7.574	21.48	88	Ra	5.277	10.14
48	Cd	8.991	16.904	89	Ac		
49	In	5.785	18.828	90	Th		
50	Sn	7.332	14.63	91	Pa		
51	Sb	8.639	19.0	92	U	4.0	

potential, and so on, can most easily be understood in terms of the greater amount of energy required to remove an electron from a $+n$ species than from a $+(n - 1)$ species.

ELECTRON AFFINITY

The *electron affinity* of an atom is defined as the energy released by a neutral gaseous atom in its lowest energy state when it accepts an electron. Thus, it is the energy of the reaction $X + e^- \rightarrow X^-$, where all species are gaseous and in their ground state. Experimentally, the electron affinity is considerably more difficult to determine than the ionization potential and has been determined only for the most electronegative elements. A direct experimental determination can be made of an electron affinity[9], but it is more common to determine it from a Born-Haber cycle as shown in Chapter 5.

The unexpectedly low value for the electron affinity of fluorine seen in Table 4–9, may be associated with electron-electron repulsion in the relatively compact $2p$ sublevel. From these values, it would appear that chlorine should be a better oxidizing agent than fluorine since more energy is released when the chlorine atom acquires an electron than when the fluorine does. However, the fluorine molecule is dissociated into single atoms with a lesser expense of energy (37.7 kcal/mole) than the corresponding dissociation of the chlorine molecule (57 kcal/mole). The low value for the dissociation energy of fluorine may be partially ascribed to the repulsion of *nonbonding* electrons, but it has generally been assumed that for chlorine, bromine, and iodine, hybridization of p and d valence shell orbitals strengthens these bonds[10].

TABLE 4–9. / **Electron Affinities of Some Elements, in Electron Volts (ev).***

Element	Electron Affinity	Element	Electron Affinity	Element	Electron Affinity	Element	Electron Affinity
F	3.62	Cl	3.82	Br	3.54	I	3.24
O	1.48 (−7.3)	S	2.07 (−3.4)	Se	... (−4.2)		
N	0.2	P	0.8				
C	1.13	Si	1.90				
B	0.3	Al	0.4				
Be	0	Mg	0				
Li	0.54	Na	0.74				
H	0.7						
Inert gases	0						

* Values in parenthesis refer to total EA for 2 electrons.

From Table 4–9, it can be seen that the electron affinities for all first members of the representative element families are lower than the respective second family members. This can be attributed to the much smaller sizes of the atoms of the first row elements which would lead to very high and unstable electron densities for their negative ions. A high electron density is opposed by interelectronic repulsion.

ELECTRONEGATIVITY

The concept of *electronegativity* has existed for many years as a qualitative measure of the relative ability of an atom in a molecule to attract electrons to itself. The concept was usually associated with the rather crude concept of the metallic or nonmetallic character of an element; the more nonmetallic an element, the greater its electronegativity. Similar correlations were also made with the activity series of the metals. The elements near the top of the series are the most active metals, and were considered to be the least electronegative and therefore the most electropositive. On the other hand, the elements approaching the bottom of the series showed a corresponding increase in electronegativity.

The first quantitative approach to the concept of electronegativity was strictly an empirical one based on the additivity of normal covalent bonds[11]. If we consider the energy E_{A-B} of a purely covalent bond between two atoms $A-B$, we might expect that it would be exactly equal to the *arithmetic mean* of the bond energies between $A-A$ and $B-B$. Thus, we would expect

$$\Delta = E_{A-B} - \tfrac{1}{2}\,(E_{A-A} + E_{B-B}) = 0 \qquad (4\text{--}7)$$

and if Δ is zero, we consider the bond $A-B$ to be a normal covalent bond. Now, if there is some difference in the two atoms, we would, in general, expect one to have somewhat more ability to attract electrons than the other; that is, one member might be more nonmetallic than the other. Or, in other words, one member might be more electronegative than the other member. From our experience with chemical bonds we know that, even in a qualitative sense, nearly pure ionic bonds are formed only between elements with extreme differences in electronegativity. Thus, it should not be unreasonable to imagine that as the difference in the electronegativity between two atoms becomes greater, the ionic character of a chemical bond between these two atoms should also become greater.

Theoretical treatments of chemical bonding show that a mixture of ionic and covalent character will give rise to a stronger bond than would be expected from a purely covalent or purely ionic bond. This additional bond energy is called the *ionic-covalent resonance energy* and is represented by the symbol Δ in Eq. (4–7). Because of the resonance energy, it is quite obvious that Δ will not be zero if there is any ionic character in the bond. Since the ionic character of a bond is related to the difference in electronegativity of the atoms making up the bond, we now have a quantitative measure of a property that is in some manner related to our concept of electronegativity. If we consider the hydrohalides listed in Table 4–10, we note that the values of Δ decrease as the electronegativity difference between the two atoms in the bond decreases. For HF, Δ is 64.2, whereas for HI, it is seen to be only 1.2. This would indicate that the amount of

TABLE 4-10. / **Bond Energies and Δ Values for the Hydrohalides.**

	H-F	H-Cl	H-Br	H-I
Bond Energy	134.6	103.2	87.5	71.4
$\frac{1}{2}(E_{A-A} + E_{B-B})$	70.4	81.1	75.2	70.2
Δ	64.2	22.1	12.3	1.2

ionic character in the H—F bond is considerably greater than in the H—I bond, and the corresponding electronegativity difference is also much less for H—I than H—F. This supports the general trend of electronegativities in a given family. The heavier elements would be expected to have a lesser ability to attract electrons than the lighter members of the same family.

In order to assign a definite numerical value for the electronegativity of an element, Pauling proposed that $\sqrt{\Delta}$ expressed in electron volts would give a good representation of the difference in electronegativity of A and B. This can be expressed as

$$0.208 \ \sqrt{\Delta_{AB}} = |x_A - x_B| \qquad (4-8)$$

where x_A is the electronegativity of element A, x_B is the electronegativity of element B, and the factor 0.208 arises from the conversion of kcal to ev.

Pauling showed that the postulate of the additivity of normal covalent bonds is valid for a large number of single bonds, and he used the Δ values obtained from Eq. (4-7) to formulate an extensive scale of electronegativities of the elements. However, the failure of the additivity postulate in certain cases, notably the alkali metal hydrides, led Pauling to postulate the *geometric mean* in place of the arithmetic mean,

$$\Delta' = E_{AB} - (E_{AA} \ E_{BB})^{\frac{1}{2}} \qquad (4-9)$$

Despite the apparently rather crude assumptions involved in Pauling's electronegativity scale, it is yet the most universally used scale today. A somewhat improved version, based on more modern thermochemical data, has been given by Huggins[4]. Since the original table of electronegativities by Pauling, several other bases for such tables have been proposed[12]. Of these, among the most important has been one proposed by Mulliken[13], in which the electronegativity of an element is given by the average of the ionization potential and the electron affinity of its atom. Unfortunately, this method may be applied rigorously only to a relatively few elements for which we have electron affinities. For these few elements, it is found that substantial agreement exists between the two tables.

Sanderson[14] has utilized the covalent radius of atoms in molecules to set up an interesting electronegativity scale. He has defined a *stability ratio*, *SR*, for an atom as the ratio of the average electron density, *ED*, around the atom to the hypothetical electron density, ED_i, it would have if it were an inert gas atom. Assuming atoms to be spherical, he calculated *ED* by dividing the number of electrons, *Z*, by the atomic volume $4\pi r^3/3$. The hypothetical electron density is calculated for the same atom by linear interpolation between the electron density values of the inert gases preceding it and following it in the periodic table. According to Sanderson, a large average electron density in an atom parallels a large electron-attracting power and hence, a high electronegativity. However, Sanderson points out that the average electron densities of the inert gases, which show no electron-attracting power, do not increase uniformly with atomic number as might be expected. Therefore, to remove that portion of the average electron density which is not related to electron-attracting power, he suggested the hypothetical electron density, ED_i.

The artificial character of the stability ratio and the problem of accurately determining covalent radii, particularly of the nonbond-forming inert gases, has prevented wide acceptance of this scale. While it has been related to the Pauling scale and gives satisfactory agreement for most of the elements, it does show trends in electronegativity values which do not appear in the Pauling scale. Furthermore, based on stability ratios, Sanderson has extended his concepts with surprising success to the determination of radii and interatomic distances.

Several other methods have been devised for the establishment of a suitable electronegativity scale. Of these, the method of Allred and Rochow[15] also depends on covalent radii. This method assumes that the electronegativity of an atom is the simple electrostatic force of attraction between the atom and an electron separated from the nucleus by the covalent radius. Thus,

$$x'_A = \frac{Z_{eff}\, e^2}{r_A{}^2} \tag{4-10}$$

The effective charge acting on the imaginary outer electron is determined by the method discussed previously.

Using the approach of Allred and Rochow, the electronegativity values can be given in terms of the Pauling scale by using the equation in the form

$$x_A = 0.359\, \frac{Z_{eff}}{r_A{}^2} + 0.744 \tag{4-11}$$

Using this equation along with recent literature data on electron configurations and covalent radii, Little and Jones[16], have calculated a complete set of electronegativity values. These, along with some values by Pauling, Huggins, and Sanderson are given in Table 4-11.

TABLE 4–11. / **A Set of Selected Electronegativity Values.***

Atomic Number	Element	x	Atomic Number	Element	x	Atomic Number	Element	x
1	H	2.1	35	Br	2.74	69	Tm	**1.11**
2	He	—	36	Kr	—	70	Yb	**1.06**
3	Li	0.97	37	Rb	0.89	71	Lu	**1.14**
4	Be	1.47	38	Sr	0.99	72	Hf	**1.23**
5	B	2.01	39	Y	1.11	73	Ta	**1.33**
6	C	2.50	40	Zr	**1.22**	74	W	**1.40**
7	N	3.07	41	Nb	**1.23**	75	Re	**1.46**
8	O	3.50▴	42	Mo	**1.30**	76	Os	**1.52**
9	F	4.10	43	Tc	**1.36**	77	Ir	**1.55**
10	Ne	—	44	Ru	**1.42**	78	Pt	**1.44**
11	Na	1.01	45	Rh	**1.45**	79	Au	**1.42**
12	Mg	1.23	46	Pd	**1.35**	80	Hg	**1.44**
13	Al	1.47	47	Ag	1.42	81	Tl	**1.44**
14	Si	1.74	48	Cd	1.46	82	Pb	**1.55**
15	P	2.06	49	In	1.49	83	Bi	**1.67**
16	S	2.44	50	Sn	1.72	84	Po	**1.76**
17	Cl	2.83	51	Sb	1.82	85	At	**1.90**
18	Ar	—	52	Te	2.01	86	Rn	—
19	K	0.91	53	I	2.21	87	Fr	**0.86**
20	Ca	1.04	54	Xe	—	88	Ra	**0.97**
21	Sc	1.20	55	Cs	0.86	89	Ac	**1.00**
22	Ti	1.32	56	Ba	0.97	90	Th	**1.11**
23	V	1.45	57	La	1.08	91	Pa	**1.14**
24	Cr	1.56	58	Ce	**1.08**	92	U	**1.22**
25	Mn	1.60	59	Pr	**1.07**	93	Np	**1.22**
26	Fe	1.64	60	Nd	**1.07**	94	Pu	**1.22**
27	Co	1.70	61	Pm	**1.07**	95	Am	**(1.2)**
28	Ni	1.75	62	Sm	**1.07**	96	Cm	**(1.2)**
29	Cu	1.75	63	Eu	**1.01**	97	Bk	**(1.2)**
30	Zn	1.66	64	Gd	**1.11**	98	Cf	**(1.2)**
31	Ga	1.82	65	Tb	**1.10**	99	Es	**(1.2)**
32	Ge	2.02	66	Dy	**1.10**	100	Fm	**(1.2)**
33	As	2.20	67	Ho	**1.10**	101	Md	**(1.2)**
34	Se	2.48	68	Er	**1.11**	102	No	**(1.2)**

The value for hydrogen is according to Pauling.[5]
The values in bold face are according to Little and Jones.[16]
The values in parenthesis are rough estimates.
The remaining values are according to Allred and Rochow.[15]

* These values are taken directly from the table by Little and Jones.[16]

In addition to those discussed, electronegativity scales have been based on such properties as dipole moments, stretching-force constants and bond distances, number of valence electrons and covalent radii, and photo-electric work functions. All of these have met with only limited success.

This would indicate that practically every element will exhibit an electro-negativity range that is dependent upon the particular circumstances of bond formation.

OXIDATION STATES OF THE ELEMENTS

The combining capacity of an element is called its valence and originally the valence was defined as the number of atoms of hydrogen that an element can combine with or replace. Since the hydrogen atom can combine with but one other atom at a time, it is termed univalent. Now, we may consider the valence of an element to be defined as the number of atoms of a univalent element with which one atom of the given element combines. Thus in H_2O the oxygen is bivalent, in NH_3 the nitrogen is tervalent, in CH_4 the carbon is quadrivalent, in PCl_5 the phosphorus is quinquevalent, in SF_6 the sulfur is sexivalent, in ReF_7 the rhenium is septivalent, and in OsO_4 the osmium is octavalent.

A more commonly used concept than valence is the near-equivalent concept of oxidation number. The latter is a positive or negative number which represents the charge that an atom would have if the electrons in a compound were assigned to the atoms in a certain way. Since this assignment is often somewhat arbitrary, the oxidation number is not always numerically equal to the valence. Nevertheless the concept is an extremely useful one. Rules for assigning oxidation numbers to every atom in a substance may be formulated as follows with the understanding that they are not entirely unambiguous:

(1) The oxidation number of an atom in an element is zero.

(2) The oxidation number of a monatomic ion is its charge.

(3) The oxidation number of each atom in a covalent compound of known structure is the charge remaining on the atom when each shared electron pair is assigned completely to the more electronegative of the two atoms sharing it. An electron pair shared by like atoms is split between them.

(4) The oxidation number of an element in a compound of uncertain structure is usually obtained by assigning reasonable oxidation numbers to the other elements in the compound.

Rules for predicting oxidation states of elements from their positions in the periodic table or even from their known electronic configurations are not nearly as clear-cut as the above rules. However, some generalizations are in order.

Representative Elements

The common oxidation states among the representative elements are readily predicted from their electron configurations providing several rules are observed. In forming molecules or ions, the atoms will always try to reach a stable arrangement for their outer electrons. Such stable arrangements are the inert gas outer configurations with two ($1s^2$) and eight (ns^2np^6) electrons, the nickel group outer configuration with 18 ($ns^2np^6nd^{10}$) electrons, and the zinc group outer configuration with 18 plus 2 ($n - 1)s^2p^6d^{10}ns^2$ electrons. Furthermore, paired electrons will tend to be lost or shared in pairs. Consequently, where several positive oxidation states occur among a family of representative elements, they are likely to differ by two units. These generalizations should be borne in mind while reading the following resume of oxidation states by families.

It should be mentioned that unusual or unexpected oxidation states are fairly numerous among the representative elements, and this subject has been reviewed several times[17].

*Group I*A. The ns^1 outer electron configuration allows only a $+1$ oxidation state for members of this family, and ions having inert gas configurations are easily formed due to the very low binding energy of the lone valence shell electron. As can be seen in Table 4–12, the lowest ionization potentials are found in this family.

TABLE 4–12. / **Ionization Potentials for Group I*A* and Group II*A* Elements.**

Element	1st IP(ev)	2nd IP(ev)	Total IP (kcal)	$-\Delta H_{hyd}$ (kcal)
Li	5.39	75.6	124.3	125
Na	5.14	47.3	118.5	100
K	4.34	31.8	100.1	79
Rb	4.18	27.4	96.3	75
Cs	3.89	23.4	89.8	68
Be	9.32	18.2	634	—
Mg	7.64	15.0	523	464
Ca	6.11	11.9	414	382
Sr	5.69	11.0	385	350
Ba	5.21	10.0	351	316

*Group I*B. It is observed that, except for family I*B* elements, no element will ever have an oxidation or valence number greater than its group number. For copper, silver, and gold, the oxidation states of $+1$, $+2$, and $+3$ are all known, except for gold $+2$, although they are not of equal stability with each element. Presumably this situation arises because the last *d* electrons to be added to the 3*d*, 4*d*, and 5*d* levels are not very different in binding energy from the 4*s*, 5*s*, and 6*s* electrons, respectively. The first and second ionization potentials for the I*B* metals are given in Table 4–13, along with the difference between the two potentials for each element. While oxidation states of $+1$, $+2$, and $+3$ for the I*B* metals do not imply that the simple ions are formed with these charges, the Δ IP values do make these oxidation states appear more reasonable. Moreover, it may be more than coincidence that the Δ IP values increase in the order Au < Cu < Ag, and the common oxidation states for the metals are Au^{3+}, Cu^{2+}, and Ag^{1+}.

TABLE 4-13. / **Ionization Potentials for Group IB and Group IIB Elements.**

Element	IP$_1$(ev)	IP$_2$(ev)	IP$_1$ + IP$_2$ (kcal)	ΔIP (ev) (IP$_2$ − IP$_1$)	−ΔH$_{hyd}$ (kcal)
Cu	7.72	20.29	646	12.57	
Ag	7.57	21.48	670	13.91	
Au	9.22	20.5	685	11.3	
Zn	9.39	17.96	631		492
Cd	8.99	16.90	598		437
Hg	10.43	18.75	674		441

*Group II*A. The outer electron configuration of ns^2 suggests that the common oxidation state for the members of this family should be +2. However, in terms of ionization potentials, one might expect the univalent ion to be quite common. As can be seen in Table 4-12, the second ionization potential is approximately twice as great as the first ionization potential for each member of the family. This apparent anomaly can be readily understood in terms of the crystal lattice energies in going from a +1 to a +2 ion as well as in terms of the hydration or solvation energies. In both cases, it is found that more than enough energy is gained to supply the energy needed to remove the second electron.

While it is doubtful that the simple Be^{2+} and Mg^{2+} ions form in any cases except with fluorine and oxygen, the +2 oxidation state is still the only common one in the more covalent compounds of these elements.

*Group II*B. The members of this family have the $(n-1)d^{10}ns^2$ electron configuration and would be expected to show a +2 oxidation state. However, the ionization potentials shown in Table 4-13 would strongly suggest the +1 state. Again, the +1 state is not observed and the reasons are apparently much the same as for the IIA family. An irregular ion does appear, however, in Hg_2^{2+}, in which the mercury must be assigned a +1 oxidation state, but the metal-metal bond has been firmly established in the mercury +1 compounds.

*Group III*B. The electron configuration ns^2np^1 suggests the two oxidation states of +1 and +3, corresponding to the involvement of the p or the p and two s electrons in bond formation. Although, there are many recent reports of +1 compounds for aluminum, gallium, and indium, the tripositive state is much more important for these elements and boron is exclusively tripositive. Thallium, the heaviest member of the family, is quite unstable in the +3 state and is readily reduced to the more stable +1 state.

The greater stability of the lower oxidation state in the heaviest family member is found not only for thallium in the IIIB family, but also in the IVB and VB families for lead and bismuth respectively. Sidgwick noticed this fact in 1933 and postulated the existence of an *inert pair* of electrons in these elements as an explanation. Grimm and Sommerfeld were the first to propose that the prominence of the lower oxidation states in these elements was due to a stabilization resulting from the completion of the *ns* orbital. Ionization potentials, however, do not support this view.

A recent explanation is that proposed by Drago[18]. By comparing thermodynamic data for the chlorides of the group IIIB and IVB elements, he has shown that the instability of the thallium (III) chloride and lead (IV) chloride can be attributed to the fact that in a given family the strength of the covalent bonds in the higher oxidation states formed by these elements decreases with an increase in atomic number. This general decrease in covalent bond-forming ability with increasing atomic number is attributed by Drago to (1) a decrease in the amount of overlap of atomic orbitals resulting from the spreading of the valence electrons over a larger area, and (2) the increased repulsion between the inner electrons of the bonded atoms.

*Group IV*B. The members of this family have the ns^2np^2 outer electron configuration which leads to the +2 and +4 oxidation states. Again, with the lighter members of this family, the maximum oxidation state is predominant. With an increase in atomic number, the lower oxidation state will become more stable, until with lead, it becomes the most stable.

*Group V*B. From the electron configuration ns^2np^3 which is characteristic of the VB family, one would predict three oxidation states. A +3 and a +5 oxidation state would be expected as a result of the tendency to give up to bonding orbitals the three p electrons or all five of the valence shell electrons respectively. In addition, it is possible for the members of this family to gain three electrons to give a completed outside shell. This, of course, would give an oxidation state of -3. The negative oxidation state is characteristic of only the lighter members of the family, but the +3 and +5 states are well known for all members. As expected, the +3 state is the more stable one for bismuth.

*Group VI*B. The ns^2np^4 electron configuration characteristic of the members of this family gives rise to oxidation states of -2, +2, +4, and +6. Being just two electrons shy of the inert gas configuration, the -2

oxidation state is quite readily formed. This is particularly true for the lighter members of the family. Indeed, oxygen stands out in its family in the ease with which it accepts two electrons to give the dinegative oxide ion. Except for the unusual negative oxidation states of oxygen in peroxides (-1), superoxides ($-1/2$), and ozonides ($-1/3$), compounds which contain oxygen-oxygen bonds, and the formal $+1$ and $+2$ states which must be ascribed to it in the compounds O_2F_2 and OF_2, oxygen will uniformly be found in the -2 oxidation state. For the remainder of the family, the negative oxidation state becomes increasingly less stable, and the positive oxidation states become increasingly more stable with the heavier members again preferring the lower of the positive states.

Group VIIB. The halogen family with the ns^2np^5 electron arrangement will show oxidation states of -1, $+5$, $+7$, $+1$, and $+3$, in the order of decreasing importance. Being one electron shy of the inert neon configuration, in addition to its small size, the fluorine atom will form exclusively the -1 oxidation state. The strong tendency toward attaining the inert gas configuration has a large effect on all of the members of the halogen family. Thus, the -1 oxidation state is found for all the elements in this family.

While the $+3$ state is relatively rare and the $+7$ state is unknown for bromine, in general it is found that the $+1$, $+5$, and $+7$ states are all quite important. Certain even oxidation states are known, particularly with chlorine, but except for the compound ClO_2, these are relatively unimportant.

Transition Elements

About the only safe statement that can be made concerning the many oxidation states of the transition metals is that the lowest common oxidation state, except for IIIA, is $+2$ and the highest possible oxidation state for a given element is the same as its group number. This is suggested from the general configuration $(n-1)d^x\ ns^2$ or $(n-1)d^{x+1}\ ns^1$, where $x+2$ is the group number. A further generalization which seems valid is that the increase in such properties as acidity, ease of hydrolysis, etc., which parallels an increase in oxidation state, also parallels an increase in atomic weight within a transition element family. Thus, the reverse of the trend found in the representative element families is observed. The heavier transition family members show increasing stability in the higher oxidation states rather than in the lower oxidation states. For instance, Mn_2O_7 decomposes at $0°C$, Tc_2O_7 melts at $119.5°C$, and Re_2O_7 melts at $220°C$ and sublimes without loss of oxygen.

A summary of the oxidation states for the transition metals is given in Table 4–14, in which the most stable oxidation states are underlined and

TABLE 4–14. / **Oxidation States of the Transition Elements.**

	IIIA	IVA	VA	VIA	VIIA	VIII		
3d	Sc 3	Ti 2 3 4	V 2 3 4 5	Cr 2 3 (4) (5) 6	Mn 2 3 4 5 6 7	Fe 2 3 (4) (5) 6	Co 2 3 (4) (5)	Ni 2 3 (4)
4d	Y 3	Zr 3 4	Nb (2) 3 (4) 5	Mo 2 3 4 5 6	Tc 4 6 7	Ru 2 3 4 (5) 6 (7) 8	Rh 2 3 4 (6)	Pd 2 (3) 4
5d	La 3	Hf (3) 4	Ta (2) (3) (4) 5	W 2 3 4 5 6	Re (2) 3 4 5 6 7	Os (2) (3) 4 6 8	Ir (2) 3 4 (6)	Pt 2 4 (6)

the very rare states are placed in parentheses. It should be noted that the tripositive state is the only state known for the IIIA metals scandium, yttrium, and lanthanum. The most stable states for the metals having a d^1 to d^5 configuration, configurations in which there is no pairing of d electrons, are the maximum valence states in which the ns and all of the $(n-1)d$ electrons are involved in the bonding. However, beyond the d^5 configuration, where electron pairing must occur, the lower oxidation states become more important. Both the decrease in size which results in an increased binding of the electrons and the additional energy necessary to unpair electrons are factors which contribute to this situation.

Actually, it is found that anomalous or unusual oxidation states are almost as numerous as the common oxidation states for the transition elements. This is found to be particularly true among the coordination compounds where certain coordinating groups stabilize the unusual oxidation states. We have omitted from Table 4–14 the large number of examples of oxidation states lower than +2. We shall only make note of the fact that the $+1$ and 0 as well as the -1 and even -2 oxidation states have been observed in recent years for many of the transition elements.

Inner Transition Elements

For the first inner transition series, the $+3$ oxidation state is common to all members. This corresponds to the use of the $6s^2$ electrons and the lone $5d$ electron, or one of the f electrons if no $5d$ electron is present. A dipositive state has been realized with europium, ytterbium, and samarium, with europium being the most stable and samarium being the least stable. As can be seen in Table 4–15, the $+2$ state is predictable for europium and ytterbium, since the former reaches the half-filled f shell structure $6s^2 4f^7$,

TABLE 4–15. / **Oxidation States of the Inner Transition Elements.**

$4f$	Ce	Pr	Nd	Pm	Sm	Eu	Gd	Tb	Dy	Ho	Er	Tm	Yb	Lu
					2	2							2	
	3	3	3	3	3	3	3	3	3	3	3	3	3	3
	4	(4)						(4)						
$5f$		Th	Pa	U	Np	Pu	Am	Cm	Bk	Cf				
		(3)	(3)	3	3	3	3	3	3	3				
		4	4	4	4	4	(4)	(4)	4					
			5	5	5	5	5							
			6	6	6	6	6							

and the latter reaches the filled f shell structure $6s^2 4f^{14}$. There appears to be no reasonable explanation for the $+2$ state for samarium. All three of the dipositive ions are strongly reducing, being oxidized readily by oxygen or even water to the tripositive state.

The tetrapositive state is well known only for cerium, which reaches the empty f shell structure of lanthanum. Indeed, the $+4$ state is more common for cerium than the $+3$ state. Praseodymium(IV) and terbium(IV) are known, but only in solid compounds. The terbium(IV) is predictable since it reaches the half-filled f shell structure of $4f^7$, characteristic of gadolinium.

The oxidation states among the second inner transition series elements are not nearly so constant as those in the first inner transition series. This is indicated in Table 4–15 in which the known oxidation states for this series of elements are listed. It is to be noted that the first three elements in the series, thorium, protactinium, and uranium, show a trend in stability of oxidation states that would indicate that they are members of families IVA, VA, and VIA, respectively. The tripositive state is not the stable state until americium is reached, presumably with six $5f$ electrons. The existence of tetravalent compounds of curium, such as CmF_4 and CmO_2, indicate that the stability of the $5f^7$ configuration is not as great as that of the $4f^7$ configuration. The existence of tetrapositive berkelium and the possible existence of divalent americium are understandable in terms of the attainment of a half-filled $5f$ shell.

BIBLIOGRAPHY

1. Wells, A., "Structural Inorganic Chemistry," 2nd ed., Clarendon Press, Oxford, 1950.
2. Rice, O., "Electronic Structure and Chemical Binding," McGraw-Hill Book Co., New York, N.Y., 1940.
3. Schomaker, V. and Stevenson, D., *J. Am. Chem. Soc.*, **63,** 37 (1941).
4. Huggins, M., *J. Am. Chem. Soc.*, **75,** 4123 (1953).
5. Pauling, L., "The Nature of the Chemical Bond," 3rd ed., Cornell University Press, Ithica, N.Y., 1960.
6. Sherman, J., *Chem. Revs.*, **11,** 93 (1932).
7. Keller, R., *J. Chem. Ed.*, **28,** 312 (1951).
8. Sisler, H. and VanderWerf, C., *J. Chem. Ed.*, **22,** 390 (1945).
9. Pritchard, H., *Chem. Revs.*, **52,** 529 (1953).
10. Mulliken, R., *J. Am. Chem. Soc.*, **77,** 884 (1955).
11. Pauling, L., *J. Am. Chem. Soc.*, **54,** 3570 (1932).
12. Pritchard, H. and Skinner, H., *Chem. Revs.*, **55,** 745 (1955).
13. Mulliken, R. S., *J. Chem. Phys.*, **2,** 782 (1934); **3,** 573 (1935).
14. Sanderson, R., *J. Inorg. Nuclear Chem.*, **7,** 157 (1958).
15. Allred, A. and Rochow, E., *J. Inorg. Nuclear Chem.*, **5,** 264, 269 (1958).
16. Little, E., Jr. and Jones, M., *J. Chem. Ed.*, **37,** 231 (1960).
17. Kleinberg, J., *J. Chem. Ed.*, **33,** 73 (1956).
18. Drago, R., *J. Phys. Chem.*, **62,** 353 (1958).

5 | *Chemical Bonding*

Before the discovery of the electron, an understanding of the nature of a chemical bond was not possible. It is true that the idea of valence existed as early as 1852, and some appreciation of molecular geometry existed shortly thereafter. In this respect, the tetrahedral structure of the carbon atom was recognized by van't Hoff and by le Bel, and the stereochemistry of complex ions was deduced by Werner. For such structures to exist, it was apparent that some type of bonding force must be present. For the lack of something better, the chemical bond was represented by a straight line between the symbols of the bonded atoms. This indicates the existence of a bond, but it, of course, fails to give any description of the nature of the bond.

Even before the discovery of the electron, the independent existence of ions was proposed by Arrhenius. In terms of this concept, several attempts were made to offer an explanation of the bonding forces between atoms. Although they were unsuccessful, they contributed to the idea of electrical charge as a basis for bond formation. Then, with the discovery of the electron, our present day advances were made possible. During the first few years, a variety of explanations of bond formation were offered in terms of positive and negative atoms, but little or no attempt was made to relate the charges to the structure of the atom. Then, in 1916, G. N. Lewis presented his theory of valence.[1] Since that time, we have made great strides in the mathematical formulation of the valency theory, but the basic ideas of the chemical bond can still be traced to the original ideas of Lewis.

According to Pauling,[2] *a chemical bond exists between two atoms when the bonding force between them is of such strength as to lead to an aggregate of sufficient stability to warrant their consideration as an independent molecular species.* Although, it would appear that this definition permits some freedom of choice, we ordinarily find it convenient to consider five types of chemical bonds. These are *ionic bonds, covalent bonds, metallic bonds, hydrogen bonds,* and *van der Waals forces.* All of these are important, and the first three are quite strong. However, in spite of its importance, we will not consider the metallic bond in this discussion. The interested student may refer to a variety of references, with reference (2) being particularly good.

THE IONIC BOND

From a mathematical standpoint, the simplest type of chemical bond is one that can be considered to be strictly electrostatic in character. Such a treatment has proved successful for the alkali halides where the bonding occurs between the cation of a highly electropositive atom and the anion of a highly electronegative atom. Although it is possible to consider a bond to be partially covalent and partially ionic, the extent of ionic character in the bond is dependent on the difference in electronegativity between the combining atoms. In the instance of the alkali halides, it would be safe to consider the bonds to be almost exclusively ionic. However, the test of this postulate will actually rest on the success we have in quantitatively evaluating various properties of the resultant compounds. In general, we

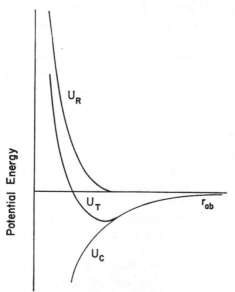

FIGURE 5–1. Potential Energy Diagram for the Formation of an Ionic Bond as a Function of Ionic Separation.

can define a bond as purely ionic in terms of the success of the electrostatic model.

As a first test of the electrostatic model, it should be possible to calculate the energy of a crystalline lattice. And, as a first-order approximation, we can consider the ions to be point charges. For the formation of a single uni-univalent molecule, we can imagine a positive and a negative point charge to be separated by an infinite distance and then allow them to approach each other. From our general knowledge of electrostatics, we are aware that an attraction will exist between the two ions that can be described by Coulomb's law. At the same time, we also know that two ions would not be expected to approach each other sufficiently closely to coalesce. Consequently, there must be a *repulsion* term that comes into play at some place apparently rather close to the equilibrium distance between the two ions. Such a situation can be described by the potential energy diagram shown in Figure 5–1. The potential energy of the system is thus seen to be expressible as the sum of the attractive potential, given by Coulomb's law, and a repulsive potential that must be represented in some alternative manner.

It should be apparent that the repulsive term is due to a short-range type of force; that is, it is not effective except when the ions are extremely close to each other. It was proposed by Born that such a term could be represented by $U_R = B/r_{ij}^n$, where r_{ij} is the distance between the two ions, and n is a parameter that is usually found to be of the order of 9. This, then, gives the mathematical description of the potential energy diagram

$$U_T = U_c + U_R$$

$$= -\frac{z_i z_j\, e^2}{r_{ij}} + \frac{B}{r_{ij}^n} \tag{5-1}$$

For a uni-univalent compound, $z_i = z_j = 1$ and in this case they can, therefore, be neglected. For this reason z_i and z_j will be omitted in the development of the pertinent equations, but they will be introduced into the final general expression.

It is possible to evaluate the coefficient, B, by recognizing that the slope of the potential curve is zero at the equilibrium distance, r_0, between the ions. Consequently, we can say that

$$\left(\frac{\partial U_T}{\partial r}\right)_{r\,=\,r_0} = \frac{e^2}{r_0^2} = \frac{Bnr_0^{n-1}}{r_0^n r_0^n} = 0$$

or

$$\frac{e^2}{r_0^2} - \frac{nB}{r_0^{n+1}} = 0 \tag{5-2}$$

Solving Eq. (5–2) for B, we obtain

$$B = \frac{e^2 r_0{}^{n-1}}{n}$$

and by substituting for B in Eq. (5–1), we obtain the expression for the potential at the equilibrium position

$$U_r = -\frac{e^2}{r_0} + \frac{e^2 r_0{}^{n-1}}{n r_0{}^n} = -\frac{e^2}{r_0} + \frac{e^2}{n r_0}$$

or

$$U_r = -\frac{e^2}{r_0}\left(1 - \frac{1}{n}\right) \tag{5–3}$$

If we now consider the energy of an entire crystal, we must multiply by the number of ions present and, in addition, we must take into consideration higher-order attractive and repulsive terms. These arise due to the effects of second, third, and so on nearest neighbors. The first factor can readily be determined by considering a crystal containing 1 mole of ions of each type. The second factor is found to be dependent on the particular crystalline structure. It has been evaluated for numerous crystal lattices and is referred to as the *Madelung constant*. For general comparison, a few examples of the Madelung constant for uni-univalent salts are given in Table 5–1. If we now incorporate these terms into our basic equation,

TABLE 5–1. / **Values of the Madelung Constant for Several Different Crystal Lattices.**

Lattice	Madelung Constant
Rock salt	1.74756
Cesium chloride	1.76267
Zinc blende	1.63806
Wurtzite	1.641

we can obtain the general expression for the lattice energy of the crystal[3]

$$U = -\frac{z_i z_j \, A N e^2}{r_0}\left(1 - \frac{1}{n}\right) \tag{5–4}$$

where A is the Madelung constant and N is Avogadro's number.

Finally, the parameter, n, can be evaluated from the compressibility of the crystal by virtue of the relationship

$$\kappa = \frac{18 r_0{}^4}{A e^2 (n - 1)} \tag{5–5}$$

where κ is the compressibility.

Although the lattice energies calculated in terms of this model are quite good, they can be improved by considering two additional factors: the repulsion arising from electron-electron interactions and the zero point energy of the ions. These have been incorporated along with a different form of the repulsion term variously by Mayer, Born, and Helmholz in the form

$$U = -\frac{z_i z_j A N e^2}{r} + NBe^{-kr} - \frac{NC}{r^6} + NE_0 \tag{5-6}$$

where k and C are two new parameters and E_0 is the zero point energy.[4]

An experimental test of the electrostatic model can be made either by a direct determination of the vapor phase equilibrium of

$$MX \rightleftarrows M^+ + X^-$$

in conjunction with the MX sublimation pressure[5] or by means of an indirect method using a cyclic process known as the *Born-Haber cycle*.[6] As it turns out, a direct measurement of a lattice energy is rather difficult to make and, for that reason, the Born-Haber cycle is more commonly used.

The Born-Haber cycle for sodium chloride can be represented as

$$
\begin{array}{ccccc}
Na_{(s)} + \frac{1}{2}Cl_{2(g)} & \xrightarrow[\frac{1}{2}D]{S} & Na_{(g)} & + & Cl_{(g)} \\
\downarrow {\scriptstyle -\Delta H} & & \downarrow {\scriptstyle I} & & \downarrow {\scriptstyle -E} \\
NaCl_{(s)} & \xleftarrow{-U} & Na^+_{(g)} & + & Cl^-_{(g)}
\end{array}
$$

Here,

$$
\begin{aligned}
S &= \text{heat of sublimation} \\
D &= \text{dissociation energy} \\
I &= \text{ionization energy} \\
E &= \text{electron affinity} \\
\Delta H &= \text{heat of formation} \\
U &= \text{lattice energy}
\end{aligned}
$$

Those quantities that require the expenditure of energy are represented as positive and those that take place with the release of energy are represented as negative. It is apparent from the cycle that

$$U = \Delta H + S + \tfrac{1}{2}D + I - E \tag{5-7}$$

Thus, if we know all the necessary quantities, we can evaluate the crystal lattice energy. Such calculations and measurements have been carried out according to the two theoretical equations as well as by direct measurement and by the Born-Haber cycle. Some idea of the success of the electrostatic model can be obtained from a comparison of these determinations as seen in Table 5-2.

TABLE 5-2.* / Comparison of the Theoretical and the Experimental Determinations of the Lattice Energies of the Alkali Halides in kcal/mole.

Compound	U_{calc}		U_{exp}	
	Eq. (5–4)	Eq. (5–6)	Born-Haber Cycle	Direct Measurement
LiF	238.9	240.1	242.8	
NaF	213.8	213.4	216.6	
KF	189.2	189.7	191.8	
RbF	180.6	181.6	184.6	
CsF	171.6	173.7	176.0	
LiCl	192.1	199.2	201.7	
NaCl	179.2	184.3	183.9	181.3
KCl	163.2	165.4	168.3	
RbCl	157.7	160.7	162.8	
CsCl	147.7	152.2	157.2	
LiBr	181.9	188.3	191.0	
NaBr	170.5	174.6	175.5	176
KBr	156.6	159.3	160.7	160
RbBr	151.3	153.5	157.1	151
CsBr	142.3	146.3	151.2	
LiI	169.5	174.1	178.4	
NaI	159.6	163.9	164.8	166
KI	147.8	150.8	151.5	153
RbI	143.0	145.3	147.9	146
CsI	134.9	139.1	143.7	141.5

* From Ketelaar, J.A.A., "Chemical Constitution," 2nd ed., Elsevier Publishing Co., Amsterdam, 1958.

THE VARIATION METHOD

Although, a simple electrostatic model is adequate for the treatment of an ionic bond, it is necessary to use a quantum mechanical approach to the covalent bond. This requires a solution of the Schroedinger wave equation. When we recall that an exact solution of the wave equation is possible only for a one-electron system, it is apparent that we must resort to approximation methods when treating a many-electron system such as we would expect to encounter in a molecule.

There are two rather common approximation methods used in quantum mechanics. These are the *perturbation method* and the *variation method*.[7] The variation method is by far the most useful in the treatment of chemical bonding, and for that reason, it will be the only method that we will consider here. Further, we will not give any proof of its validity, but rather, we will only illustrate its application to the problem of chemical bonding.

It can readily be seen that the time-independent wave equation

$$\nabla^2 \psi + \frac{8\pi^2 m}{h^2} (E - V) \psi = 0 \qquad (2\text{--}13)$$

can be rearranged to the form

$$\left(-\frac{h^2}{8\pi^2 m} \nabla^2 + V \right) \psi = E\psi$$

The term on the left side of the equation contains the differential operator, ∇^2, and some multiplying constants as well as the wave function, ψ. The quantities within the parenthesis can be considered, together, to be an operator acting on ψ. Consequently, the equation may be expressed in the more convenient form

$$H \psi = E \psi \qquad (5\text{--}8)$$

where H represents this operator and is known as the *Hamiltonian operator*.

Now, if we multiply both sides of Eq. (5–8) by ψ^* and integrate over the configuration space, we will obtain the expression

$$\int \psi^* H\psi \, d\tau = E \int \psi\psi^* \, d\tau$$

or

$$E = \frac{\int \psi^* H\psi \, d\tau}{\int \psi\psi^* \, d\tau} \qquad (5\text{--}9)$$

Assuming that we know ψ as well as the form of the Hamiltonian operator, and assuming that we can solve the equations, we obviously have an expression that will permit the calculation of the energy of the system. As it turns out, we **can** ordinarily set up the Hamiltonian operator for a given problem, but it would be unusual if we happened to know the form of ψ. Nevertheless, it is still possible to use the variation principle to obtain an approximate wave function.

To begin with, we can guess a wave function and calculate the energy in terms of this proposed function. If we were so fortunate as to guess the correct one, we would obtain the correct energy of the system. On the other hand, if we happened to choose a poor wave function, we would expect to get a rather poor value for the energy. Thus, it would appear that unless we had some means of making a particularly good choice of wave functions, Eq. (5–9) would be of little value. However, this is not the case. According to the variation principle, it can readily be shown that if ψ_0 is the correct wave function for a system, that is, the one that will give the correct energy of the system, E_0, then any other acceptable wave function, ψ_i, will give an energy greater than E_0. Therefore, any energy, E_i, obtained from a wave function, ψ_i, will be greater than E_0. And although this will not give us the correct wave function, it will, at least, tell us which of several trial wave functions is closest to the true wave function in the sense of giving the best energy.

The problem is really not as bad as it may at first appear. In choosing a reasonable wave function, one is often aided by his chemical intuition, and a reasonable choice is often quite obvious. In addition, it is possible to consider a general group or family of wave functions at one time. This can be done by introducing one or more variable parameters in the trial function and then minimizing the energy with respect to the parameters. Of course, the more parameters that are introduced in a given trial function, the closer one comes to the actual wave function, but at the same time, the more parameters used, the greater will be the work involved in the computation.

Ground-State Energy of the Hydrogen Atom

As a simple example of the use of the variation method, we can consider the calculation of the ground-state energy of the hydrogen atom. We are already aware of the fact that the wave function is of the general form

$$\psi = e^{-ar}$$

and to illustrate the method, we will choose our trial function to be of this same form. The problem now becomes one of evaluating the two integrals $\int \psi^* H \psi \, d\tau$ and $\int \psi \psi^* \, d\tau$. For the ground state of the hydrogen atom, the potential energy term will be $-e^2/r$, and this leads to the expression for the Hamiltonian operator

$$H = -\frac{h^2}{8\pi^2 m} \nabla^2 - \frac{e^2}{r} \tag{5-10}$$

From our discussion of the hydrogen atom, we should recall that the energy term occurs only in the radial equation, and for this reason we will need only to consider the radial portion of the Laplacian operator. In the spherical coordinates, this can be seen from Eq. (2–43) to be

$$\nabla^2 = \frac{1}{r^2} \frac{\partial}{\partial r} \left(r^2 \frac{\partial}{\partial r} \right)$$

Applying the indicated operation to ψ gives

$$\nabla^2 \psi = \left[\frac{1}{r^2} \frac{\partial}{\partial r} \left(r^2 \frac{\partial}{\partial r} \right) \right] e^{-ar}$$

$$= \frac{1}{r^2} \left[-r^2 \left(-a^2 e^{-ar} \right) + \left(ae^{-ar} \right) \left(-2r \right) \right]$$

$$= \left(a^2 - \frac{2a}{r} \right) e^{-ar} \tag{5-11}$$

The limits of integration are determined by considering the electron to be in a spherical shell at a distance of r to $r + dr$ from the nucleus as r goes from zero to infinity. The volume of such a spherical shell at a distance, r, from the nucleus is given by $4\pi r^2 dr$, and this, when substituted into Eq. (5–9) along with the value for $\nabla^2\psi$, leads to

$$E = \frac{\int \psi^* H\psi \, d\tau}{\int \psi\psi^* \, d\tau}$$

$$= -\frac{\int_0^\infty e^{-ar}\left[-\frac{h^2}{8\pi^2 m}\left(a^2 - \frac{2a}{r}\right)e^{-ar} - \frac{e^2}{r}e^{-ar}\right]4\pi r^2 dr}{\int_0^\infty e^{-2ar} \, 4\pi r^2 dr}$$

$$= \frac{\int_0^\infty -\frac{h^2 a^2}{8\pi^2 m} r^2 e^{-2ar} \, dr + \int_0^\infty \frac{2h^2 a}{8\pi^2 m} re^{-2ar}dr - \int_0^\infty e^2 r e^{-2ar} \, dr}{\int_0^\infty r^2 e^{-2ar} \, dr}$$

The solutions to these integrals are readily obtained from the relation

$$\int_0^\infty x^n e^{-ax} \, dx = \frac{\Gamma(n+1)}{a^{(n+1)}}$$

where, if n is an integer $\Gamma_{(n)} = (n-1)!$

Substituting the solutions to the integrals, we can obtain the expression for the energy

$$E = \frac{-\frac{h^2 a^2}{8\pi^2 m}\left(\frac{2}{8a^3}\right) + \frac{h^2 a^2}{4\pi^2 m}\left(\frac{1}{4a^2}\right) - e^2\left(\frac{1}{4a^2}\right)}{\left(\frac{2}{8a^3}\right)}$$

$$= \frac{h^2 a^2}{8\pi^2 m} - e^2 a$$

The best energy obtainable from this wave function will be the minimum energy, and this will depend on the magnitude of the parameter, a. Therefore, it will be necessary to choose a in such a manner as to give a minimum energy value. This can be done by minimizing E with respect to a:

$$\frac{\partial E}{\partial a} = \frac{2h^2}{8\pi^2 m} a - e^2 = 0$$

or

$$a = \frac{4\pi^2 m e^4}{h^2}$$

If we now substitute the value for a into the general expression for the energy, we obtain

$$E_{\min} = -\frac{2\pi^2 me^4}{h^2}$$

which is the same as the ground-state energy of the hydrogen atom as obtained in Chapter 2 by the closed-form calculations. Of course, we would not have obtained the exact energy of the ground state of the hydrogen atom if we had not used the correct form of the wave function. However, we could have taken a variety of trial functions, and the closer we came to the proper function, the better would have been our energy calculation.

The Secular Equations

In most instances, it is desirable to express the variation function in terms of a set of functions, φ_i. These functions will be of the class Q and will frequently, but not necessarily, be normalized. Accordingly,

$$\psi = a_1\,\varphi_1 + a_2\,\varphi_2 + \cdots + a_n\varphi_n \tag{5-12}$$

where the $a_1, a_2, \ldots, a_n$ are arbitrary parameters that can be varied to give a minimum in the energy. Actually, it is often found that the wave function can be adequately represented simply as

$$\psi = a_1\varphi_1 + a_2\varphi_2$$

and for convenience, we will consider the variation function in terms of this representation.

If we now substitute for ψ in Eq. (5-9), we obtain

$$E = \frac{\int (a_1\varphi_1^* + a_2\varphi_2^*)\, H\, (a_1\varphi_1 + a_2\varphi_2)\, d\tau}{\int (a_1\varphi_1^* + a_2\varphi_2^*)\, (a_1\varphi_1 + a_2\varphi_2)\, d\tau}$$

or

$$E \int (a_1\varphi_1^* + a_2\varphi_2^*)\, (a_1\varphi_1 + a_2\varphi_2) d\tau = \int (a_1\varphi_1^* + a_2\varphi_2^*)\, H\, (a_1\varphi_1 + a_2\varphi_2) d\tau$$

which leads to

$$E \left(a_1^2 \int \varphi_1^*\varphi_1 d\tau + 2a_1a_2 \int \varphi_1^*\varphi_2 d\tau + a_2^2 \int \varphi_2^*\varphi_2 d\tau \right) =$$

$$a_1^2 \int \varphi_1^* H \varphi_1 d\tau + 2a_1a_2 \int \varphi_1^* H \varphi_2 d\tau + a_2^2 \int \varphi_2^* H \varphi_2 d\tau \tag{5-13}$$

Since we desire the minimum value of E, it is necessary to minimize E with respect to both a_1 and a_2. Using the differentiation with respect to a_1 as an example we find that

$$E \left[2a_1 \int \varphi_1^* \varphi_1 d\tau + 2a_2 \int \varphi_1^* \varphi_2 d\tau \right] + \frac{\partial E}{\partial a_1} \left[a_1^2 \int \varphi_1^* \varphi_1 d\tau + 2a_1 a_2 \int \varphi_1^* \varphi_2 d\tau + \right.$$

$$\left. a_2^2 \int \varphi_2^* \varphi_2 d\tau \right] = 2a_1 \int \varphi_1^* H \varphi_1 d\tau + 2a_2 \int \varphi_1^* H \varphi_2 d\tau \qquad (5\text{--}14)$$

and, of course, an equivalent equation would be obtained for a_2. Now, in order to minimize E with respect to a_1 and a_2 it is necessary that

$$\left(\frac{\partial E}{\partial a_1} \right)_{a_2} = \left(\frac{\partial E}{\partial a_2} \right)_{a_1} = 0$$

For the sake of simplicity, it is desirable to introduce the symbolism

$$H_{ij} = \int \varphi_i^* H \varphi_j d\tau \quad \text{and} \quad S_{ij} = \int \varphi_i^* \varphi_j d\tau \qquad (5\text{--}15)$$

If this is done, and we apply the condition $\partial E / \partial a_1 = 0$ to Eq. (5–14), we can obtain, on rearrangement,

$$(H_{11} - ES_{11}) a_1 + (H_{12} - ES_{12}) a_2 = 0 \qquad (5\text{--}16a)$$

The equivalent equation obtained by applying the condition $\partial E / \partial a_2 = 0$ will be

$$(H_{21} - ES_{21}) a_1 + (H_{22} - ES_{22}) a_2 = 0 \qquad (5\text{--}16b)$$

These two equations are known together as the *secular equations*.

It is to be noted that the secular equations are of the form

$$ax + by = 0$$
$$cx + dy = 0$$

and if we solve this set of linear homogeneous equations, we see that

$$(ad - bc) y = 0$$

In order for this equality to be valid, it is apparent that either y is identically zero or else the coefficient of y is zero. If y is zero, no problem really exists; therefore, a nontrivial solution requires that the coefficient of y be zero. This can be expressed in determinental form as

$$\begin{vmatrix} a & b \\ c & d \end{vmatrix} = 0$$

Obviously, the same condition applies to our secular equations, and they can, therefore, be expressed as

$$\begin{vmatrix} H_{11} - ES_{11} & H_{12} - ES_{12} \\ H_{21} - ES_{21} & H_{22} - ES_{22} \end{vmatrix} = 0 \qquad (5\text{--}17)$$

To be more general, if we express ψ in terms of n independent terms, then the secular determinant becomes

$$
\begin{vmatrix}
H_{11} - ES_{11} & H_{12} - ES_{12} \cdots H_{1n} - ES_{1n} \\
H_{21} - ES_{21} & H_{22} - ES_{22} \cdots H_{2n} - ES_{2n} \\
\vdots & \vdots \qquad\qquad \vdots \\
H_{n1} - ES_{n1} & H_{n2} - ES_{n2} \cdots H_{nn} - ES_{nn}
\end{vmatrix} = 0 \qquad (5\text{--}18)
$$

MOLECULAR ORBITAL THEORY

In the variation method we have a means of approximating the energy of a system, but it is still necessary to choose a trial wave function. This is not always an easy task, and for the calculation of molecular energy levels two basic approaches to the problem have evolved. These are referred to as the *molecular orbital theory* and the *valence bond theory*. The two theories lead to quite different means of constructing a trial function, but equally important, they reflect quite different conceptual approaches to the basic structural model of a molecule.

The valence bond theory was developed several years prior to the molecular orbital theory, but it would appear that in recent years the latter theory has generally become the more popular of the two. This can be attributed to the greater conceptual and mathematical simplicity of the molecular orbital theory. However, with respect to certain aspects of molecular structure, the valence bond theory offers a simpler pictorial representation and therefore has been more frequently used for qualitative considerations.

Whereas the valence bond theory retains the individuality of the atoms composing a molecule, the molecular orbital theory attempts to construct a molecule in terms of the basic concepts of atomic structure. Just as there are atomic orbitals in an atom, there are *molecular orbitals* in a molecule. The most obvious difference is that the molecular orbitals are *polycentric*. Nevertheless, the molecular orbital theory attempts to construct a wave function for an electron in a molecule that lends itself to the same interpretations that proved valid for the wave function of an electron in an atom. Thus, the probability that the electron will be confined to a volume element, $d\tau$, will be proportional to $\int \psi \psi^* d\tau$ and, as with atomic orbitals, each molecular orbital will be dependent on a set of quantum numbers that determine its energy and spatial distribution. It is also assumed that the building-up or *aufbau* principle holds for the molecule just as it does for an atom. That is, each molecular orbital can accommodate two electrons with opposite spins, and, starting with the lowest-energy orbital, the electrons must go into the available molecular orbitals one at a time.

According to the molecular orbital theory, if we have a simple covalent bond composed of two electrons described by one-electron molecular orbital wave functions, ψ_1 and ψ_2, respectively, these can be combined to give the configurational wave function for the system

$$\psi_{MO} = \psi_1 \psi_2$$

Or, in general, if there are n electrons, the configurational wave function will be

$$\psi_{MO} = \psi_1 \psi_2 \cdot \cdot \cdot \psi_n \tag{5-19}$$

where the ψ_i are one-electron molecular orbitals. In determining the individual one-electron molecular orbitals such as ψ_1 and ψ_2, a linear combination of the bonding atomic orbitals of the atoms composing the molecule can be used.

The Hydrogen Molecule Ion

As an example, we can consider the simplest possible molecular species, the hydrogen molecule ion.[8] If we are interested in determining the ground-state energy of this species, we can construct our trial wave function from a linear combination of the $1s$ orbitals of the hydrogen atoms. We can begin by imagining the nuclei to be separated to an infinite distance, thereby leading to the arrangement

$$H \cdot \qquad\qquad H^+$$
$$(a) \qquad\qquad (b)$$

In this instance we have the electron on atom a, and in the ground state, the molecular orbital will be represented by the atomic orbital $\psi_a = \psi_{1s_a}$. If the other extreme is considered, the ground-state molecular orbital will be the atomic orbital $\psi_b = \psi_{1s_b}$, indicating that the electron is associated with atom b. If the two nuclei are now allowed to come together, it would be reasonable to consider that the resultant one-electron molecular orbital will be characteristic of the two atomic orbitals. This leads to the approximation of *linear combination of atomic orbitals (LCAO)*. Thus, we can say that the one-electron molecular orbital for the first electron is

$$\psi_1 = a_1 \psi_a + a_2 \psi_b \tag{5-20}$$

For this particular problem, there is only one electron, and the total wave function is $\psi = \psi_1$. However, if we were considering the hydrogen molecule, the configurational wave function would be

$$\psi_{MO} = \psi_1 \psi_2 = \{a_1 \psi_a(1) + a_2 \psi_b(1)\}\{a_3 \psi_a(2) + a_4 \psi_b(2)\}$$

where $\psi_a(1)$ is the wave function for electron 1 on atom a, $\psi_a(2)$ is the wave function for electron 2 on atom a, and so on. Of course, due to the symmetry of the hydrogen molecule, the absolute magnitudes of all of the coefficients a_i are the same.

Since the molecular orbital of the one electron in the hydrogen molecule ion is here represented as a linear combination of two independent terms, the secular determinant will take the same form we have already developed in Eq. (5–17)

$$\begin{vmatrix} H_{aa} - ES_{aa} & H_{ab} - ES_{ab} \\ H_{ba} - ES_{ba} & H_{bb} - ES_{bb} \end{vmatrix} = 0$$

This can be simplified considerably by noting the symmetry of this particular molecule. Since the hydrogen atoms, and therefore, the ground-state atomic orbitals, are identical, it should be apparent that

$$H_{aa} = H_{bb}$$
$$H_{ba} = H_{ab}$$

and

$$S_{ba} = S_{ab}$$

Further, if we use normalized wave functions, $S_{aa} = S_{bb} = 1$. Consequently, the secular determinant can now be reduced to

$$\begin{vmatrix} H_{aa} - E & H_{ba} - ES \\ H_{ba} - ES & H_{aa} - E \end{vmatrix} = 0 \qquad (5\text{–}21)$$

and this leads to the expression*

$$(H_{aa} - E)^2 - (H_{ba} - SE)^2 = 0 \qquad (5\text{–}22)$$

If this expression is now rearranged and solved for E by means of the quadratic equation, two roots are obtained,

$$E_S = \frac{H_{aa} + H_{ba}}{1 + S} \qquad (5\text{–}23a)$$

and

$$E_A = \frac{H_{aa} - H_{ba}}{1 - S} \qquad (5\text{–}23b)$$

where E_S and E_A denote *symmetric* and *antisymmetric* energy states, respectively.

Bonding and Antibonding Orbitals. Here we note that the original $1s$ energy states of the two hydrogen atoms are degenerate, but, on combination, they split into two new energy states, one of lower energy and one of higher energy than the original atomic $1s$ states. This is represented schematically in Figure 5–2. In terms of the molecular orbital theory, the lower-energy orbital is considered to be a *bonding orbital* and the higher-energy orbital is considered to be an *antibonding orbital*. Both orbitals can accommodate a pair of electrons, but the bonding orbital, since it is of

---

* Very often, this equation is seen in terms of the symbolism $H_{aa} = E_a$, $H_{bb} = E_b$, and $H_{ab} = \beta$.

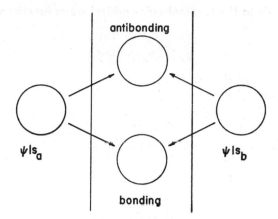

FIGURE 5-2. Combination of Two Atomic Orbitals
to Form Two Molecular Orbitals.

lower energy, will be filled first. Thus, for the hydrogen molecule ion, the
electron will go into the bonding orbital. However, for more complex systems, we shall see that the occupancy of an antibonding orbital is extremely
important in determining bond character.

Electron Distribution in the Hydrogen Molecule Ion. Along with the
energy states, it is also interesting to consider the electron distribution in
the hydrogen molecule ion for both the symmetric and the antisymmetric
states. From Eq. (5–20) we have seen that the wave function for the
hydrogen molecule ion is

$$\psi_{MO} = a_1 \psi_a + a_2 \psi_b$$

Now, from the fact that two energy states were obtained, we can conclude
that two wave functions must exist: one for the symmetric state and one
for the antisymmetric state. These can be determined from the general
expression relating a_1 to a_2,

$$(H_{11} - ES_{11})a_1 + (H_{12} - ES_{12})a_2 = 0 \tag{5–16a}$$

In terms of our present symbolism, this can be represented as

$$(H_{aa} - E)a_1 + (H_{ba} - ES_{ba})a_2 = 0$$

In order to obtain the symmetric solution, it is necessary to substitute E_S
for E in this equation, and for the antisymmetric solution, it is necessary
to substitute E_A for E. If this is done, and the resultant expression is solved,
it is found, respectively, that

$$a_1 = a_2$$

and

$$a_1 = -a_2$$

This, then, leads to the two molecular orbital wave functions

$$\psi_S = N_S(\psi_a + \psi_b) \tag{5-24a}$$

$$\psi_A = N_A(\psi_a - \psi_b) \tag{5-24b}$$

where N is a normalizing constant.

In order to get the final wave functions, it is necessary to carry out the normalization of ψ_S and ψ_A. This can be done quite simply for both the symmetric and the antisymmetric functions. Using the symmetric function to illustrate the procedure, we can recognize that for a normalized function

$$\int \psi_S{}^* \psi_S d\tau = 1$$

or

$$\int N_S{}^2 (\psi_a + \psi_b)^* (\psi_a + \psi_b) d\tau = 1$$

On expansion, this becomes

$$N_S{}^2 \left[\int \psi_a{}^2 d\tau + 2 \int \psi_a \psi_b d\tau + \int \psi_b{}^2 d\tau \right] = 1 \tag{5-25}$$

The complex conjugate forms can be dropped here since both ψ_a and ψ_b are real. Now, if we have originally chosen ψ_a and ψ_b to be normalized wave functions, it follows that

$$\int \psi_a{}^2 d\tau = \int \psi_b{}^2 d\tau = 1$$

and by definition

$$\int \psi_a \psi_b d\tau = S_{ab}$$

Thus, we see that Eq. (5-25) becomes

$$N_S{}^2(1 + 2S_{ab} + 1) = 1$$

or

$$N_S = \frac{1}{\sqrt{2 + 2S_{ab}}} \tag{5-26a}$$

In the same manner, it can be shown that

$$N_A = \frac{1}{\sqrt{2 - 2S_{ab}}} \tag{5-26b}$$

This now gives us the normalized wave functions

$$\psi_S = \frac{1}{\sqrt{2 + 2S_{ab}}} (\psi_a + \psi_b) \tag{5-27a}$$

and

$$\psi_A = \frac{1}{\sqrt{2 - 2S_{ab}}} (\psi_a - \psi_b) \tag{5-27b}$$

From the wave functions we can determine the distribution of the electron charge in the molecule, and from the expressions for the energy states, we can calculate the molecular energy levels. Considering the charge distribution first, we can see that if S_{ab} is sufficiently near to zero, then

$$\psi_S{}^2 = \frac{1}{2} \{\psi_a{}^2 + \psi_b{}^2 + 2\,\psi_a\,\psi_b\} \qquad (5\text{–}28a)$$

and

$$\psi_A{}^2 = \frac{1}{2} \{\psi_a{}^2 + \psi_b{}^2 - 2\,\psi_a\,\psi_b\} \qquad (5\text{–}28b)$$

Here we see that the symmetric function leads to an increase in electron charge density in the region of overlap between the two atoms over that of the individual atoms as described by the functions $\psi_a{}^2$ and $\psi_b{}^2$. On the other hand, the antisymmetric function leads to a decrease in the charge density. This is represented graphically in Figure 5–3. The dotted lines represent the respective charge densities on the individual atoms when separated to infinity, and the heavy line represents the electron charge distribution in the hydrogen molecule ion along a line through the nuclei. It is apparent that the bonding orbital favors a charge distribution that is concentrated between the nuclei, whereas the antibonding orbital tends

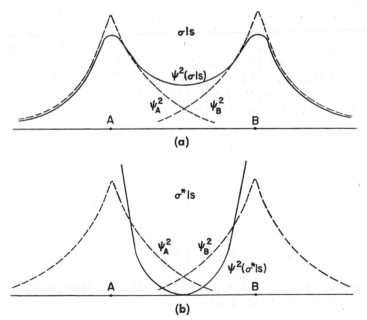

FIGURE 5–3. Electron Densities Along the Nuclear Axis for (a) the Symmetrical and (b) the Antisymmetrical States of the Hydrogen Molecule Ion.

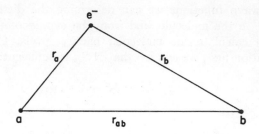

FIGURE 5–4.   Coordinates for the Hydrogen
Molecule Ion.

to decrease the charge density in this region and to concentrate it around
the individual atoms. Since we consider the formation of a covalent bond
to be associated with an electron charge buildup in the region of the bond,
it would seem that only the symmetric function should lead to the formation of a stable molecule.

Stability of the Hydrogen Molecule Ion. If the hydrogen molecule ion
actually does form a stable species, we should expect a potential energy
diagram as a function of the distance of separation of the two nuclei to
show a minimum at some equilibrium separation of the two atoms, a and b.
It should be possible to plot such a curve if we can evaluate the expression
for the energy of the molecule as a function of the internuclear separation.
Immediately, we should recognize that two potential energy diagrams will
be obtained: one for the bonding orbital and one for the antibonding
orbital. In both E_S and E_A the same integrals will appear, but the energies
will be different due to the signs of the various terms. From Eq. (5–23),
it can be seen that these integrals are

$$H_{aa} = \int \psi_a H \psi_a d\tau$$

$$H_{ba} = \int \psi_b H \psi_a d\tau$$

and

$$S_{ba} = \int \psi_b \psi_a d\tau$$

Now, according to Figure 5–4, it can be seen that the Hamiltonian operator
for the hydrogen molecule ion is

$$H = -\frac{h^2}{8\pi^2 m} \nabla^2 - \frac{e^2}{r_a} - \frac{e^2}{r_b} + \frac{e^2}{r_{ab}} \tag{5–29}$$

and H_{aa} will therefore become

$$H_{aa} = \int \psi_{1sa} \left[-\frac{h^2}{8\pi^2 m} \nabla^2 - \frac{e^2}{r_a} - \frac{e^2}{r_b} + \frac{e^2}{r_{ab}} \right] \psi_{1sa} \, d\tau \qquad (5\text{–}30)$$

This integral can be simplified by recognizing that

$$-\frac{h^2}{8\pi^2 m} \nabla^2 - \frac{e^2}{r_a}$$

is the Hamiltonian operator for the hydrogen atom with the electron around atom a, and since, in general,

$$H\psi = E\psi$$

the Hamiltonian operator for the hydrogen molecule ion can be expressed as

$$H = E_0 - \frac{e^2}{r_b} + \frac{e^2}{r_{ab}} \qquad (5\text{–}31)$$

where E_0 is the ground-state energy of the hydrogen atom. This then gives

$$H_{aa} = \int \psi_{1sa} \left[E_0 - \frac{e^2}{r_b} + \frac{e^2}{r_{ab}} \right] \psi_{1sa} \, d\tau$$

Now E_0 and r_{ab} are both constants, and for this reason it is possible to remove them from under the integral sign, giving

$$H_{aa} = E_0 \int \psi_{1sa} \psi_{1sa} \, d\tau + \frac{e^2}{r_{ab}} \int \psi_{1sa} \psi_{1sa} \, d\tau - e^2 \int \frac{1}{r_b} \psi_{1sa} \psi_{1sa} \, d\tau$$

But, since the $1s$ wave functions are normalized, it follows that

$$H_{aa} = E_0 + \frac{e^2}{r_{ab}} - J \qquad (5\text{–}32)$$

where J denotes the integral

$$J = e^2 \int \frac{1}{r_b} \psi_{1sa} \psi_{1sa} \, d\tau \qquad (5\text{–}33)$$

The evaluation of this integral is not a simple matter, and for that reason it will not be considered here. Nevertheless, it will yet be possible to discuss the shape of the potential energy diagram in terms of its contribution to the total energy of the system.

After introducing the Hamiltonian operator, the integral H_{ba} becomes

$$H_{ba} = \int \psi_{1sa} \left(E_0 + \frac{e^2}{r_{ab}} - \frac{e^2}{r_b} \right) \psi_{1sb} \, d\tau$$

and in the same manner as with the integral H_{aa}, the integral H_{ba} can be represented as

$$H_{ba} = E_0 \int \psi_{1sa} \psi_{1sb} \, d\tau + \frac{e^2}{r_{ab}} \int \psi_{1sa} \psi_{1sb} \, d\tau - e^2 \int \frac{1}{r_b} \psi_{1sa} \psi_{1sb} \, d\tau$$

Since $\int \psi_{1sa} \psi_{1sb} d\tau$ is defined as S_{ab}, then H_{ba} can be expressed as

$$H_{ba} = E_0 S_{ab} + \frac{e^2}{r_{ab}} S_{ab} - K \tag{5-34}$$

where K denotes the integral

$$K = e^2 \int \frac{1}{r_b} \psi_{1sa} \psi_{1sb} \, d\tau \tag{5-35}$$

Just as with the integral J, the integral K is rather difficult to evaluate, but it can be helpful to see how it will, in general, effect the energy of the molecule.

When the solutions of the various integrals are substituted into the equations for the energy states, we obtain for the symmetric state,

$$E_S = \frac{H_{aa} + H_{ba}}{1 + S_{ba}}$$

$$= \frac{E_0 + \dfrac{e^2}{r_{ab}} - J + E_0 S_{ba} + \dfrac{e^2}{r_{ab}} S_{ba} - K}{1 + S_{ba}}$$

or

$$E_S - E_0 = \frac{e^2}{r_{ab}} - \frac{J + K}{1 + S_{ba}} \tag{5-36a}$$

For the antisymmetric state, it is found that the corresponding equation is

$$E_A - E_0 = \frac{e^2}{r_{ab}} - \frac{J - K}{1 - S_{ba}} \tag{5-36b}$$

Although the arithmetic is rather complex, it is possible to evaluate the integrals J and K as a function of the internuclear separation of the hydrogen nuclei. This result can be represented by means of a potential-energy diagram such as that shown in Figure 5–5. Here the antisymmetric state is seen to correspond to an unstable energy state, and if the electron were in the antisymmetrical orbital, we could conclude that the hydrogen molecule ion would be an unstable species. On the other hand, the symmetric energy state leads to a potential minimum and, therefore, a stable molecular species.

Using the particular wave function we have chosen, the potential energy minimum is equivalent to a dissociation energy of 1.76 ev and an

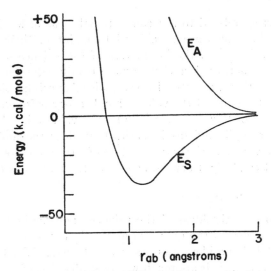

FIGURE 5–5. Potential Energy Diagram for the Hydrogen Molecule Ion Showing the Symmetrical (E_S) and the Antisymmetrical (E_A) Energy States.

equilibrium separation of 1.32Å. Experimentally, it is found that the dissociation energy is 2.791 ev, and the equilibrium separation is 1.06Å. Thus, our calculations indicate that the hydrogen molecule ion is a stable species, but they also indicate that the trial wave function we have used can be improved. A first step in this direction would be to introduce a variable parameter. Such a trial function that has proven successful is

$$\psi_a = \left(\frac{\alpha^3}{\pi} \right)^{\frac{1}{2}} e^{-\alpha r_a}$$

If the energy is minimized with respect to the parameter, α, somewhat closer agreement between theory and experiment is obtained than with our original wave function, but some difference yet exists. Finally, James used the function

$$\psi = e^{-c_1(r_a + r_b)} \{ 1 + c_2(r_a + r_b)^2 \}$$

and obtained very good agreement between theory and experiment. This function is of particular interest in that it is not based on the *LCAO* method, and the concept of resonance does not appear.

THE VALENCE BOND THEORY

The natural extension of the Lewis concept of an electron pair bond finds its quantum mechanical expression in the valence bond theory. Just as with the molecular orbital theory, the valence bond theory is also an approximation method. However, its basic approach to the structure of a molecule is closely related to our conventional ideas of localized chemical bonds. Here, the atoms are considered to maintain their individuality, and the bond arises from the interaction of the valence electrons as the atoms come together. Such a view is more readily adapted to qualitative arguments than that presented by the molecular orbital theory, and for this reason the language of the valence bond theory is frequently the more familiar. In spite of this desirable feature, the valence bond method often leads to more complicated mathematics than does the molecular orbital theory. And, in addition, the determination of a trial function for a complex molecule is not so straightforward as it is in the molecular orbital theory.

The Hydrogen Molecule

To some extent, the ideas of the valence bond method can be appreciated by an analysis of the quantum mechanical treatment of the hydrogen molecule.[9] This problem was first treated successfully by Heitler and London in 1927, and their approach was basically that of the valence bond method. The trial wave function will be somewhat different in the simple valence bond theory than it is in the simple molecular orbital theory. According to the molecular orbital theory, the wave function for electron (1) is made up of a linear combination of the hydrogen $1s$ orbitals just as it is in the hydrogen molecule ion. Thus,

$$\psi_1 = \psi_a(1) + \psi_b(1)$$

But, in the hydrogen molecule there are two electrons, and a one-electron molecular orbital wave function for the second electron will be

$$\psi_2 = \psi_a(2) + \psi_b(2)$$

This then leads to the configurational wave function

$$\psi_{\text{MO}} = \psi_1 \psi_2 = \{\psi_a(1) + \psi_b(1)\} \{\psi_a(2) + \psi_b(2)\} \tag{5–37}$$

In this case it is seen that the configurational wave function is expressed as a product of one-electron molecular orbital wave functions.

A quite different construction is used in the valence bond method. Here it is proposed that if two unconnected systems can be separately described by wave functions ψ_a and ψ_b, respectively, then the wave function for the combined system will be

$$\psi_I = \psi_a \psi_b \tag{5–38}$$

Consequently, for the hydrogen molecule

$$\psi_I = \psi_{1s_a}(1) \ \psi_{1s_b}(2) \tag{5–39}$$

This wave function places electron (1) on atom a and electron (2) on atom b.

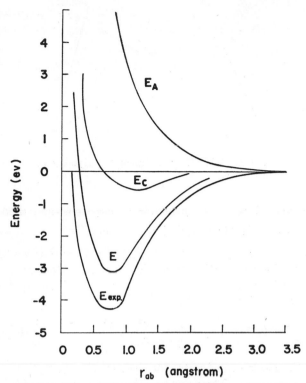

FIGURE 5–6.   Potential Energy Diagram for the Hydrogen Molecule Showing the Antisymmetrical State (E_A), the Classical Coulombic Interaction (E_C), the Simple Valence Bond Energy (E), and the Experimental Curve (E_{exp}).

Although the potential energy diagram that results from this wave function has a minimum, thereby indicating a stable molecule, the agreement with experiment is not good. However, a much better trial function can be obtained by introducing what has now become a fundamental principle of quantum mechanics. In the wave function ψ_I we have arbitrarily placed electron (1) on atom a and electron (2) on atom b. There is no basis for such a choice, and it is equally valid to reverse this arrangement, giving

$$\psi_{II} = \psi_{1sa}(2)\ \psi_{1sb}(1) \tag{5–40}$$

This emphasizes the fact that the electrons are *indistinguishable*, and it is significant that this recognition leads to a much better trial function. This is evident from Figure 5–6 where the potential energy diagram for the hydrogen molecule is plotted for various trial functions. This new effect can be introduced into the total wave function by taking the usual linear

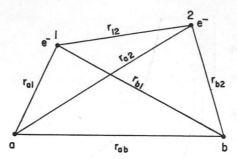

FIGURE 5–7. Coordinates of the Hydrogen Molecule.

combination according to the principle of superposition, thereby giving

$$\psi_{vs} = \psi_{1s_a}(1)\ \psi_{1s_b}(2) + \psi_{1s_a}(2)\ \psi_{1s_b}(1) \tag{5–41}$$

Symmetric and Antisymmetric Energy States. Now that we have a trial wave function, the problem is essentially the same as that of the hydrogen molecule ion. Using the symbolism of Figure 5–7, the Hamiltonian operator for the hydrogen molecule will be

$$H = \left[-\frac{h^2}{8\pi^2 m}\ (\nabla_1{}^2 + \nabla_2{}^2) - \frac{e^2}{r_{a1}} - \frac{e^2}{r_{b1}} - \frac{e^2}{r_{a2}} - \frac{e^2}{r_{b2}} + \frac{e^2}{r_{12}} + \frac{e^2}{r_{ab}} \right] \tag{5–42}$$

where $\nabla_1{}^2$ is the Laplacian operator for electron (1) and $\nabla_2{}^2$ is the Laplacian operator for electron (2). The wave function can be expressed in the general form

$$\psi_{vs} = a_1\ \psi_{\mathrm{I}} + a_2\ \psi_{\mathrm{II}} \tag{5–43}$$

and this leads to the same secular determinant that was used for the hydrogen molecule ion. Additionally, we will also obtain the symmetric and antisymmetric energy terms

$$E_S = \frac{H_{11} + H_{12}}{1 + S_{12}}$$

and

$$E_A = \frac{H_{11} - H_{12}}{1 - S_{12}}$$

The resultant integrals, however, will be more complex than those encountered in the hydrogen molecule ion.

The integral H_{11} is now defined as

$$H_{11} = \int\int \psi_{\mathrm{I}} H \psi_{\mathrm{I}} d\tau_1 d\tau_2$$

where the double integral results from a consideration of the coordinates of both electron (1) and electron (2). On introducing the Hamiltonian operator, the integral becomes

$$H_{11} = \int\int \psi_a(1)\,\psi_b(2)\left\{-\frac{h^2}{8\pi^2 m}\,(\nabla_1{}^2 + \nabla_2{}^2) - \frac{e^2}{r_{a1}} - \frac{e^2}{r_{b1}} - \frac{e^2}{r_{a2}} - \frac{e^2}{r_{b2}}\right.$$

$$\left. + \frac{e^2}{r_{12}} + \frac{e^2}{r_{ab}}\right\} \psi_a(1)\,\psi_b(2)\,d\tau_1 d\tau_2$$

Now,

$$\left(-\frac{h^2}{8\pi^2 m}\,\nabla_1{}^2 - \frac{e^2}{r_{a1}}\right)\psi_a(1) = E_0\psi_a(1)$$

and

$$\left(-\frac{h^2}{8\pi^2 m}\,\nabla_2{}^2 - \frac{e^2}{r_{b2}}\right)\psi_b(2) = E_0\psi_b(2)$$

where E_0 is the ground-state energy of the hydrogen atom. Therefore, the integral H_{11} can be expressed more simply as

$$H_{11} = \int\int \psi_a(1)\psi_b(2)\left(2E_0 + \frac{e^2}{r_{ab}} + \frac{e^2}{r_{12}} - \frac{e^2}{r_{a2}} - \frac{e^2}{r_{b1}}\right)\psi_a(1)\,\psi_b(2)\,d\tau_1 d\tau_2$$

Or, since the 1s wave functions are assumed to be normalized,

$$H_{11} = 2E_0 + \frac{e^2}{r_{ab}} + J_1 - 2J_2 \qquad (5\text{--}44)$$

Here,

$$J_1 = e^2 \int\int \frac{1}{r_{12}}\,[\psi_a(1)\,\psi_b(2)]^2\,d\tau_1 d\tau_2 \qquad (5\text{--}45)$$

and, because of the equivalence of the two electrons,

$$J_2 = e^2 \int\int \frac{1}{r_{a2}}\,[\psi_a(1)\,\psi_b(2)]^2\,d\tau_1 d\tau_2 \qquad (5\text{--}46a)$$

$$= e^2 \int\int \frac{1}{r_{b1}}\,[\psi_a(1)\,\psi_b(2)]^2\,d\tau_1 d\tau_2 \qquad (5\text{--}46b)$$

The solution of these integrals is even more complicated than that for the corresponding integrals of the hydrogen molecule ion, and for this reason they will not be treated further here. However, it will again be useful to consider the basic form of the energy expression.

By the same general argument as was used for H_{11}, it can be shown that

$$H_{12} = 2E_0 S_{12} + \frac{e^2}{r_{ab}} + K_1 - 2K_2$$

where

$$K_1 = e^2 \int \int \frac{1}{r_{12}} [\psi_a(1) \ \psi_b(2) \ \psi_a(2) \ \psi_b(1)] \ d\tau_1 d\tau_2 \qquad (5\text{--}47)$$

and, again because of the equivalence of the electrons,

$$K_2 = e^2 \int \int \frac{1}{r_{a1}} [\psi_a(1) \ \psi_b(2) \ \psi_a(2) \ \psi_b(1)] \ d\tau_1 d\tau_2 \qquad (5\text{--}48a)$$

$$= e^2 \int \int \frac{1}{r_{b2}} [\psi_a(1) \ \psi_b(2) \ \psi_a(2) \ \psi_b(1)] \ d\tau_1 d\tau_2 \qquad (5\text{--}48b)$$

If these results are now substituted into the expressions for the energy states of the hydrogen molecule and are rearranged, we can obtain

$$E_S - 2E_0 = \frac{e^2}{r_{ab}} + \frac{J_1 - 2J_2 + K_1 - 2K_2}{1 + S_{12}} \qquad (5\text{--}49a)$$

and

$$E_A - 2E_0 = \frac{e^2}{r_{ab}} + \frac{J_1 - 2J_2 - K_1 + 2K_2}{1 - S_{12}} \qquad (5\text{--}49b)$$

which correspond to the symmetric and the antisymmetric wave functions, respectively.

The potential-energy curves resulting from both the symmetric and the antisymmetric states are seen in Figure 5-6. By setting the ground-state energies of the isolated hydrogen atoms equal to zero, that is, $E_0 = 0$, then the resultant potential-energy curve represents the *interaction energy* between the two hydrogen atoms as they form the hydrogen molecule. The antisymmetric state fails to show a minimum, and as would be expected, it represents an unstable state. On the other hand, the symmetric state shows a relatively deep minimum in the curve, thereby indicating a stable molecular species. It is significant that the potential minimum using this trial function is considerably closer to the experimental potential minimum than that obtained by ignoring the indistinguishability of the electrons. However, we should also note that better agreement can be obtained by using still other wave functions.

The Classical Interaction Energy. Acknowledging the indistinguishability of the electrons in the hydrogen molecule is comparable to admitting the existence of the two structures

$$H_a(1) \quad H_b(2) \quad \text{and} \quad H_a(2) \quad H_b(1)$$
$$\text{I} \qquad\qquad\qquad\qquad \text{II}$$

Because of the identity of any two isolated hydrogen atoms, the wave function and the energy of structures I and II are identical. Now, in order to appreciate the significance of the indistinguishability of the two electrons, it is necessary to interpret the molecular energy in terms of either one or the other of these structures. If, for example, we consider structure I, we can recall that the corresponding wave function is

$$\psi_I = \psi_a(1)\ \psi_b(2)$$

and the energy of the system will be given by

$$E = \frac{\displaystyle\int \psi H\ \psi d\tau}{\displaystyle\int \psi\ \psi d\tau}$$

$$= \frac{\displaystyle\int \psi_a(1)\ \psi_b(2)\ H\ \psi_a(1)\ \psi_b(2)d\tau}{\displaystyle\int \psi_a(1)\ \psi_b(2)\ \psi_a(1)\ \psi_b(2)\ d\tau}$$

or simply

$$E_c = \frac{H_{11}}{S_{11}}$$

This can be simplified further by using normalized $1s$ wave functions. If this is done, $S_{11} = 1$, and

$$E_c = H_{11} \tag{5-50}$$

Earlier, it was shown that

$$H_{11} = 2E_0 + \frac{e^2}{r_{ab}} + J_1 - 2J_2 \tag{5-44}$$

Therefore, we can say that

$$E_c = 2E_0 + \frac{e^2}{r_{ab}} + J_1 - 2J_2 \tag{5-51}$$

The interaction energy of the two atoms can be determined by equating the energy of the isolated atoms, E_0, to zero. The resultant potential-energy diagram then gives the decrease in energy of the system over that of the isolated atoms as the two hydrogen atoms are allowed to approach each other. If a potential minimum as a function of r_{ab} is observed, then the theory would predict a stable molecule. In Figure 5-6, the second line represents E_c, and it is seen to show a slight minimum in the potential diagram. This indicates that the molecule is stable, but the calculated dissociation energy is seen to be only about one-tenth of the experimental value.

If we consider the various terms in the energy expression, we can conclude that E_c is essentially the classical coulombic interaction between the two hydrogen atoms. The integral J_1 was seen to be

$$J_1 = e^2 \int \int \frac{1}{r_{12}} \psi_a{}^2(1) \; \psi_b{}^2(2) \; d\tau_1 d\tau_2$$

The term e^2/r_{12} represents the electrostatic repulsion between two unit charges and $\psi_a{}^2(1)$ and $\psi_b{}^2(2)$ represent the charge densities of electron (1) and electron (2). We can, therefore, conclude that J_1 represents the electrostatic repulsion between the charge clouds of electron (1) and electron (2).

On the other hand, the integral J_2 was seen to be

$$J_2 = e^2 \int \int \frac{1}{r_{a2}} \psi_a(1)\psi_b(2)\psi_a(1)\psi_b(2)d\tau_1 d\tau_2$$

$$= e^2 \int \int \frac{1}{r_{b1}} \psi_a(1) \; \psi_b(2) \; \psi_a(1) \; \psi_b(2)d\tau_1 d\tau_2$$

and these reduce effectively to

$$J_2 = e^2 \int \frac{1}{r_{a2}} \psi_b{}^2(2) \; d\tau_2$$

$$= e^2 \int \frac{1}{r_{b1}} \psi_a{}^2(1) \; d\tau_1$$

This can be seen to represent the attraction between the electron charge around each individual atom and the opposite nucleus. For instance, it is the attraction between the positively charged nucleus b and the negatively charged electron cloud around nucleus a.

Finally, e^2/r_{ab} represents the nuclear repulsion between the two positively charged nuclei. Thus, we have the two electrostatic repulsion terms, e^2/r_{ab} and J_1, and we have the one electrostatic attraction term $2J_2$. E_c should then represent the classical electrostatic attraction between the two hydrogen atoms. This leads to a stable hydrogen molecule, but it is not nearly so stable according to this picture as it is experimentally known to be.

Resonance. It is here that the significance of the indistinguishability of the electrons can be appreciated. By recognizing that the two structures I and II can exist, a new wave function is seen to result that leads to a dissociation energy that is about 70 per cent of the experimental value. When we recall that the simple electrostatic interaction gives a dissociation energy of only about 10 per cent of the experimental value, it is understandable why the effect is considered as a quantum mechanical principle.

It is interesting to note that there is no classical analog of this effect, but in terms of our quantum mechanical model it has meaning. In valence bond language, this effect is referred to as *resonance*, and it plays a critical role in the valence bond theory.

Mathematically, one might conclude that electron (1) exists on atom a and electron (2) exists on atom b at a given instant, and at another instant the reverse arrangement exists. Thus, the electrons could be considered to resonate between the two structures. This conclusion, however, is not the presently accepted conclusion. It is more realistic to say that the actual state of the system is represented by neither structure I nor II at any instant of time, but rather the actual structure is some intermediate one that has some of the character of each of the independent structures. Thus, we are constructing a wave function to describe the actual structure by introducing the various common characteristics expressed by each individual structure. Carrying out this construction results in a significant increase in stability of the system with respect to any single structure, and this difference in energy is referred to as the resonance energy.

It is important to recognize that the concept of resonance is, in a sense, a *fictitious* concept. It has its existence by virtue of the mode of construction of the trial wave function, and its reality is thus a product of the quantum mechanical model used to describe the system. As long as we use the valence bond theory, resonance has a reality for it is basic to the language and concepts of this theory. However, in terms of another equally good model, it may have no meaning and, therefore, no existence. The same argument, of course, applies to any scientific concept, but because of the success and use of some concepts, they are often given more credence than they deserve. Resonance falls into this category. Thus, in terms of the valence bond theory, resonance will have an existence, and we will feel justified in speaking as if it were a fact. But in terms of other models, we may tend to deny its existence.

Contribution of Ionic Terms. Using the language of the valence bond theory, we can improve the trial function by recognizing that two additional structures may contribute to the total wave function of the hydrogen molecule. These are the ionic structures

$$:H_a^- \quad H_b^+ \quad \text{and} \quad H_a^+ \quad :H_b^-$$
$$\text{III} \qquad\qquad\qquad \text{IV}$$

in which both of the electrons are placed on either atom a or atom b. These structures obviously cannot be of equal weight with the homopolar structures I and II. Consequently, the total wave function can be represented as

$$\psi_{vB} = a\,\psi_I + a\,\psi_{II} + b\,\psi_{III} + b\,\psi_{IV}$$
$$= a\,\psi_a(1)\,\psi_b(2) + a\,\psi_a(2)\,\psi_b(1) + b\,\psi_a(1)\,\psi_a(2) + b\,\psi_b(1)\,\psi_b(2)$$

Here we note that the two homopolar terms are of equal weight and the two ionic terms are also of equal weight. If the atoms were not the same, this would not be true. Thus, in general, it can be said that

$$\psi_{vB} = a\,\psi_I + b\,\psi_{II} + c\,\psi_{III} + d\,\psi_{IV} + \cdots \qquad (5\text{–}52)$$

The values of the parameters a, b, c, d, etc., can be determined by minimizing the energy of the system with respect to each of the parameters. Such a calculation for the hydrogen molecule implies that the bond has about 17 per cent ionic character. It is of interest to note that the simple molecular orbital wave function for the hydrogen molecule contains the ionic terms represented by structures III and IV, but they are given the same weight as the homopolar terms. This can be seen by multiplying out the function

$$\psi_{MO} = \{\psi_a(1) + \psi_b(1)\}\{\psi_a(2) + \psi_b(2)\} \qquad (5\text{–}37)$$

to give

$$\psi_{MO} = \psi_a(1)\,\psi_b(2) + \psi_a(2)\,\psi_b(1) + \psi_a(1)\,\psi_a(2) + \psi_b(1)\,\psi_b(2)$$

Thus, it would appear that the simple molecular orbital theory places too much emphasis on the ionic terms. This, of course, can be remedied by arbitrarily introducing parameters to give the proper weight to the various terms.

In addition to the resonance effect, the valence bond function can be further improved by introducing other parameters. These are usually attributed to various physical aspects of the molecular structure. For instance, we can represent the $1s$ wave function as $\psi = (1/\pi a_0^3)e^{-\alpha r/a_0}$ rather than $\psi = (1/\pi a_0^3)e^{-r/a_0}$. The parameter, α, can then be used to minimize the energy, and at the same time it can be justified in terms of a contraction of the electron orbit due to an attraction to two nuclear centers. Of course, no justification is really necessary. The more parameters that are used in the trial function, the more adaptable it should be, if we ignore the effort required to solve the resultant equations. In fact, essentially exact agreement between theory and experiment was obtained by James and Coolidge using a wave function with 13 terms.[10]

DIATOMIC MOLECULES

In the construction of the one-electron molecular orbitals for the hydrogen molecule, we used linear combinations of the atomic $1s$ orbitals of the separated hydrogen atoms. In this instance, the isolated atoms are identical, and the ground state in each is the same. If, on the other hand, a molecule is to be constructed from two different atoms, it would be very unlikely that the same orbitals would be used from both atoms. If, for instance, we consider the molecule HCl, it is obvious that, although the $1s$ orbital of the hydrogen atom is used, the $1s$ orbital of the chlorine atom will contribute nothing to the formation of the bond. This emphasizes an important point with regard to bond formation. In order for two orbitals to make an effective molecular orbital, it is necessary that they be of comparable energies. In this particular instance, the $1s$ orbital of the chlorine atom is at a much lower energy than the $1s$ orbital of the hydrogen atom, and the two will, therefore, not combine.

It is also important to consider the extent of *overlap* between the combining orbitals. Although, the overlap is, by itself, an insufficient criterion for bond formation, it nevertheless is important. Mathematically, the overlap is expressible in terms of the overlap or orthogonality integral, $S_{ab} - \int \psi_A \psi_B d\tau$. When S_{ab} is large, the overlap of the orbitals ψ_A and ψ_B is large. In directional bonding, the overlap criterion will be of extreme importance. However, in general, we will say that it is one of the factors that must be considered in the choice of atomic orbitals to be used in the construction of the molecular orbital.

Along the same lines, it is important to consider the symmetry of the combining orbitals. We can recall that a p orbital has a positive and a negative lobe whereas a $1s$ orbital is everywhere positive. Now, as can be seen in Figure 5–8, two s orbitals overlap effectively as do an s and a p_x

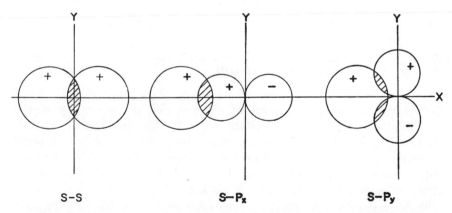

S–S   S–P$_x$ S–P$_y$

FIGURE 5–8. Overlap of s and p-Type Orbitals with Respect to Axial Symmetry.

orbital. However, it is apparent that the symmetry of the p_y and p_z orbitals prevent an effective overlap with the s orbital. Here we see that both the positive and the negative lobes of the p_y orbital overlap with the s orbital and each exactly cancels the effect of the other. The p_z orbital would, of course, give the same result as the p_y orbital. Just as no overlap at all causes $S_{ab} = 0$, the type of overlap observed with the p_y and p_z orbitals also leads to $S_{ab} = 0$. Thus, it is evident that we must consider

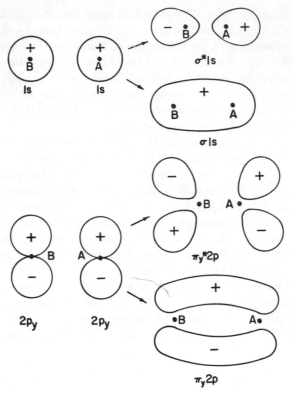

FIGURE 5–9. Formation of σ and π-Type Molecular Orbitals from Atomic Orbitals.

the relative energies, the extent of overlap, and the symmetry of the combining orbitals in the construction of a molecular orbital wave function.

In the case of homonuclear diatomics, we can give a simple pictorial representation of the molecular orbitals as they are formed from the individual atomic orbitals. For the s and p states, we can obtain two distinct types of molecular orbitals, as can be seen in Figure 5–9. The atomic orbitals combine to form two molecular orbitals, the bonding and the antibonding molecular orbitals corresponding to the symmetric and the antisymmetric functions, respectively. The molecular orbitals formed from the $1s$ atomic orbitals have cylindrical symmetry about the line of centers between the two atoms, **A** and **B**. Such bonds are referred to as σ bonds. σ bonds would also be expected from the combination of two p_x orbitals or an s orbital with a p_x orbital. To the contrary, the p_y orbitals shown in Figure 5–9, show a quite different symmetry with respect to the bond axis. These bonds are called π bonds, and since they can be formed from either the p_y or the p_z atomic orbitals, it is necessary to designate them as π_y and π_z, respectively.

In addition to the source of the orbitals, it is also necessary to differentiate between the bonding and the antibonding orbitals. This can be done by designating an antibonding σ bond as σ^* and an antibonding π bond as π^*. The same symbolism can be used for δ bonds which originate from atomic d orbitals, and so on.

Just as there is an order of filling of atomic orbitals, there is also an order of filling of molecular orbitals. This latter order has not been determined strictly from theoretical considerations because of mathematical complexity, but in conjunction with spectroscopic evidence, it has been concluded that for homonuclear diatomic molecules of the first-row elements the order is

$$\sigma_{1s} < \sigma^*{}_{1s} < \sigma_{2s} < \sigma^*{}_{2s} < \sigma_{2p} < \pi_{y2p} = \pi_{z2p} < \pi^*{}_{y2p} = \pi^*{}_{z2p} < \sigma^*{}_{2p}$$

Once this order is established, it is possible to consider the formation of a homonuclear diatomic molecule between the first-row elements. This can be done in much the same manner as that used to build up the electron levels in an atom. Considering first the hydrogen molecule, we can recognize that there will be two electrons to place in the molecular orbitals, and since each orbital will accommodate two electrons, we can represent the molecular formation as

$$\text{H } [1s^1] + \text{H } [1s^1] \rightarrow \text{H}_2 \, [(\sigma_{1s})^2]$$

This tells us that the hydrogen molecule has two electrons in the bonding σ_{1s} orbital which was constructed from the atomic $1s$ states of the isolated hydrogen atoms. Since both electrons are in the bonding orbital, the resultant molecule should be stable. We should also recognize that the hydrogen molecule ion should be stable. Its configuration is $\text{H}_2{}^+ \, [(\sigma_{1s})]$ and the one electron in the bonding orbital should lead to a stable species.

The next normal homonuclear diatomic molecule is He_2, and with four electrons, it can be represented as

$$\text{He } [1s^2] + \text{He } [1s^2] \rightarrow \text{He}_2 \, [(\sigma_{1s})^2 \, (\sigma^*{}_{1s})^2]$$

Here, we see that there are two electrons in the bonding orbital and two electrons in the antibonding orbital. These latter electrons cancel the effect of the bonding electrons, and a stable He_2 molecule should not exist. This, of course, is what is observed. However, the helium molecule ion, $\text{He}_2{}^+$, has been detected. Its stability can be attributed to an excess of bonding over antibonding electrons. But it should be mentioned that an antibonding electron more than compensates for the bonding effect of a single bonding electron. Thus, the helium molecule ion would not be expected to be as stable as a molecule having a simple one-electron bond.

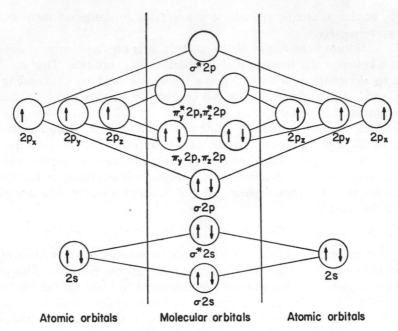

Atomic orbitals   Molecular orbitals   Atomic orbitals

FIGURE 5–10. Molecular Orbitals and Their Occupancy for the Nitrogen Molecule.

Two molecules that are of particular interest are nitrogen and oxygen. The bond formation in nitrogen can be considered to be

$$\text{N } [1s^2 2s^2 2p^3] + \text{N } [1s^2 2s^2 2p^3] \rightarrow \text{N}_2 \, [KK(\sigma_{2s})^2(\sigma^*_{2s})^2(\sigma_{2p})^2(\pi_{2p})^4]$$

The KK indicates the completion of the K shell, namely $(\sigma_{1s})^2(\sigma^*_{1s})^2$, and $(\pi_{2p})^4$ represents the occupancy of the $\pi_{y_{2p}}$ and the $\pi_{z_{2p}}$ orbitals. Here, we see a total of six bonding electrons distributed in three molecular orbitals. We can consider this to represent a triple bond, composed of a σ type bond and two π type bonds. It is of interest to consider the formation and the occupancy of the molecular orbitals for this molecule. As can be seen in Figure 5–10, the bonding results from the σ_{2p} and the two equivalent bonding π orbitals.

The oxygen molecule has the unusual property of being paramagnetic in its ground state, and any valency theory must adequately explain this property. If we consider the bond formation for this molecule, we see that it is

$$\text{O } [1s^2 2s^2 2p^4] + \text{O } [1s^2 2s^2 2p^4] \rightarrow \text{O}_2 \, [KK(\sigma_{2s})^2(\sigma^*_{2s})^2(\sigma_{2p})^2(\pi_{2p})^4(\pi^*_{2p})^2]$$

Two of the electrons go into the antibonding π orbitals leading effectively to a double bond. Now, if we look at the diagram of the oxygen molecular orbitals shown in Figure 5–11, we see that rather than pair up, the electrons

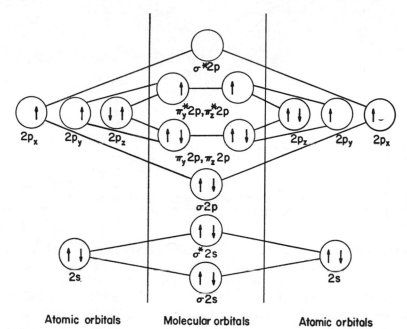

Atomic orbitals   **Molecular orbitals**   **Atomic orbitals**

FIGURE 5-11. Molecular Orbitals and Their Occupancy for the Oxygen Molecule.

located in the antibonding orbitals go into different orbitals of equal energy according to Hund's rule. This still gives the double bond character demanded but, at the same time, it gives two unpaired electrons. This, then, explains the resultant paramagnetic susceptibility of the oxygen molecule.

DIRECTIONAL BONDING

One of the more outstanding accomplishments of the quantum mechanical approach to molecular structure has been its success in the treatment of molecular geometry. If we consider the bonds between the atoms in a molecule to be associated with the overlap of atomic orbitals, we would then expect a definite geometry to be associated with the molecule. There are a variety of ways to handle molecular structure, and the approach used in the treatment of stereochemistry in Chapter 6 will be different than the one used here. However, the use of localized atomic orbitals in terms of the valence bond theory has proved so successful that it is worthy of discussion.

In terms of the valence bond approach to molecular structure, we can imagine a covalent bond to be formed as the result of the pairing of two electrons in the atomic orbitals of two different atoms. The bond, then should lie along the directions of the overlapping atomic orbitals, and we

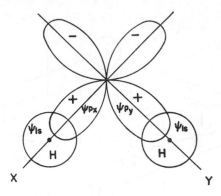

FIGURE 5–12. Overlap of Bonding Orbitals
in the Water Molecule.

would expect the strongest bond to be formed in the position that permitted
the maximum possible extent of overlap between the two orbitals. For the
sake of illustration, we can consider the water molecule. The two hydrogen
atoms will, of course, use $1s$ orbitals in the bond formation. However, the
oxygen atom has the electron configuration $1s^2 2s^2 2p_x^2 2p_y^1 2p_z^1$, and since
we are considering the bond to be formed from the pairing of electrons,
it would appear that the p_y and p_z orbitals of the oxygen atom must be
used. In Figure 5–12, the yz plane of the water molecule is shown, and we
see that the p_y and p_z orbitals lie mutually perpendicular to each other
in this plane. In order to obtain a maximum possible overlap between the
$1s$ orbitals of the hydrogen atoms and the p_y and p_z orbitals of the oxygen
atom, it is necessary for the hydrogen atoms to approach along the y and
the z axes. This leads to the overlap shown, and the HOH bond angle
should amount to 90°. This is not exactly in agreement with experiment.
The angle has been shown to be 104°31′. However, the deviation from 90°
can be attributed to a repulsion between the two hydrogen atoms and to
the effect of some contribution to the bond of the $2s$ electrons of the oxygen
atom. Subsequently, we will see that the bond may also be treated as an
sp^3 hybrid bond.

The same structure would be expected for H_2S, H_2Se, and H_2Te as is
predicted for H_2O. And, in fact, the agreement between experiment and
theory is found to be quite good for these molecules. The HXH angle for
H_2S is observed to be 92.2°, for H_2Se it is 91.0°, and for H_2Te it is 89.5°.
The same general arguments may also be applied to the series NH_3, PH_3,
AsH_3, and SbH_3. Here, all three of the p orbitals are involved in the
bonding and the HXH bond angles should again be 90°. Experimentally,
the angles are found for the series to be 107.3°, 93.3°, 91.8°, and 91.3°,
respectively. Various explanations can be given for these deviations within

the structure of the valence bond picture as well as explanations in terms of different theoretical models. However, we can see from this simple picture that a basis for molecular geometry exists in terms of the overlap of atomic orbitals.

Hybridization

Although the simple approach based on the overlap of s and p atomic orbitals works well for a variety of molecules, it is seen to fail completely for the organic compounds of carbon. The occupancy of the atomic orbitals of the carbon atom is

$$\underset{1s}{\underline{\uparrow\downarrow}}\ \underset{2s}{\underline{\uparrow\downarrow}}\ \underset{2p_x}{\underline{\downarrow}}\ \underset{2p_y}{\underline{\downarrow}}\ \underset{2p_z}{\underline{\hphantom{\downarrow}}}$$

From this configuration we might expect a molecular formation similar to water, where the carbon atom has a valency of 2 with the bonds being mutually perpendicular. This, of course, is not what is observed for carbon. The quadrivalency and tetrahedral structure of carbon are well established.

It is possible to justify the quadrivalency of carbon by the promotion of one of the $2s$ electrons to the empty $2p_z$ orbital. This would lead to the configuration

$$\underset{1s}{\underline{\uparrow\downarrow}}\ \underset{2s}{\underline{\downarrow}}\ \underset{2p_x}{\underline{\downarrow}}\ \underset{2p_y}{\underline{\downarrow}}\ \underset{2p_z}{\underline{\downarrow}}$$

Although this gives the known quadrivalency, it still does not agree with observation. According to the valence bond picture, such a configuration would predict that three of the hydrogen atoms in a molecule such as CH_4 are equivalent in energy and are also mutually perpendicular, but the fourth hydrogen atom is held by a weaker bond at an angle of about $125°$ with respect to the other bonds. Again, this result is contrary to the known geometry of the organic carbon atom.

In spite of the apparent difficulties, it is possible to resolve the problem within the framework of the valence bond approach.[11] In our previous application of the valence bond theory, it was found that the wave function was improved by taking linear combinations of several reasonable functions which described different representations or resonance structures of the system. We might likewise imagine that the actual wave functions for the four carbon bonds are represented by a mixture of the s and p orbitals available for bond formation. This character would be introduced into the various total wave functions by taking linear combinations of the s and p wave functions. The best combination should be the one that would lead to the strongest bond.

Although it is quite reasonable to assume that the best wave function will be the one that gives the strongest bond, it is not obvious what basis we can use to measure the strength of the bond. It would seem reasonable, however, to assume that the strongest bond would be the one that permitted the maximum possible overlap between the bonding orbitals. This is referred to as *the criterion of maximum overlap,* and it is fundamental to the valence bond treatment of directional bonding.

sp³ Hybridization. In the construction of the hybrid orbitals, it is of importance to note that the radial portions of the orbitals in a given shell are approximately the same. This is apparent from a comparison of the radial portions of the $2s$ and the $2p$ orbitals shown in Figure 2–8. On this basis, it is assumed that the hybridized orbitals can be constructed from the angular parts of the individual wave functions. Thus, for the quadrivalent carbon atom, these should be four bonds of the form

$$\psi_i = a_i \, \psi_s + b_i \, \psi_{px} + c_i \, \psi_{py} + d_i \, \psi_{pz} \qquad (5\text{--}53)$$

where the ψ_i are now purely angular wave functions.

Inasmuch as we are neglecting the radial portion of the wave functions, the individual angular wave functions can be expressed in terms of spherical harmonics as seen in Table 2–6. Here, we note that $\psi_s = 1/\sqrt{4\pi}$ and the p orbitals all contain the term $\sqrt{3/4\pi}$. For simplicity, ψ_s is set equal to unity, and the functions will all be normalized to 4π. This results in the equations for the individual angular wave functions

$$\psi_s \;= 1 \qquad (5\text{--}54\text{a})$$

$$\psi_{px} = \sqrt{3} \; \sin \theta \cos \varphi \qquad (5\text{--}54\text{b})$$

$$\psi_{py} = \sqrt{3} \; \sin \theta \sin \varphi \qquad (5\text{--}54\text{c})$$

$$\psi_{pz} = \sqrt{3} \; \cos \theta \qquad (5\text{--}54\text{d})$$

Applying the normalization requirement, we can say that for each of these functions, as well as a linear combination of them

$$\int \psi_i \, \psi_i^* \, d\tau = 1$$

Or, in terms of θ and φ over the surface of a sphere,

$$\int_0^{2\pi} \int_0^{\pi} \psi_i \, \psi_i^* \sin \theta \, d\theta \, d\varphi = 4\pi$$

Because of the orthogonality of the various atomic orbitals, this leads to the restriction on the coefficients in Eq. (5–53)

$$a_i{}^2 + b_i{}^2 + c_i{}^2 + d_i{}^2 = 1 \qquad (5\text{--}55)$$

In determining the angular relationship between the bonds, it is convenient to let the first bond lie along one of the axes, say the x axis. If this is done, the p_y and p_z orbitals should make no contribution to the bond. For this reason, c_i and d_i will both be zero and

$$\psi_1 = a_1 \, \psi_s + b_1 \, \psi_{px} \tag{5-56}$$

Since

$$a_1{}^2 + b_1{}^2 = 1$$

we can say that

$$\psi_1 = a_1 \, \psi_s + \sqrt{1 - a_1{}^2} \; \psi_{px}$$

If we now substitute the wave functions expressed in terms of ψ_s equal to unity, we obtain,

$$\psi_1 = a_1 + \sqrt{1 - a_1{}^2} \; \sqrt{3} \; \sin \theta \cos \varphi \tag{5-57}$$

We have decided that the bond will be formed in such a manner as to give the strongest bond possible, and if we are to use the principle of maximum overlap, then we are interested in choosing a_1 so as to make ψ_1 as large as possible in the direction of the bond. This is based on the assumption that the larger the extension of the orbital in space, the stronger the bond it will be able to form. Now, the value of ψ_1 along the x axis is given by

$$\psi_1 = a_1 + \sqrt{3} \; \sqrt{1 - a_1{}^2}$$

The $\sin \theta \cos \varphi$ term is unity here because $\theta = \pi/2$ and $\varphi = 0$. This, of course, is the maximum possible value for this term. If we differentiate with respect to a_1 and set the result equal to zero, we obtain

$$1 - a_1 \sqrt{3} \; (1 - a_1{}^2)^{-\frac{1}{2}} = 0 \tag{5-58}$$

from which it can be seen that $a_1 = 1/2$ and $b_1 = \sqrt{3}/2$. This, then, gives us the wave function for the first hybrid bond,

$$\psi_1 = 1/2 + (\sqrt{3}/2)\sqrt{3} \; \sin \theta \cos \varphi$$

which, in terms of the orbital symbols, can be expressed as

$$\psi_1 = 1/2 \, \psi_s + (\sqrt{3}/2) \, \psi_{px} \tag{5-59}$$

Previously, we have set the value of ψ_s at unity, and in terms of this value, the p orbitals assume the form shown in Eq. (5-54). If we evaluate their maximum magnitude in space on this basis by setting $\sin \theta$ and $\cos \varphi$ each equal to unity, we obtain a value of 1.732. This would indicate that a p orbital is capable of a greater amount of overlap than a pure s orbital, and according to the principle of maximum overlap, it should form a stronger bond. On the same basis, we can evaluate the magnitude of the hybrid bond ψ_1. By setting $\sin \theta$ and $\cos \varphi$ both equal to unity, it is seen that a value of 2 is obtained for ψ_1 in the direction of the bond. This is considerably greater than either a pure s or a pure p orbital, and we would,

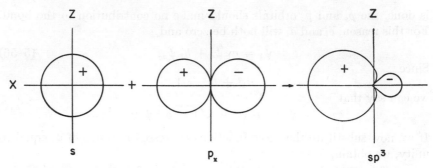

FIGURE 5–13. Formation and Structure of an *sp* Hybrid Orbital.

therefore, expect the hybrid bond to form a stronger bond than either a pure *s* or a pure *p* bond.

The formation of the hybrid bond can be pictured in the manner shown in Figure 5–13. The *s* orbital is everywhere positive and the *p* orbital has a positive and a negative lobe. The positive lobe of the *p* orbital combines with the *s* orbital and the negative lobe of the *p* orbital is reduced by the mixing.

The second of the hybrid bonds can be chosen to lie in the *xz* plane. Here, the p_y orbital will make no contribution, and the new wave function will be

$$\psi_2 = a_2\,\psi_s + b_2\,\psi_{px} + d_2\,\psi_{pz} \tag{5–60}$$

It can be seen from Figure 2–4, that since the orbital will lie in the *xz* plane, the angle φ will be 0° or 180° for the bond direction. However, for $\varphi = 0°$, we are in the region of ψ_1. Therefore, ψ_2, will have its maximum value when φ is 180°, and $\cos \varphi$ will be -1. Using this fact and substituting the expressions for the wave functions into Eq. (5–60), we obtain

$$\psi_2 = a_2 - b_2\,\sqrt{3}\,\sin\theta + d_2\,\sqrt{3}\,\cos\theta$$

This equation can be expressed in terms of the parameter b_2 and the angle θ by using the two relations

$$a_2{}^2 + b_2{}^2 + d_2{}^2 = 1$$

and

$$a_1 a_2 + b_1 b_2 = 0$$

This latter expression arises from the orthogonality condition. Since d_1 is zero, the *d* parameters vanish. Knowing the values for a_1 and b_1, we can evaluate a_2 and d_2 in terms of b_2. Thus

$$a_2 = -(b_1/a_1)b_2 = -\frac{\sqrt{3/2}}{1/2}\,b_2 = -\sqrt{3}\,b_2$$

and

$$d_2 = \pm\sqrt{1 - a_2{}^2 - b_2{}^2} = \pm\sqrt{1 - 3b_2{}^2 - b_2{}^2} = \pm\sqrt{1 - 4b_2{}^2}$$

It is immaterial which sign is chosen for $|d_2|$, so for convenience we will use the positive sign. Now we can express ψ_2 as

$$\psi_2 = -b_2\sqrt{3}\,(1 + \sin\theta) + \sqrt{3(1 - 4b_2{}^2)}\,\cos\theta \qquad (5\text{--}61)$$

Just as with the first hybrid orbital, it is again necessary to maximize the orbital in the bond direction in order to evaluate the parameter, b_2. However, we find that in this case, the angle, θ, is also a variable and it determines the bond direction, θ_2. Consequently, it is necessary to maximize the function with respect to both b_2 and θ. This leads to two equations which can be solved simultaneously. The first of these can be obtained by differentiating ψ_2 with respect to b_2 and setting the differential equal to zero. This is seen to result in the following equation

$$\left(\frac{\partial\psi}{\partial b_2}\right)_\theta = -\sqrt{3}\,(1 + \sin\theta_2) + (\tfrac{1}{2})\,(3 - 12b_2{}^2)^{-\frac{1}{2}}\,(-24b_2)\cos\theta_2 = 0$$

or

$$-\sqrt{3}\,(1 + \sin\theta_2) - \frac{12b_2}{\sqrt{3 - 12b_2}}\cos\theta_2 = 0 \qquad (5\text{--}62)$$

Similarly,

$$\left(\frac{\partial\psi}{\partial\theta}\right)_{b2} = -b_2\sqrt{3}\,\cos\theta_2 - \sqrt{3 - 12b_2{}^2}\,\sin\theta_2 = 0$$

or

$$-b_2\sqrt{3}\,\cos\theta_2 - \sqrt{3 - 12b_2{}^2}\,\sin\theta_2 = 0 \qquad (5\text{--}63)$$

These two equations can now be used to determine the angle, θ_2, and the parameter, b_2. If we rearrange them to the form

$$-\frac{12b_2}{\sqrt{3 - 12b_2{}^2}} = \frac{\sqrt{3}\,(1 + \sin\theta_2)}{\cos\theta_2}$$

and

$$-\frac{\sqrt{3}b_2}{\sqrt{3 - 12b_2{}^2}} = \frac{\sin\theta_2}{\cos\theta_2}$$

it can be seen that

$$\frac{12\sin\theta_2}{\sqrt{3}\cos\theta_2} = \frac{\sqrt{3}\,(1 + \sin\theta_2)}{\cos\theta_2}$$

And this equation can be solved for $\sin\theta_2$ to give $\sin\theta_2 = 1/3$. Once $\sin\theta_2$ is known we can evaluate b_2, and this is found to be $b_2 = -(\tfrac{1}{2}\sqrt{3}\,)$. If these two quantities are both known, we can calculate the magnitude of the new hybrid orbital and we can determine its angle with respect to the first hybrid orbital. In terms of Eq. (5–61), the magnitude is seen to be

$$\psi_2 = -\left(-\frac{1}{2\sqrt{3}}\right)\sqrt{3}\left(1 + \frac{1}{3}\right) + \sqrt{3 - 12\left(\frac{1}{2\sqrt{3}}\right)^2}\left(\frac{2\sqrt{2}}{3}\right) = 2$$

This is the same value that was obtained for ψ_1. Therefore, we can conclude that the two bonds are of equal strength.

In considering the angle, θ_2, it is seen that for the sin θ_2 to equal $1/3$, θ_{max} will equal 19° 28′ or 160° 32′. The former corresponds to choosing the positive sign for d_2. Since it was necessary to consider the angle φ to be 180°, it is apparent that, with respect to the first bond, the angle θ_2 is 90° + 19° 28′, or 109° 28′.

This same general procedure can be continued to determine the angles and magnitudes of the remaining two bonds. The general forms of the wave functions of these orbitals along with those of the first two orbitals are

$$\psi_1 = \frac{1}{2}\,\psi_s + \sqrt{3}/2\,\psi_{p_z}$$

$$\psi_2 = \frac{1}{2}\,\psi_s - \frac{1}{2\sqrt{3}}\,\psi_{p_x} + \frac{\sqrt{2}}{\sqrt{3}}\,\psi_{p_z}$$

$$\psi_3 = \frac{1}{2}\,\psi_s - \frac{1}{2\sqrt{3}}\,\psi_{p_x} + \frac{1}{\sqrt{2}}\,\psi_{p_y} - \frac{1}{\sqrt{6}}\,\psi_{p_z}$$

$$\psi_4 = \frac{1}{2}\,\psi_s - \frac{1}{2\sqrt{3}}\,\psi_{p_x} - \frac{1}{\sqrt{2}}\,\psi_{p_y} - \frac{1}{\sqrt{6}}\,\psi_{p_z}$$

Needless to say, the angles all turn out to be 109° 28′, and the relative magnitudes are all 2. In the methane molecule, we know that all four of the bonds are equivalent and the HCH angles are all 109° 28′. Thus, it would appear that the valence bond theory is capable of giving a satisfactory treatment of the tetrahedral carbon atom. The tetrahedral hybrid bonds are constructed from one s orbital and three p orbitals, and for this reason, they are referred to as sp^3 *hybrids*.

sp^2 *and sp Hybridization.* The treatment of double-bonded structures is in terms of sp^2 hybrid orbitals. For a molecule such as ethylene, we can imagine the *skeletal* structure to be

It can be seen that there are three sigma bonds from each carbon atom. These can be considered to arise from the 2s and two of the three 2p elec-

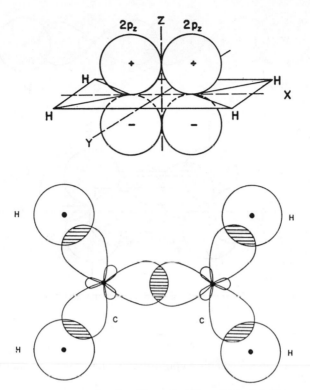

FIGURE 5–14. Overlap of σ and π-Type Orbitals in the
Ethylene Molecule.

trons of the carbon atom in the form of an sp^2 hybridization. This leaves
one unused $2p$ electron on each carbon atom. By hybridizing these three
orbitals, it is found that three equivalent bonds are obtained that lie in a
plane at an angle of 120° with respect to one another. This is in general
agreement with experiment.[2] Further, their magnitude compared to unity
for an s orbital is 1.991. This is less than that of an sp^3 hybrid, but it is
considerably greater than that of a pure p orbital or a pure s orbital.

The double bond character of the carbon—carbon bond can be attributed to the overlap of the p orbitals occupied by the unused p electrons.
This is illustrated in Figure 5–14. The overlap of the sp^2 hybrid orbitals
leads to the sigma bonds and the overlap of the p orbitals leads to a pi
bond. From the figure, it is apparent why restricted rotation should exist
around a double bond. In order for one of the carbon atoms to rotate around
an axis through the line of centers of the two carbon atoms, it is necessary
to break the overlap of the π orbitals.

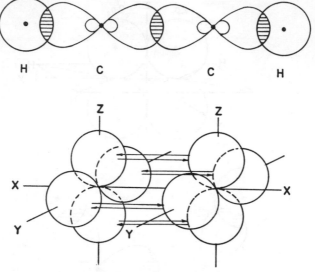

FIGURE 5–15. Overlap of σ and π-Type Orbitals in the Acetylene Molecule.

Finally, for the acetylenic type linkage, the skeletal structure is

$$H—C—C—H$$

This structure requires the use of only one of the $2p$ orbitals along with the $2s$ orbital to form the hybrid bond. Here, we have two p electrons on each carbon atom that are unused in the formation of the sigma bond. The calculations of the geometry and relative strengths of two equivalent sp hybrids are again found to be in agreement with the experimentally determined structure of the molecule. Both bonds are of equal strength and they are linear. The triple-bond character of the acetylenic linkage can then be attributed to the overlap of the two p orbitals that are left on each carbon atom, as can be seen in Figure 5–15.

Hybridization with d Orbitals. In addition to its success in the treatment of the stereochemistry of the carbon compounds, the valence bond theory has also proved moderately successful in its treatment of the structure of coordination compounds. Here, it is usually necessary to consider the effects of the d orbitals. The most common structures that result from the hybridization of d orbitals are the dsp^2 hybrid bonds, which lead to square planar structures, and the d^2sp^3 hybrid bonds which lead to octahedral structures. These are discussed in some detail in Chapter 9, and for that reason they will not be considered further here. However, a summary of the more common bonds, along with their geometry and their relative strengths, are listed in Table 5-3. In all cases the strength of the bonds is based on a value of unity for the pure s orbital.

TABLE 5-3. / **Relative Strengths and Angular Distributions of Bonding Orbitals.**

Coord. No.	Orbitals Used	Angular Distribution	Relative Strength
1	s	none	1.000
3	p	mutually $\perp$	1.732
2	sp	linear	1.932
3	sp^2	planar 120°	1.991
4	sp^3	tetrahedral	2.000
4	dsp^2	square planar	2.694
6	d^2sp^3	octahedral	2.923

Hybridization in Water and Ammonia. Previously, we considered the structures of water and ammonia as well as the analogous compounds in their families in terms of pure p bonding. This would predict HXH bond angles of 90°, and these were seen to differ considerably from the experimental values for both water and ammonia. Another means of considering the structures of these compounds is in terms of hybridization.[12] If we take the three molecules, CH_4, NH_3, and H_2O, we note that they are isoelectronic, each having 10 electrons. Now, the methane molecule is considered to be using sp^3 hybrid orbitals, and its structure, therefore, is tetrahedral. If we consider an imaginary process whereby a proton from one of the hydrogen atoms coalesces with the carbon nucleus, we have the ammonia molecule. Further, if we imagine a proton from one of the hydrogen atoms in the ammonia molecule coalescing with the nitrogen nucleus, we have a water molecule. The only difference between the three structures is the exchange of a M—H bond for a *lone pair* of electrons on the $(M + 1)$ nucleus. We can now wonder whether a lone pair of electrons on an atom can occupy a tetrahedral position just as can a *bonding pair* of electrons. If this is possible, and it is certainly reasonable, then we can consider the water molecule as well as the ammonia molecule to be tetrahedral structures based on sp^3 hybridization, and our problem is no longer one of understanding a deviation from 90°, but rather one from 109.5°. This idea has been developed with some success, but it will not be considered further here. The details of stereochemistry will be discussed in Chapter 6.

THE PAULI EXCLUSION PRINCIPLE

In our previous discussion of the hydrogen molecule, it was seen that both a symmetrical and an antisymmetrical function arose. In terms of the valence bond language, these can be represented respectively as

$$\psi_S = \psi_a(1) \, \psi_b(2) + \psi_a(2) \, \psi_b(1)$$

and

$$\psi_A = \psi_a(1) \, \psi_b(2) - \psi_a(2) \, \psi_b(1)$$

Now, if we take the electrons in the system described by these two wave functions and exchange the coordinates of electron (1) with the coordinates of electron (2), we will obtain for the symmetric function

$$\psi_{S'} = \psi_a(2) \, \psi_b(1) + \psi_a(1) \, \psi_b(2)$$

But, this is the same as ψ_S. Therefore, on exchange of coordinates, we can say that $\psi_S = \psi_{S'}$. On the other hand, if we exchange the coordinates of the electrons in the antisymmetrical function, we obtain

$$\psi_{A'} = \psi_a(2) \, \psi_b(1) - \psi_a(1) \, \psi_b(2)$$

This expression is not the same, but rather, it is opposite in sign from ψ_A. Consequently, in this case, we can say that, for the exchange of coordinates $\psi_A = -\psi_{A'}$.

Up until this point, we have considered only the *orbital wave functions*, and these are based on the spatial quantum numbers n, l, and m. Thus, we have neglected the *spin wave functions*. For a simple discussion of valency, it is possible to separate the spin wave functions from the orbital wave functions because spin-orbit interactions are generally negligible. Nevertheless, we should recognize that the electron spin must be included in any complete description of the system.

Since an electron must have a spin of either $+1/2$ or $-1/2$, we can represent these as α or β, respectively. If both electrons in an electron pair have spins of $+1/2$, then their combined wave function will be $\alpha(1) \, \alpha(2)$. If both of the electrons have a spin of $-1/2$, then their combined wave function will be $\beta(1) \, \beta(2)$. Finally, if one of the electrons has a spin of $+1/2$ and the other has a spin of $-1/2$, the combined wave function will be

$$\alpha(1) \, \beta(2) \doteq \alpha(2) \, \beta(1)$$

The linear combination of wave functions arises here because of the indistinguishability of the electrons just as it did in the treatment of the hydrogen molecule. Further, if we exchange the electrons we can see that the function

$$\alpha(1) \, \beta(2) + \alpha(2) \, \beta(1)$$

is a symmetrical function, but the function

$$\alpha(1)\ \beta(2) - \alpha(2)\ \beta(1)$$

is an antisymmetrical function.

Now that we have both the spatial portion and the spin portion of the system, it is necessary to combine these to give the total wave function including spin. In Chapter 2, it was seen that the total wave function for the hydrogen atom could be expressed as a product of the individual wave functions, such that

$$\psi_T = R_{(r)}\Theta_{(\theta)}\Phi_{(\varphi)}$$

If we introduce a fourth degree of freedom, we should expect the product relationship to still hold. Thus, the total wave function for the hydrogen molecule, including spin, should be formed from the product of the orbital function and the spin function. That is, for this system

$$\psi_T = \{\psi_a(1)\ \psi_b(2) \pm \psi_a(2)\ \psi_b(1)\}\ \{\text{spin functions}\}$$

Immediately, we can see that this leads to the eight possible combinations

$$\{\psi_a(1)\ \psi_b(2) + \psi_a(2)\ \psi_b(1)\}\ \begin{cases} \alpha(1)\ \beta(2) - \alpha(2)\ \beta(1) \\ \alpha(1)\ \alpha(2) \\ \beta(1)\ \beta(2) \\ \alpha(1)\ \beta(2) + \alpha(2)\ \beta(1) \end{cases}$$

$$\{\psi_a(1)\ \psi_b(2) - \psi_a(2)\ \psi_b(1)\}\ \begin{cases} \alpha(1)\ \alpha(2) \\ \beta(1)\ \beta(2) \\ \alpha(1)\ \beta(2) + \alpha(2)\ \beta(1) \\ \alpha(1)\ \beta(2) - \alpha(2)\ \beta(1) \end{cases}$$

The question now arises as to whether all eight of these combinations are significant. The answer lies in the Pauli exclusion principle. As it was first enunciated in 1925, it was stated, in essence, that *no two electrons in the same system can have the same values for all four quantum numbers.* In terms of quantum mechanics, however, it takes on the more subtle form: *every total wave function must be antisymmetric in the exchange of the coordinates of every pair of electrons.* In terms of this restriction, only four of the eight combinations will be acceptable. These are

$$\{\psi_a(1)\ \psi_b(2) + \psi_a(2)\ \psi_b(1)\}\ \{\alpha(1)\ \beta(2) - \alpha(2)\ \beta(1)\}$$

$$\{\psi_a(1)\ \psi_b(2) - \psi_a(2)\ \psi_b(1)\}\ \begin{cases} \alpha(1)\ \alpha(2) \\ \beta(1)\ \beta(2) \\ \alpha(1)\ \beta(2) + \alpha(2)\ \beta(1) \end{cases}$$

Thus, it would appear that there are three states corresponding to the antisymmetric spatial function, whereas there is only one state corresponding to the symmetric spatial function. Accordingly, we refer to the ground state as a singlet state and to the repulsive or antisymmetric state as a triplet state.

On the surface, the relationship between the quantum mechanical statement of the exclusion principle and the more familiar statement in terms of the four quantum numbers may not be evident. However, it can readily be shown that the original statement of the exclusion principle is a necessary feature of the more general statement of the principle in terms of symmetry. If we take the total ground state function

$$\psi_\tau = \{\psi_a(1)\,\psi_b(2) + \psi_a(2)\,\psi_b(1)\}\{\alpha(1)\,\beta(2) - \alpha(2)\,\beta(1)\}$$

we obtain on multiplication

$$\psi_\tau = \psi_a(1)\alpha(1)\,\psi_b(2)\beta(2) - \psi_a(2)\alpha(2)\,\psi_b(1)\beta(1) + \psi_a(2)\beta(2)\,\psi_b(1)\alpha(1) \\ - \psi_a(1)\beta(1)\,\psi_b(2)\alpha(2)$$

This can be expressed more conveniently in the determinantal form

$$\psi_\tau = \begin{vmatrix} \psi_a(1)\alpha(1) & \psi_b(1)\beta(1) \\ \psi_a(2)\alpha(2) & \psi_b(2)\beta(2) \end{vmatrix} - \begin{vmatrix} \psi_a(1)\beta(1) & \psi_b(1)\alpha(1) \\ \psi_a(2)\beta(2) & \psi_b(2)\alpha(2) \end{vmatrix}$$

If we consider the three quantum numbers n, l, and m to be identical for both electrons, then $\psi_a = \psi_b$, and the determinant can be expressed as

$$\psi_\tau = \begin{vmatrix} \psi_a(1)\alpha(1) & \psi_a(1)\beta(1) \\ \psi_a(2)\alpha(2) & \psi_a(2)\beta(2) \end{vmatrix} - \begin{vmatrix} \psi_a(1)\beta(1) & \psi_a(1)\alpha(1) \\ \psi_a(2)\beta(2) & \psi_a(2)\alpha(2) \end{vmatrix}$$

or

$$\psi_\tau = 2 \begin{vmatrix} \psi_a(1)\alpha(1) & \psi_a(1)\beta(1) \\ \psi_a(2)\alpha(2) & \psi_a(2)\beta(2) \end{vmatrix}$$

Now, if we permit α to equal β, the two rows of the determinant become identical and the determinant vanishes. Thus, the wave function is seen to be equal to zero when all four quantum numbers are the same for two different electrons in the same system. And this, of course, is what is demanded by the Pauli exclusion principle.

ATOMIC SPECTRA AND TERM SYMBOLS

In expressing the energy of an electron in terms of s, p, d, and f states, we are actually taking into account only two of the four quantum numbers necessary to completely describe the energy of an electron in an atom. In general, such a configuration will be highly degenerate because we are ignoring both *interelectronic repulsion* and *spin-orbit interactions*. While these forces may be relatively small, they nevertheless serve to remove the otherwise high degeneracy of a given electron configuration involving electrons outside a closed shell. In order to see how these additional interactions remove the degeneracy of a given electron configuration, it will be desirable to consider two extreme situations commonly referred to as *Russell-Saunders* or *LS coupling* on the one hand and *jj coupling* on the other.

The more common of these is the Russell-Saunders coupling in which it is assumed that the interaction among the individual orbital moments and among the individual spin moments is stronger than the spin-orbit or *ls* interaction. This assumption appears to be valid for elements lighter than approximately $Z = 30$. In Russell-Saunders coupling, we can assume that all of the angular momenta of the different electrons, l_i, in an atom couple together to give a total or resultant orbital angular momentum quantum number L. L must be zero or integral according to the quantum restrictions applying to the addition of vector quantities, and it is the vectorial sum of the l values for all of the electrons. The summation is simplified by the fact that the electrons in closed shells do not contribute to L since their orbital angular momenta as well as their spin angular momenta add up to zero. Therefore, only electrons outside a closed shell need be considered.

As an example, we can consider a general case where two electrons have the azimuthal quantum numbers l_1 and l_2. In this instance, L would take on the values

$$L = l_1 + l_2, l_1 + l_2 - 1, l_1 + l_2 - 2, \cdots, l_1 - l_2$$

For three electrons, the L values are obtained by first finding those values for two of the electrons, and then adding vectorially the l value for the third electron, and so on. To illustrate this point, we can consider three electrons with the configuration sp^2. For the s electron $l = 0$, and therefore $L_1 = 0$. For the two p electrons, the l values are $l_1 = l_2 = 1$, and therefore, L_2 is given by

$$L_2 = 1 + 1, 1 + 1 - 1, 1 + 1 - 2 (= l - l)$$

or

$$L_2 = 2, 1, 0$$

In a similar manner, the individual spins couple together to give a total or resultant spin angular momentum quantum number, S. S is obtained as the algebraic sum of the s values for the separate electrons, i.e.,

$$S = \sum_i s_i$$

Finally, just as the l and s values may couple (spin-orbit interaction) to give a j for a single electron, so the L and S values may couple to give a series of J values for all of the electrons. J is called the *total angular momentum quantum number* and its possible values are

$$J = L + S, L + S - 1, L + S - 2, \cdots, |L - S|$$

J may only have positive values or be zero, and it will have integral values when S is an integer and half-integral values when S is a half-integer.

An atomic state with given L and S values thus consists of a group of components having energies that are generally relatively close together. The number of components of the group is equal to the number of possible J values. The particular state is then said to be a *multiplet* and to have a *multiplicity* equal to the number of J values. If, for instance, $S = 1/2$, then

$$J = L + 1/2$$

and

$$J = L + 1/2 - 1 = L - 1/2$$

Therefore, the multiplicity is 2, and we have a *doublet*. If we consider a case where $S = 1$, then

$$J = L + 1$$
$$J = L + 1 - 1 = L$$

and

$$J = L + 1 - 2 = L - 1$$

Here, the multiplicity is 3 and we have a *triplet*. In general, the multiplicity will be $2S + 1$, provided that L is geater than S. If $L < S$, there is only one possible value of J, although, $2S + 1$ may be greater than unity. For instance, a lone s electron outside a closed shell would have $l = 0 = L$ and $s = 1/2 = S$, so that J can only be $1/2$. Thus, the state is a singlet even though $2S + 1 = 2$.

In order to represent more completely the electronic state of an atom, a scheme based on the use of spectral term symbols was introduced in 1925 by H. N. Russell and F. A. Saunders. The term letters are arrived at as follows:

$$L = 0, 1, 2, 3, 4, 5, \cdots$$
$$\text{Term letter} = S, P, D, F, G, H, \cdots$$

The term letter is preceded by a superscript representing the multiplicity of the term, i.e., $2S + 1$, and it is followed by a subscript giving the corresponding J value. Thus,

$$^{2S+1}L_J = \text{term symbol}$$

For example, suppose that $L = 2$ and $S = 1$, then the term symbol would be ^3D, and since the possible J values are 3, 2, and 1, the three states of the triplet are $^3D_3$, $^3D_2$, and $^3D_1$.

It is now possible to consider a specific atom and construct the term symbols representing the various energy states in which the atom may be found. If we take the carbon atom with the ground state configuration $1s^2 2s^2 2p^2$, we see that both L and S will be determined only by the two p electrons. L may be 2, 1, or 0 corresponding to D, P, and S states, respectively. S may be 0 or 1, corresponding to multiplicities of 1 and 3, respectively. Therefore, we can have the following states: ^3D, ^3P, ^3S, ^1D, ^1P, and ^1S. However, application of the Pauli exclusion principle will show that not all of these states are allowed. We may say that some are forbidden, and for the p^2 configuration, the only allowed states are ^3P, ^1D, and ^1S. In Table 5–4 a list of the allowed Russell-Saunders states is given

TABLE 5–4.	Allowed Russell-Saunders States for Equivalent s, p, and d Electrons.

Equivalent s Electrons					
s	^2S				
s^2	^1S				

Equivalent p Electrons					
p^1 or p^5		^2P			
p^2 or p^4	^1S,		^1D,	^3P	
p^3		^2P,	^2D,	^4S	
p^6	^1S				

Equivalent d Electrons					
d^1 or d^9	^2D				
d^2 or d^8	$^1(SDG)$,	$^3(PF)$			
d^3 or d^7	^2D,	$^2(PDFGH)$,	$^4(PF)$		
d^4 or d^6	$^1(SDG)$,	$^3(PF)$,	$^1(SDFGI)$,	$^3(PDFGH)$,	^5D
d^5	^2D,	$^2(PDFGH)$,	$^4(PF)$,	$^4(SDFGI)$,	$^4(DG)$, ^6S

for equivalent s, p, and d electrons. It should be noted that an atom or ion consisting of closed shells only is always in a $^1S_0$ state.

For the carbon atom, we will have the states $^3P_0$, $^3P_1$, $^3P_2$, $^1D_2$ and $^1S_0$. Once these terms are known, it is necessary to determine which of the components lies lowest in energy, that is, which represents the ground state. In order to do this, we rely on a set of rules called *Hund's rules*. These are as follows:

(1) Of the Russell-Saunders states arising from a given electron configuration and allowed by the Pauli principle, the most stable state will be the one with the greatest multiplicity.

(2) Of a group of terms with a given value of S, the one with the largest value of L lies lowest in energy.

(3) Of the states with given L and S values in a configuration consisting of less than half the electrons in a subgroup, the state with the smallest

value of J is usually the most stable. And for a configuration consisting of more than half the electrons in a subgroup, the state with the largest J is the most stable. The multiplets of the former are called *normal* multiplets, and those of the latter are called *inverted* multiplets.

In addition to the splitting we have thus far considered, a further splitting of the energy levels can occur from the action of an external magnetic field on the atom. Under these conditions, the total angular momentum quantum number, J, is split into $2J + 1$ equally spaced levels corresponding to the number of values that can be assumed by the magnetic quantum number M. These values are $- J, \cdots 0, \cdots , + J$.

Now we are in a position to write out the various energy levels arising from the p^2 configuration, and these are shown in Figure 5–16. It is seen that the p^2 configuration is actually 15-fold degenerate. If the n value of the two p electrons is different, then even more energy levels will arise.

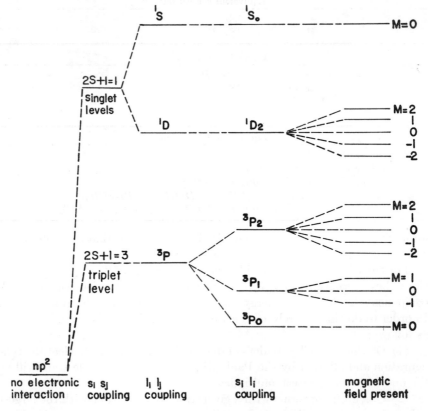

FIGURE 5–16. Energy Levels for the Electron Configuration $(np)^2$. (Adapted from Eyring, H., Walter, J., and Kimball, G., "Quantum Chemistry," John Wiley & Sons, Inc., New York, N. Y., 1944).

For example, the configuration $2p3p$ will split upon application of a magnetic field into 36 energy levels.

The essential importance of the term symbol lies in the fact that in a large number of cases it can be determined from atomic spectra. And from this, it is possible to obtain information regarding electronic configurations. In Table 3–4, the term symbols for the ground state are given for the various elements along with their electron configurations in terms of s, p, d, and f orbitals.

Finally, a few words are in order concerning the more complex jj coupling. For the Russell-Saunders coupling scheme to be applicable it was necessary to assume that the interaction of the individual l_i vectors and of the individual s_i vectors is strong. However, in some cases, the interaction of the l_i with the s_i, that is, the spin-orbit interaction is stronger for each electron than the individual orbital and spin interactions. This occurs in the heavy elements where the central field forces are quite large. The result here is jj coupling. The l_i and s_i moments of each electron are combined to give a j value and the coupling of these for all of the electrons in the atom determines the total J. The number of terms remains the same as for LS coupling, but the selection rules are different.

VAN DER WAALS FORCES

Although the covalent, ionic, as well as the metallic bond can be used to explain the structural characteristics and the solid, liquid, and gaseous states of many substances, there is yet a large number of systems that do not fit into these categories. We can look at the inert gases as the most obvious example. These atoms are spherically symmetrical and incapable of forming any of the above-mentioned bonds. Yet, there must be some force active between adjacent atoms if a liquid or solid state exists above absolute zero. We can go further and recognize that the same necessity exists for the multitude of saturated molecules such as H_2, N_2, CH_4, and so on. These species have used their available electrons in the formation of the molecule and thus have no apparent means to bond to adjacent molecules.

There is one particularly significant characteristic of these forces. They are extremely weak in comparison to ionic or covalent forces. This is evident from the observable properties of substances that are predominantly dependent on such forces. In an ionic crystal where each atom is held by a number of ionic interactions, the boiling point of the substance will be quite high. However, substances in which the adjacent molecules are held together by these apparently very weak forces are frequently gases at room temperature, and in many instances their boiling points are extremely low. This is particularly true for the inert gases. As a comparison with a covalent bond, we can consider the sublimation of Cl_2. Here, the heat of sublimation of Cl_2 is of the order of 5 kcal/mole, whereas the Cl—Cl bond dissociation energy is 57 kcal/mole. Obviously, the forces holding one Cl_2 molecule to another Cl_2 molecule are extremely weak in comparison to the covalent bond holding one chlorine atom to the other chlorine atom in a Cl_2 molecule.

The existence of such weak attractive forces was first recognized by van der Waals as early as 1813. At that time, he introduced the a/v^2 term in his equation of state to allow for such interactions. It is for this reason that these forces are referred to as *van der Waals forces*.

If we carefully consider the systems involved, we can find two obvious sources of the van der Waals forces. First, if the molecules have a permanent dipole, it is easy to see that a weak attractive force should exist simply from the electrostatic interactions of two *dipoles*. This would be the case for any polar molecule. In molecules like HCl and H_2O the effect should be rather large. However, in a molecule such as CO, which has an anomalously low dipole moment, the effect will be present, but much smaller than in the former instances. The interaction energy of this particular effect is found to be expressable as

$$E_K = -\frac{2\ \mu^4}{3r^6kT} \tag{5-64}$$

where r is the distance between centers of the dipoles, μ is the permanent dipole moment, and k and T have their usual significance.

A second source of the van der Waals interaction is that of a *dipole-induced dipole* type. This results from the polarization of one molecule by the dipoles of the surrounding molecules. This effect can be superimposed upon the dipole-dipole interaction and thus lead to a slight increase in the attraction. This particular aspect of the van der Waals interaction can be expressed as

$$E_D = -\frac{2\alpha\mu^2}{r^6} \tag{5-65}$$

where α represents the polarizability.

Although, these two factors are important in the evaluation of the van der Waals interaction, they are obviously not the only factors to be considered. Neither of these effects can be used to explain the solid or liquid states of such species as the inert gases, Cl_2, H_2, N_2, CH_4, etc. In addition, it is also found that neither of the equations or the combination of the equations gives any agreement with experiment.

A third contributing term to the total van der Waals energy was developed in 1930. This particular term represents the *London dispersion forces.* Using a quantum mechanical treatment, London arrived at the equation

$$E_L = -\frac{3\,\alpha^2 h\nu_0}{4r^6} \qquad (5\text{--}66)$$

where $h\nu_0$ is the zero point energy which is inherently present in any atom or molecule. The London dispersion forces are existent between any atoms or molecules regardless of their geometry. Pictorially, the dispersion forces can be thought to arise from the synchronization of instantaneous dipoles in the interacting species. For the sake of argument, we can consider a helium atom. This atom can certainly be considered to be spherically symmetrical, and consequently, to have no dipole moment. However, this is based on a time average. If we were to take an instantaneous photograph of a helium atom, we should find a quite unsymmetrical distribution of the electrons around the nucleus at that moment. Consequently, a temporary dipole should exist. This instantaneous dipole can act to induce an instantaneous dipole in an adjacent atom and this then leads to a synchronized field throughout the system. Such an effect will lead to a lowering of the energy of the system, but it will necessarily be a very weak interaction.

In terms of the three contributing effects to the total van der Waals interaction, quite satisfactory agreement can be obtained between theory and experiment. For a symmetrical atom or molecule, the London term is the only term operative. However, the more polar a molecule becomes and the more polarizable it becomes, the more significant will be the first two effects. This can be appreciated from Table 5–5, where the contributions of the three terms to the total van der Waals attraction are given.

TABLE 5–5. / **Contributions to the Total van der Waals Lattice Energy in kcal/mole.**

Molecule	Dipole-Dipole	Dipole-induced Dipole	Dispersion	Total	B. Pt., °K
Ar	0.000	0.000	2.03	2.03	76
CO	0.000	0.002	2.09	2.09	81
HCl	0.79	0.24	4.02	5.05	188
NH_3	3.18	0.37	3.52	7.07	239.6
H_2O	8.69	0.46	2.15	11.30	373.1

Dipole-quadrapole and *quadrapole-quadrapole* interactions can also be considered, but they result in $1/r^8$ and $1/r^{10}$ effects respectively, and these can generally be neglected.

THE HYDROGEN BOND

It has long been recognized that a hydrogen atom can be attracted simultaneously to two different atoms, thereby showing a coordination number of two. Under these circumstances, the hydrogen atom serves as a bridge between the two species and can be considered as the basis of a bond between the two atoms. The resultant bond is much weaker than a covalent bond. Nevertheless, the effects of the hydrogen bond are of considerable significance. This is evident in many physical and structural properties of matter, and it is known to be of particular significance in physiological processes.[13]

We can imagine the hydrogen bond to be formed by a process of the type

$$X - H + Y \qquad X - H \text{ - - - } Y$$

where X and Y can be the same atom or different atoms. This reaction implies that the hydrogen atom is bonded simultaneously to both atom X and atom Y. In addition, it implies that the bond to Y is different in some respect from the bond to X. This is found to be the case in every instance except for the ion FHF^-. The structure of the hydrogen bond can be appreciated from a consideration of the dimer of formic acid. The geometry of the dimer, including the bond distances and bond angles, is shown in Figure 5–17. Here we see that the hydrogen atom is bonded to two different oxygen atoms. However, from the bond distances, it is apparent that the bonding is not identical. The O—H bond still retains its identity, but it is seen to be elongated from its normal distance of 0.97Å in the monomer to a value of 1.07Å in the dimer.

In an attempt to determine the nature of the hydrogen bond, we can consider several different approaches. In terms of purely covalent bonding, it can be assumed that the hydrogen atom can be divalent. This would require the use of the $1s$ orbital for the formation of one bond and either

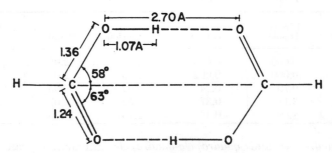

FIGURE 5–17. Hydrogen Bonding in the Dimer of Formic Acid.

the 2s or the 2p orbital for the second bond. Because of the extreme difference in energy between the 1s state and the 2s or 2p states of the hydrogen atom, a divalent hydrogen is not very likely. A second possibility involves the existence of resonance structures, and a third possibility is that the bond can be treated as if it were purely electrostatic in origin. All three of these possibilities have been seriously considered, and it is now generally assumed that we can satisfactorily treat the hydrogen bond in terms of electrostatic interactions.

If we can consider the hydrogen bond to be solely electrostatic in origin, it would appear that the van der Waals-type forces would be adequate to describe its character. The major contribution to the bond energy arises from the dipole-dipole interaction with the dipole-induced dipole and the dispersion forces making lesser contributions. This basic structure is supported by the fact that the bond occurs only when the atoms X and Y are the highly electronegative atoms F, O, N, and Cl. The surprisingly large magnitude of the dipole-dipole interaction can be attributed to the small size of the hydrogen atom and the absence of inner electron shells. This combination permits the close approach of a second atom that is not possible with other positive ions such as those of lithium or sodium.

Although the hydrogen bond can generally be treated solely in terms of electrostatic interactions, in valence bond language, there is evidence of resonance contributions in terms of the structures

$$
\begin{array}{lll}
\text{(a)} & X\text{—H} & :Y \\
\text{(b)} & X\!:^-\!\text{H}^+ & :Y \\
\text{(c)} & X\!:^-\!\text{H}\!\text{——}\!:Y^+ &
\end{array}
$$

It would be expected that structure (a), where the normal X—H bond exists, will be the most important of these three structures. In structure (c), the H——Y bond is a long bond, and a covalent bond over this distance should be insignificant. In ice, X and Y will both represent oxygen atoms, and knowing that there is only a trivial shift in the normal O—H bond distance, we can say that the long bond is about 0.80Å longer than the normal O—H bond. On this basis, it has been shown that the relative weights of the three structures are 61 per cent, 34 per cent, and 5 per cent, respectively.[14] Thus, we can see that, because of the small contribution of structure (c), it is legitimate to consider the bond to be essentially electrostatic in origin.

There are instances, however, where it appears that the three resonance structures contribute more equally to the final state of the system. This occurs when there is a decrease in the $X \cdots X$ distance over what is normally observed. Such is found to be the case in the β-form of oxalic acid where the O $\cdots$ O distance is approximately 2.5Å, but it is particularly true in the extreme case of FHF⁻ as found in KHF₂. In this instance, the hydrogen atom is located at the midpoint between the two fluorine atoms. Further, it is observed that the H—F distance is only 0.21Å greater than in the isolated HF molecule. Both of these facts indicate that all three of the resonance structures

$$\text{(a)} \quad \text{F:}^- \quad \text{H} - \text{F}$$
$$\text{(b)} \quad \text{F} - \text{H} \quad \text{:F}^-$$
$$\text{(c)} \quad \text{F:}^- \quad \text{H}^+ \quad \text{:F}^-$$

probably contribute about equally to the bond. In this particular case, the hydrogen bond energy is of the order of eight times greater than is usually observed, being of the order of 40 kcal/mole.

The relative ability of atoms in a given family to form hydrogen bonds is evident from a consideration of the boiling points of the nonmetallic hydrides. In Figure 5–18, these are given for the four nonmetal families. According to molecular weight considerations and van der Waals forces, we observe the expected trend for CH_4, SiH_4, GeH_4, and SnH_4 as well as for the three heavier members of each of the other families. However, we note the anomalous behavior of the lightest member of each of these three latter families. The unusually high boiling points for HF, H_2O and NH_3 must be attributed to the existence of hydrogen bonding. It is interesting to note that a stronger hydrogen bond exists in HF than in H_2O,

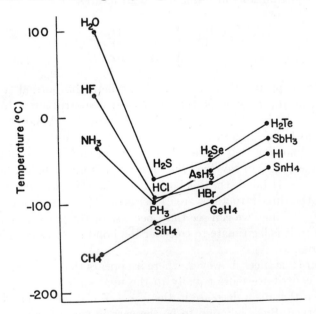

FIGURE 5–18. The Effect of Hydrogen Bonding on the Boiling Points of Non-metal Hydrides.

yet the boiling point of water is the higher. This can be attributed to the statistical fact that water can form two such bonds to one for hydrogen fluoride.

Thus far, we have considered only intermolecular hydrogen bonding. However, there is also the possibility of the formation of intramolecular hydrogen bonds where the hydrogen bond exists between two atoms of the same molecule. This type of hydrogen bonding is quite common, and it can also have a marked effect on the chemical and physical properties of the molecule. As an example, we can consider the three isomers of chlorophenol. For the *ortho* isomer, we should expect to find both the *cis* and the *trans* form of the molecule, as shown in Figure 5–19. From the proximity of the

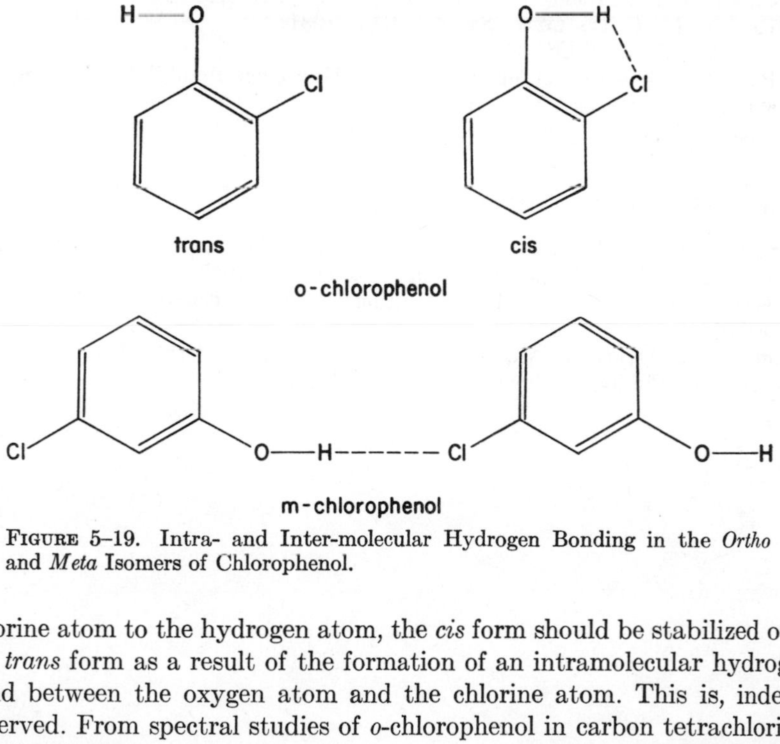

o - chlorophenol

m - chlorophenol

FIGURE 5–19. Intra- and Inter-molecular Hydrogen Bonding in the *Ortho* and *Meta* Isomers of Chlorophenol.

chlorine atom to the hydrogen atom, the *cis* form should be stabilized over the *trans* form as a result of the formation of an intramolecular hydrogen bond between the oxygen atom and the chlorine atom. This is, indeed, observed. From spectral studies of o-chlorophenol in carbon tetrachloride, the distribution is approximately 91 per cent *cis* and 9 per cent *trans*. The possibility of hydrogen bond formation is also reflected in the physical properties of the chlorophenols. For instance, the boiling point of the o-chlorophenol is 176°C, whereas, it is considerably greater for both the *meta* and the *para* isomers. In the latter two structures intermolecular hydrogen bonding plays a much more important part than it does in the *ortho* isomer.

BIBLIOGRAPHY

1. Lewis, G., *J. Am. Chem. Soc.*, **38,** 762 (1916).
2. Pauling, L., "The Nature of the Chemical Bond," 3rd ed., Cornell University Press, Ithica, N.Y., 1960.
3. Born, M. and Lande, A., *Preuss. Akad. Wiss. Berlin, Ber.*, **45,** 1048 (1918).
4. Mayer, J. and Helmholz, L., *Z.f. Physik*, **75,** 1 (1932).
5. Helmholz, L. and Mayer, J., *J. Chem. Phys.*, **2,** 245 (1934).
6. Born, M., *Verhandl. deut, physik. Ges.*, **21,** 13 (1919); Haber, F., *Verhandl. deut. physik. Ges.*, **21,** 750 (1919).
7. Glasstone, S., "Theoretical Chemistry," D. Van Nostrand Co., Inc., New York, N.Y., 1944.
8. Pauling, L., *Chem. Revs.*, **5,** 173 (1928).
9. Heitler, W. and London, F., *Z.f. Phys.*, **44,** 455 (1927).
10. James, H. and Coolidge, A., *J. Chim. phys.*, **1,** 825 (1933).
11. Pauling, L., *J. Am. Chem. Soc.*, **53,** 1367 (1931).
12. Bent, H., *J. Chem. Ed.*, **37,** 616 (1960).
13. Pimentel, G. and McClellan, A., "The Hydrogen Bond," W. H. Freeman Co., San Francisco, Cal., 1959.
14. Pauling, L., *J. Chim.phys.*, **46,** 435 (1949).

SUGGESTED SUPPLEMENTARY READING

Sherman, J., "Crystal Energies of Ionic Compounds," *Chem. Revs.* **11,** 93 (1932).
Coulson, C., "Valence," The Clarendon Press, Oxford, 1952.
Ketelaar, J. A. A., "Chemical Constitution," 2nd ed., Elsevier Publishing Co., Amsterdam, 1958.
Syrkin, Y. and Dyatkina, M., "Structure of Molecules and the Chemical Bond," Interscience Publishers, Inc., New York, N.Y., 1950.

6 | *Inorganic Stereochemistry*

Theories of valence and stereochemistry were developed in the last century side by side, usually the one being the result of the other. In 1852 Frankland proposed the concept of valence and he indicated that the elements form compounds by combining with a definite number of what we now call equivalents of other elements. Kekule (1858) and Kolbe (1859) extended the valence idea and postulated the quadrivalency of the carbon atom. In 1858, Kekule suggested that carbon atoms may bond to one another in an indefinite number to form chains, and in the same year Couper introduced the concept of a valence bond and drew the first structural formulas. The term *chemical structure* was introduced by Butlerov in 1861, who stressed the importance of writing a single formula for a compound showing how the atoms are linked together in one of its molecules. He also stated that the properties of compounds are determined by their molecular structure, and that if we can determine the latter, we may predict the former. However, it was not until 1874 that the first major step was taken toward a visualization and assignment of molecular structures in three dimensions. It was in that year that J. H. van't Hoff and J. A. le Bel independently postulated the tetrahedral disposition of the four valence bonds of the carbon atom and thereby placed classical organic stereochemistry at least twenty years ahead of inorganic stereochemistry.

The Coordination Theory of A. Werner (1893) may be considered the beginning of inorganic stereochemistry, as it was concerned with the spatial arrangement of molecules and ions about a central metal ion. For many years after the Werner theory, inorganic chemists were occupied with the preparation and characterization of a great number of new complex compounds and the deduction of their stereochemistries. Such deductions were based primarily on chemical methods of study, and these are necessarily limited. The great strides that have subsequently been made in the field of stereochemistry can be attributed to two completely independent developments, both beginning at about the same time, in the second decade of this century. The first of these was the development of physical methods for the determination of structure. This began with the development of the X-ray diffraction method of structural analysis and was followed by the newer physical techniques which include the diffraction of electron waves, the measurement of electric and magnetic dipole moments, and the interpretation of infrared, Raman, microwave, and nuclear magnetic resonance spectra. All of these methods are capable of revealing three-dimensional geometry and have served to stimulate the interest in, and rapid growth of, inorganic stereochemistry. At the same time the electronic theory of valency stimulated the later development of quantum chemistry and its application in new theories of the chemical bond and chemical structure. The application of these powerful experimental and theoretical methods for the past thirty years has produced a great wealth of structural information as well as uncovering new structural principles which have produced a greater understanding of the properties of compounds. It will be the primary purpose of this chapter to point out the principles which underlie the modern approach to stereochemistry and to show how they may be applied in specific cases.

It is apparent at the outset that we shall have to limit somewhat severely the scope of the presentation. For example we shall not consider the structures of crystalline solids, although we recognize the existence of at least four types of solid lattices: (1) *ionic,* in which the lattice sites are occupied by ions held in position by strong electrostatic forces and the geometry is dependent upon the relative numbers, sizes, and charges of the constituent ions; (2) *molecular,* in which the lattice sites are occupied by discrete molecules held together by relatively weak dipole or van der Waals forces and the geometry is determined largely by the size and polarizability of the molecules and the strength of the interactions between them; (3) *metallic,* in which metallic ions occupying the lattice sites are held in position by their mutual attraction for electrons which are more or less free to move within the metallic lattice from ion to ion, and the geometry is dependent largely upon the size and electronic configuration of the metallic atoms; and (4) *covalent,* in which atoms occupy the lattice positions and are covalently bound in three dimensions to the neighboring atoms in a repeating pattern throughout the crystal, forming a so-called giant molecule, and the geometry is determined by the number and multiplicity of the covalent bonds which the constituent atoms can form.

Furthermore, no attempt will be made to discuss what little information is available concerning the structure of liquids. It should be mentioned, however, that currently there is under way extensive theoretical and experimental research in this highly complex area. What we shall be concerned with primarily, then, is the stereochemistry of molecules in the solid, liquid, or gaseous phase which are derived from multivalent atoms. *Bond lengths* and *bond angles* will be the important experimental quantities considered.

Many of the basic ideas necessary for a discussion of stereochemistry have already been introduced in Chapter 5, and in Chapter 9 the stereochemistry of complex ions and molecules has been briefly considered. Therefore, we will limit our discussion here primarily to simple inorganic molecules and to inorganic ions, such as ICl_4^-, which are not discussed in Chapter 9 since the central atom is a nonmetallic one.

EXPERIMENTAL METHODS

The stereochemistry of a molecule will be considered as defined by stating the spatial positions of the atoms or groups of atoms relative to a given polyvalent atom to which they are attached through bonds having some substantial degree of covalent character. Thus, for the elucidation of the stereochemistry of a molecule, we require precise internuclear distances (bond lengths) and the angles (bond angles) between imaginary lines joining the centers of the bonded atoms. The main experimental methods used for obtaining such structural information may be grouped conveniently into four categories:

(1) *Diffraction methods*
(2) *Spectroscopic methods*
(3) *Resonance methods*
(4) *Other physical methods*

Because chemical methods are in general fewer and less accurate, and their applicability is sharply limited, they will not be discussed here.

Diffraction Methods

In the first category are included X-ray, electron, and neutron diffraction. The most direct method for the determination of internuclear distances in individual molecules is one which utilizes the diffraction of radiation having wave lengths comparable to molecular dimensions. For example, the wave lengths for bombarding X rays and neutrons range from about 0.7 Å to about 2.5 Å, and those for electrons range from 0.05 Å to 0.07 Å. X-ray diffraction has been a powerful tool for structure determination ever since Bragg, in 1912, determined the structure of NaCl, KCl and ZnS by directing a beam of monochromatic X rays on crystals of these compounds. Several excellent texts[1,2,3] devoted entirely to X-ray methods and the interpretation of X-ray data are available, and the student should consult these for details.

Any particle moving with a momentum, mv, has associated with it a de Broglie wave length, $\lambda = h/mv$, and a beam of such particles can give rise to diffraction phenomena under appropriate conditions. Beams of monochromatic electrons are used primarily for investigations of molecular structure in the gaseous state,[4] although in recent years they have also been used for studying the surface and internal structures of crystals. Neutrons, unlike X rays and electrons, which interact with the orbital electrons of the atoms they encounter, are scattered by the atomic nuclei. Neutron diffraction[5] is particularly valuable in that it provides a means of locating hydrogen atoms in molecules. Thus, for example, hydrogen atoms scatter neutrons as well as do potassium atoms. This is in marked contrast to X rays, where the scattering increases smoothly with an increase in the number of orbital electrons in the scattering atom. Another advantage of neutron diffraction over X-ray diffraction is that two chemically dissimilar atoms having nearly the same number of extra-nuclear electrons cannot be distinguished by the latter method. Yet neutron diffraction may easily distinguish between them. For example, it has been shown that in spinel, $MgAl_2O_4$, the magnesium atoms occupy tetrahedral sites in the crystal, and the aluminum atoms are in octahedral sites.

Spectroscopic Methods

Spectroscopic methods of structural analysis are concerned primarily with the absorption of radiant energy by molecules. Although the divisions are not sharply defined, we can generally state that molecules may absorb energy in the four regions of the electromagnetic spectrum illustrated in Figure 6–1, giving rise to spectra labeled *rotation, vibration-rotation, vibration,* or *electronic.* Excitation of electrons generally involves energies in the range of 1.5 to 8.0 electron volts (ev) which require radiation in the

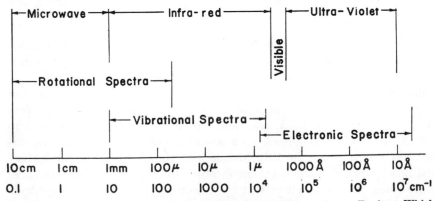

FIGURE 6–1. Electromagnetic Spectrum Showing the Approximate Regions Which Give Rise to Rotational, Vibrational, and Electronic Spectra.

visible and *near ultraviolet* region of the spectrum, i.e., wave lengths in the 1500 to 8000 Å* range. The electronic spectra may yield structural information on both the ground and the excited states of a molecule, although this method has not been used as extensively as the other spectral methods for molecular structure determination. However, the recent emphasis being placed upon electronic spectra of transition metal complexes (Chapter 9), and the attempts at the correlation and determination of the structures of these ions from the spectra, would indicate an increasing interest in this method.

The energy differences existing between vibrational energy levels within a molecule fall in the energy range from about 0.05 to 1.2 ev. This corresponds to absorptions during vibrational excitation of approximately 1×10^4 to 2.5×10^5 Å. In terms of microns, this would be 1.0 to 25μ, where $1\mu = 10^4$ Å. This spectral region is often referred to as the *near infrared* and the absorptions due to the fundamental stretching vibrations of most bonds, as well as many other vibrational modes, occur here. Being one of the most widely used methods of spectral analysis, infrared methods and the interpretations of infrared spectra have been extensively discussed in several texts.[6-8]

Often the use of infrared spectral data for structure determinations must be supplemented by Raman spectral data. The Raman effect, which gives rise to the Raman spectra, may be pictured briefly as arising in the following manner: A beam of monochromatic light from any convenient source and with almost any desired frequency passing through a gas, liquid, or transparent solid, is partially scattered. Most of the scattered light has the same frequency as the incident light, but a small fraction has slightly altered frequencies, the differences being called *Raman frequencies*. The alteration in frequency arises from the partial removal of energy by a molecule from an incident photon which it absorbs, causing the rotational or vibrational energy of the molecule to be increased by a discrete amount, and the remainder of the energy to be re-emitted as a lower-frequency photon. It is also possible for a higher-energy molecule to transfer energy to the incident photon and thereby increase the frequency of the scattered light. The photons with altered energy are recorded in a spectrogram as lines shifted from the strong line due to the incident light.

The selection rules that prescribe the number of lines obtained in the infrared or Raman spectra are strongly dependent upon the molecular symmetry. For example, a linear triatomic molecule XAX has two strong lines in its infrared spectrum and only one strong line in its Raman spectrum. The two spectra of a given molecule are said to be *complimentary* or *mutually exclusive* if a strong line in one does not appear in the other. This

---

* The relationship between energy in ev and wave length in Å is $E \times \lambda = 12{,}400$.

is theoretically the situation that must occur if a molecule has a center of symmetry. If the same vibration gives lines in both the infrared and Raman spectra, the molecule has no symmetry center. So, for example, the appearance of three lines in both spectra of SO_2 rule out linearity for this molecule. In general, we may say that any vibrational mode that involves a change in the dipole moment of the molecule should give rise to an infrared absorption line, while any vibration which causes a change in the polarizability of a molecule should produce a Raman shift.

The rotation spectra of polar gas molecules lies in the *far infrared* and *microwave* regions of the electromagnetic spectrum.[9-10] The study of rotation spectra, which give the energy differences existing between rotational energy levels, yields the moments of inertia of molecules. The latter may be used to derive very precise bond lengths and bond angles when combined with similar data for isotopic molecules which are justifiably expected to have the same bond lengths and bond angles. The great precision of the method arises from the high resolving power attainable in the microwave region, where spectral lines as close as 4×10^{-6} cm^{-1} can be separated.

Resonance Methods

Structural information is attainable by other recent methods which employ energies in the *radio-frequency* range. They include nuclear magnetic resonance[11-14] and paramagnetic resonance.[9,13-16] Nuclei which possess magnetic moments may exist in various quantum states in the presence of an applied magnetic field. The nuclear resonance effect arises from transitions among the energy levels corresponding to different orientations of nuclear magnetic moments with respect to the external field. The energy separation of the quantum states is very small, lying in the frequency range 10 to 60 megacycles (i.e., the 30- to 5-m wave length range). Since the field which determines the energy gaps depends partially upon the electron distribution about the nucleus, variations in the latter caused by changes in bonding or molecular environment produces shifts, termed *chemical shifts*, in the position of the resonance peaks. These chemical shifts therefore lead, in principle, to structure information.

Paramagnetic resonance absorption spectroscopy is a technique which may be applied to molecules containing atoms or solids containing ions which have unpaired electrons. Magnetic moments here are approximately 2000 times greater than those observed for nuclei, thereby causing the absorption of energy in the microwave region (usually the 4- to 1-cm wave length range). This results in a change in the orientation of the magnetic moment from one allowed position to another. The actual frequency absorbed is dependent upon the magnetic field and thus, by varying the field, the absorption may be detected at some appropriate microwave frequency.

Finally, it should be mentioned that certain general structural information may also be obtained by dipole moment and magnetic susceptibility determinations. However, these methods do not yield bond lengths or bond angles directly, and in certain cases they may be misleading and thereby result in misinterpretations in structure.

MODERN STEREOCHEMICAL THEORIES

In the years following the introduction of the valence-bond method and its application to the hydrogen molecule by Heitler and London (1927), Pauling,[17] Slater,[18] and others extended the theory and were able to explain the shapes of simple molecules formed by polycovalent atoms. We have seen in Chapter 5 that the valence bond approach, because of its emphasis upon localized hybrid orbitals with definite directional properties, is particularly well suited to stereochemical descriptions. Thus, it is possible to predict the stereochemistry of a molecule with nearly the same degree of certainty that we have of the orbitals which are hybridized on the central polyvalent atom. For example, the description of the tetrahedral disposition of the four valencies of the carbon atom in methane in terms of sp^3 hybrid orbitals is certainly a significant theoretical accomplishment of this approach. We need not discuss the application of the valence bond theory for predicting and describing stereochemistry as this has already been done in Chapter 5 for simple compounds of the nontransitional elements and in Chapter 9 for complex compounds of the transitional elements. Rather we will show that the shapes of molecules can be explained in terms of simpler theories requiring fewer assumptions than the valence bond method. Furthermore, it should be pointed out that the valence bond concepts of hybridization, resonance, and exchange are merely convenient mathematical descriptions, but they do not constitute explanations for the actual cause of the phenomena they are used to describe.[19]

Bases For a New Theory

The foundations for a new theory were laid in 1940, when Sidgwick and Powell[20] surveyed the then known inorganic stereochemistry and concluded that the spatial arrangements of the bonds in polycovalent atoms are related in a very simple way to the total number of valency shell electrons. They suggested that the electron pairs present in the valency shell of a polyvalent atom are always arranged in such a way as to minimize the repulsions between them, regardless of whether they are *shared* (bonding) *pairs* or *unshared* (nonbonding or lone) *pairs*. According to this picture, two pairs will be arranged linearly, three pairs in a plane triangle, four pairs tetrahedrally, five pairs in the form of a trigonal bipyramid, and six pairs octahedrally. It is noteworthy that these configurations, arrived at so simply, have been found to correctly predict the arrangements in all known compounds of the non-transitional elements for which the valence shell electron pairs are all bonded to identical atoms or groups. If one or more electron pairs are unshared, or if there are two or more different kinds of bonded atoms, deviations from the regular structures are expected.

Perhaps one of the most valuable ideas to be introduced into stereochemical considerations following the early applications of the valence bond theory is that unshared or *lone pairs* of electrons are just as important in determining the stereochemistry of a compound of the non-transitional elements as are the bonding pairs. We shall see shortly just what role these lone pairs play in the stereochemical picture, but we should point out here that they do not appear to have the same prominent role in determining the stereochemistry of compounds of the transitional elements as they do for the non-transitional elements. In the transitional elements, the lone pairs and the single unpaired electrons are in the penultimate shell, $(n - 1)d$, and may be treated as though they are in unhybridized metal atomic orbitals, whereas in the non-transitional elements they are in the outermost quantum shell and are believed to be in hybrid orbitals. For example, the octahedral configuration of transition metal complexes is found to be quite independent of the number of nonbonding electrons. As a further, more specific example, the ion $Mo(CN)_8^{4-}$ is found to have a dodecahedral (symmetrical eight-cornered) arrangement despite the fact that the valency shell of the molybdenum contains nine electron pairs.

Importance of the Pauli Exclusion Principle

During the past decade Lennard-Jones, Pople, Linnett, Walsh, and others, have treated the problems of molecular geometry from yet a new theoretical approach. Their method, while it uses some of the same mathematics and fundamental ideas as the valence-bond and localized molecular orbital theories, places the most emphasis upon merely the number of valence shell electrons and their inherent properties. There is a very simple property possessed by all electronic systems (atoms, molecules, or solids), namely, *electrons of like spin tend to avoid being in the same region of space*. For the simple reason that all electrons are negatively charged, they will repel one another according to a coulombic law of force. However, even more important in the determination of the shapes and properties of molecules is the result that electrons having the same spin are found to have a very low probability of being close together because of the more subtle demands of the Pauli exclusion principle.[21] In fact it has been possible from a consideration of the latter interaction alone, ignoring the perturbations due to electrostatic repulsions, to deduce the electron arrangements cited earlier for 2, 3, 4, 5, and 6 electron pairs.

The Pauli (or antisymmetry) principle, in wave-mechanical terms, states that electrons having the same spin must avoid being in the same region of space because the complete wave function, Ψ, representing the actual state of a system containing two or more electrons, must be anti-symmetrical to electron interchange. That is, if the coordinates, three space and one spin, are interchanged for any two electrons, the wave function must change its sign. The Pauli principle cannot be derived, but it is justified by the conclusions which can be drawn from it. In 1954, Lennard-Jones made the following statement concerning the Pauli principle: "Its all-pervading influence does not seem hitherto to have been fully realized by chemists, but it is safe to say that ultimately it will be regarded as the most important property to be learned by those concerned with molecular structure." Thus, from the point of view of modern theory, we must consider the Pauli exclusion principle along with the usual inter-electronic forces, and the interactions of the atomic nuclei.

APPLICATION OF THE PAULI PRINCIPLE TO STEREOCHEMISTRY

It can readily be shown that the application of the Pauli principle will lead to the same conclusions as the valence-bond method. The general procedure is basically as follows: The valence electrons are assigned to appropriate s, p, and d atomic orbitals. Next, the complete antisym-metrical determinantal wave function, Ψ, for these electrons is written out, thereby taking into account the Pauli principle and the indistinguish-ability of electrons. The value of the wave function, then, for any con-figuration in which two electrons have the same spin and position vectors is zero, so that the probability of such a configuration is also zero. It is in this way that the exclusion principle operates to keep electrons with the same spin apart. This will become clearer shortly when we consider a specific example. To find the probability of any particular spatial configuration, Ψ is squared and then integrated over all spin coordinates leaving a prob-ability function dependent only upon electron space coordinates. The value of the coordinates which causes this probability to be a maximum is deter-mined by setting the first derivative equal to zero. The type of wave func-tion used is generally a simple hydrogen-like function, but others have also been tried. Quantitative results as, for example, in the determination of bond angles or energies, are markedly dependent upon the exact form taken for the wave function, but qualitative results are not. As a first approximation no terms involving interelectronic distances are included. This, then, ignores the effects of interelectronic repulsions on the electron distribution, Ψ^2. Interelectronic repulsions may be taken into account, but it has been found that for stereochemical results the far more important effect arises from the Pauli antisymmetry principle.

For a two-electron system such as the helium atom in the $1s^{1}2s^{1}$ state, the electrons in the *singlet state* (spins opposed) have a tendency to be drawn together, whereas in the *triplet state* (spins parallel) the opposite is observed.[19,22] Furthermore, this is not a result of the usual type of force between the electrons, but rather it is a consequence of the form required of the wave functions arising from the indistinguishability of the electrons. For this case, in which the electrons are in nondirectional s orbitals, the spatial distributions of the electrons in the two states are found to be as follows: For the symmetric or singlet state, three configurations have a high probability — two in which one electron is near the nucleus and the other farther out, and the third in which both are simultaneously near the nucleus. For the antisymmetric or triplet state, only two configurations have high probability, and both are for one electron near the nucleus and the other far from the nucleus. Thus, because the s orbitals have no angular dependence, the *electron correlation* (correlation between the electron positions) is radial only. From the standpoint of stereochemistry, we are interested in wave functions which involve angular terms. Consequently, it will be of interest to consider in some detail the helium atom in the $1s^{1}2p_{z}^{1}$ state.

The Helium Atom in the Excited State, $1s^{1} 2p^{1}$

For this particular case, we can designate the two occupied orbitals as ψ_{a} and ψ_{b}. Each of these represents a solution of the one-electron problem and is, therefore, an unperturbed wave function. Thus, they neglect interelectronic repulsion effects. Satisfactory solutions to the unperturbed Schrodinger equation for electrons (1) and (2) will be

$$\psi_{(1,2)} = \psi_{a}(1)\ \psi_{b}(2) \tag{6-1a}$$

and

$$\psi_{(2,1)} = \psi_{a}(2)\ \psi_{b}(1) \tag{6-1b}$$

Since electrons are indistinguishable, the probability, ψ^{2}, for a configuration in which electron (1) is at position a and electron (2) is at position b must always equal the probability of the configuration for which the electrons are interchanged. That is,

$$[\psi_{(1,2)}]^{2} = [\psi_{(2,1)}]^{2} \tag{6-2}$$

Therefore

$$\psi_{(1,2)} = +\psi_{(2,1)} \tag{6-3}$$

and

$$\psi_{(1,2)} = -\psi_{(2,1)} \tag{6-4}$$

Now two solutions to the Schrodinger equation which satisfy the conditions set forth in Eqs. (6–3) and (6–4) are, respectively:

$$\psi_S = \frac{1}{\sqrt{2}} \, [\psi_a(1) \, \psi_b(2) + \psi_a(2) \, \psi_b(1)] \tag{6–5}$$

$$\psi_A = \frac{1}{\sqrt{2}} \, [\psi_a(1) \, \psi_b(2) - \psi_a(2) \, \psi_b(1)] \tag{6–6}$$

The factor $1/\sqrt{2}$ insures that the probability of finding the electrons in the whole of space is unity. The wave function, ψ_S, has the property expressed by Eq. (6–3), and ψ_A the property expressed by Eq. (6–4). This may be verified by interchanging the numbers representing the electrons. ψ_S is said to be symmetric to the interchange of electrons because it obeys Eq. (6–3), and ψ_A is said to be antisymmetric to the interchange of electrons because it obeys Eq. (6–4).

For the specific case of helium $1s^1 2p_z^1$, we have

$$\psi_a = \psi_{1s} = N_{1s} \exp{(-\alpha r_1)} \tag{6–7}$$
$$= f_{1s}(r_1)$$

$$\psi_b = \psi_{2p} = N_{2p} r_2 \exp{(-\alpha r_2)} \cos \theta \tag{6–8}$$
$$= f_{2p}(r_2) \cos \theta$$

where N_{1s}, N_{2p}, and α are constants, r_1 and r_2 are the distances of electrons (1) and (2) from the nucleus, θ is the angle between a line joining the electron and the nucleus and a fixed axis about which the wave function is symmetric, and $f_{1s}(r_1)$ and $f_{2p}(r_2)$ are the radial functions of the s and p states.

These give rise to the symmetric and antisymmetric wave functions:

$$\psi_S = \frac{1}{\sqrt{2}} \, [\psi_{1s}(1) \, \psi_{2p}(2) + \psi_{1s}(2) \, \psi_{2p}(1)] \tag{6–9}$$

$$\psi_A = \frac{1}{\sqrt{2}} \, [\psi_{1s}(1) \, \psi_{2p}(2) - \psi_{1s}(2) \, \psi_{2p}(1)] \tag{6–10}$$

which may be rewritten using Eq. (6–7) and Eq. (6–8) as follows:

$$\psi_S = f_{1s}(r_1) \cdot f_{2p}(r_2) \cos \theta_2 + f_{1s}(r_2) \cdot f_{2p}(r_1) \cos \theta_1 \tag{6–11}$$
$$\psi_A = f_{1s}(r_1) \cdot f_{2p}(r_2) \cos \theta_2 - f_{1s}(r_2) \cdot f_{2p}(r_1) \cos \theta_1 \tag{6–12}$$

If both electrons are at the same radius, $r = r_1 = r_2$, then Eq. (6–11) and Eq. (6–12) become

$$\psi_S = f_{1s}(r) f_{2p}(r) \, [\cos \theta_2 + \cos \theta_1] \tag{6–13}$$

$$\psi_A = f_{1s}(r) f_{2p}(r) \, [\cos \theta_2 - \cos \theta_1] \tag{6–14}$$

ψ_S^2 is a maximum when $\theta_1 = \theta_2 = 0$, or $\theta_1 = \theta_2 = \pi$; and ψ_A^2 is a maximum when $\theta_1 = 0$ and $\theta_2 = \pi$, or vice versa. Physically these results are interpreted to mean that for electrons at the same or even different radii, the singlet state will have electrons on the same side of the nucleus whereas the triplet state will have them on opposite sides.

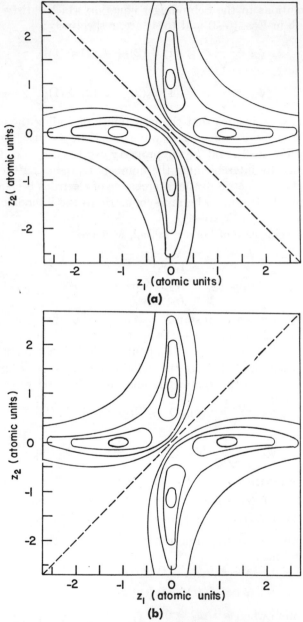

FIGURE 6–2. Contour Diagrams of the Wave Function Dependence on Electron Positions z_1 and z_2 Along the Chosen Fixed z Axis, for the Helium Atom in the $1s^1 2p^1$ Configuration: (a) the singlet, ψ_s, state; (b) the triplet, ψ_A, state.

We may construct *contour diagrams* of the dependence of these wave functions on the positions z_1 and z_2 of the two electrons, where z is the chosen fixed axis, and the subscripts refer to electrons (1) and (2). These are shown in Figure 6–2 (a) and (b). The former shows the contour of ψ_S, the singlet state, with electrons (1) and (2) located on the fixed z axis, and the latter shows the contour of ψ_A, or the triplet state, on that axis. It can be seen that in both cases there are maxima for the configurations in which one electron is at the nucleus, where the $1s$ orbital has its maximum, and one removed from the nucleus by the radius at which the $2p$ orbital has its maximum. More significantly, it can be observed from the contour diagram for the singlet state that configurations having both electrons on the same side of the nucleus are favored, whereas for the triplet state, configurations having the electrons on opposite sides of the nucleus are favored. In fact, electrons with the same spin will have a maximum probability of being located on opposite sides of the nucleus on a straight line passing through the nucleus, that is, at an angle of 180° with respect to each other. This is seen to be the same result as is obtained by hybridization of an s and a p atomic orbital to yield the two equivalent sp hybrid orbitals. The only point of difference here is that we have considered the atomic configurations $1s^1 2p^1$ rather than $ns^1 np^1$ which is necessary for forming equivalent hybrid orbitals. But, that was only for simplicity of presentation. The *angular correlation*, which is what we were after, is the same regardless of whether or not the s and p orbitals have the same principal quantum number.

MOLECULES HAVING REGULAR GEOMETRIES

Four or Less Valency Shell Electron Pairs

It is now possible to understand why atoms such as beryllium, zinc, cadmium, and mercury, which can adopt the $ns^1 np^1$ configuration with the electron spins parallel, will form bicovalent compounds with bonds at an angle of 180°. In an analogous way, we can arrive at the conclusion that the boron atom in the configuration $1s^2 2s^1 2p_x^1 p_y^1$, with three electrons having parallel spin, must adopt as its most probable stereochemical arrangement the equilateral triangle with 120° bond angles (cf. sp^2 hybrid orbitals). Furthermore, Zimmerman and van Rysselberghe[23] have shown for the carbon atom in the configuration $1s^2 2s^1 2p_x^1 p_y^1 p_z^1$, with four spins parallel, that as a consequence of the Pauli principle, the most probable distribution of the four unpaired electrons is at the vertices of a regular tetrahedron (cf. sp^3 hybrid orbitals).

Thus far we have really considered only the situations in which a given isolated atom in an excited state has two, three, or four unpaired electrons. We cannot verify our predictions of the radial or angular distribution of electrons for the isolated atoms, but we can study the molecules which they form. In the covalent molecules in which the unpaired electrons have become paired with electrons from the surrounding atoms, we still predict that the electrons with parallel spins will distribute themselves as far apart as possible under the operation of the Pauli principle and in accordance with their indistinguishability. To illustrate, consider the neon atom which possesses four electron pairs in its outer shell. Lennard-Jones[21] has utilized the Pauli principle to predict that the most probable arrangement of each set of four parallel-spin electrons is at the vertices of a tetrahedron. Furthermore, if we disregard coulombic repulsion, there will be no correlation between these two sets of opposite spin, and they will be equally likely to be found in any relative orientation. However, we should recall that there is some tendency for electrons of opposite spin to be drawn together, but this is opposed by coulombic repulsion (*charge correlation*). Although we have no method to verify our conclusion about neon atoms, it is interesting to note that Ne, Ar, Kr, and Xe all have a cubic close-packed solid-state structure like the tetrahedral methane rather than the hexagonal close-packed structure found for He. The latter structure is expected for all of the inert gases, assuming their atoms to be spherical.[19]

Now let us consider methane in which the carbon may be pictured hypothetically as C^{4-} with the neon electronic arrangement. When the four protons are brought up to the C^{4-} to form CH_4, the attractions of the protons for the electrons will cause the two sets of independent tetrahedra to come into alignment. This prediction is verifiable although the mechanism is not, as the methane molecule is indeed tetrahedral. We may draw the important conclusion that the most probable arrangement for n electrons of the same spin will also be the most probable arrangement for n pairs of electrons.

Five or More Valency Shell Electron Pairs

If we consider now single atoms with five or more electrons of the same spin or polyvalent atoms in molecules with five or more electron pairs, the most probable arrangements are perhaps not so obvious.[24] The problem here is that electrons in d orbitals must be included, and the d orbitals are not all equivalent. For example, in writing the complete antisymmetric wave function for five or more unpaired electrons, a choice must be made among the nonequivalent d orbital wave functions. From the hybrid orbital picture, we would predict the square pyramid arrangement for five electron pairs if the hybrid set were $sp^3d_{x^2-y^2}$, and the trigonal bipyramid, if it were $sp^3d_{z^2}$. For six electron pairs an octahedral structure arises from the hybrid set $sp^3d_{x^2-y^2}d_{z^2}$, and a trigonal prism arises from the hybrid set $sp^3d_{xy}d_{yz}$.[25] Likewise for seven and eight electron pairs there are several arrangements possible for each, depending upon which d or f orbitals are hybridized with the s and p orbitals.

Gillespie[24] has considered the stereochemical problems of five to nine unpaired electrons, or electron pairs, from a simple and somewhat novel viewpoint. He first assumes that the valency shell electron pairs are at the same average distance from the nucleus. Strictly speaking this will only be exact for two, three, four, and six electron pairs which are bonding the central atom to a set of identical atoms or groups. He then reasons that the determination of the most probable distribution of these electron pairs is the same as the determination of the arrangement of a set of particles on the surface of a sphere under the action of an appropriate force law. Since electrons of the same spin must obey the Pauli principle, they therefore behave as though there were a force between them. Since this force increases rapidly with the increasing overlap of the orbitals of electrons with the same spin, the force is assumed to vary inversely with some large power of the interelectron distance,[26] viz., $1/r^n$. The arrangement of particles on the surface of a sphere obeying such a force law is obtained by maximizing the least distance between any two particles. This problem and the identical one of assuming an inverse square force law, $1/r^2$ (i.e., where the arrangement is determined only by electrostatic forces), have been solved mathematically and the results are given in Table 6-1. Both

TABLE 6-1. / **Equilibrium Arrangements of Like Particles on the Surface of a Sphere Obeying a Force Law $1/r^n$ or $1/r^2$.**

No. of Particles (or electron pairs)	Arrangement
2	linear
3	equilateral triangle
4	tetrahedron
5	trigonal bipyramid
6	octahedron
7	1:3:3* or pentagonal bipyramid (1:5:1)
8	square antiprism
9	tripyramid**

* Irregular octahedron plus an extra particle opposite one face.
** A trigonal prism plus an extra particle opposite each of the three rectangular faces.

force laws are found to lead to the same arrangements except for the case of seven particles (or electron pairs). For seven electron pairs the $1/r^2$ law predicts a pentagonal bipyramid (I) (1:5:1), the $1/r^n$ law predicts an irregular octahedron (II) with the seventh pair opposite the middle of one octahedral face (1:3:3), and an intermediate force law, $1/r^m$ (where $n > m > 2$), predicts an irregular trigonal prism (III) with the seventh pair opposite one rectangular face[24] (1:4:2). Examples of molecules or ions having structure I are IF_7, UF_7^{3-} and $UO_2F_5^{3-}$; some having structure II

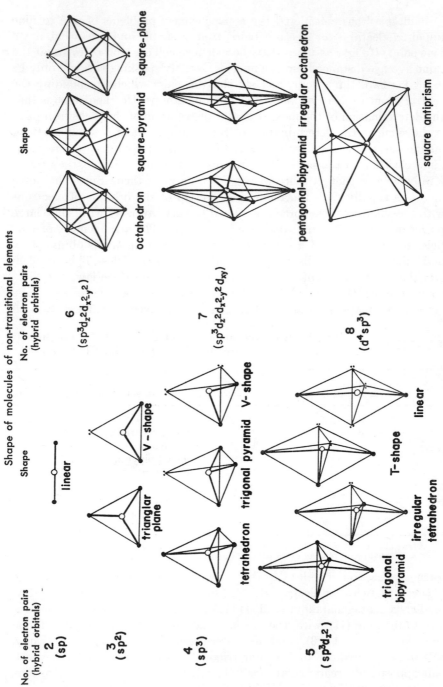

FIGURE 6-3. Shapes of Molecules of Non-transitional Elements.

are the A-modification oxides, X_2O_3, of La, Ce, Pr and Nd; and some having structure III are the ions TaF_7^{2-}, NbF_7^{2-} and $NbOF_6^{3-}$.

It is significant that for any number of electron pairs from two to six, whether or not they are equivalent, the arrangements given in Table 6–1 correctly predict the shapes of molecules of the non-transitional elements.[27] Some examples are given in Table 6–2, and Figure 6–3 illustrates the shapes

| TABLE 6–2. | The Arrangements of Electron Pairs in Valency Shells and the Shapes of Molecules of Non-transitional Elements. |

No. of Valency Shell Electron Pairs	Electron Pair Arrangement	No. of Bond Pairs	No. of Lone Pairs	Molecular Shape	Examples
2	linear	2	0	linear	$Ag(NH_3)_2^+$, $HgCl_2$, $ZnCl_2$, $AgCl_2^-$, UO_2^{2+}
3	triangular-plane	3	0	triangular-plane	$BX_3(X=F,Cl,Br)$, GaX_3, $InX_3(X=Cl,Br,I)$
		2	1	V-shape	SnX_2 (gas), PbX_2 $(X=Cl, Br,I)$
4	tetrahedron	4	0	tetrahedron	CH_4, GeF_4, BH_4^-, NH_4^+
		3	1	trigonal pyramid	NH_3, NF_3, PF_3, H_3O^+
		2	2	V-shape	H_2O, F_2O, SCl_2, $TeBr_2$, NH_2^-
5	trigonal-bipyramid	5	0	trigonal-bipyramid	PCl_5 (gas)
		4	1	irregular tetrahedron*	$TeCl_4$
		3	2	T-shape*	ClF_3, BrF_3
		2	3	linear*	ICl_2^-, I_3^-
6	octahedron	6	0	octahedron	SF_6, PCl_6^-
		5	1	square pyramid	IF_5, BrF_5
		4	2	square plane*	ICl_4^-
7	pentagonal-bipyramid	7	0	pentagonal-bipyramid	IF_7
		6	1	irregular octahedron*	$SbBr_6^{3-}$, $SeBr_6^{2-}$

* For these cases, alternative molecular shapes are possible since there are alternative positions for the one or more lone pairs. However, the choice has been made on the basis of considerations found in the text (pp. 203-205).

TABLE 6–3. / **The Shapes of Molecules Containing Multiple Bonds.**

No. of σ-Bonds Plus Lone Pairs	Arrangement	No. of σ-Bonds	No. of Lone Pairs	Molecular Shape	Examples*
2	linear	2	0	linear	$O{=}C{=}O$, $H{-}C{\equiv}N$ $O{=}\overset{+}{N}{=}O$
3	triangular plane	3	0	triangular plane	$Cl_2C{=}O$, $HClC{=}O$, $O_2S{=}O$
		2	1	V-shape	SO_2 , O_3 , $NOCl$, NO_2^-
4	tetrahedral	4	0	tetrahedral	SO_2Cl_2, SO_3^{2-}(O, Cl), $O{=}P(Cl)(Cl)Cl$
		3	1	triangular pyramid	$S(O)(O)Cl$, $S(O)(O)O^-$, ClO_3^-
		2	2	V-shape	BrO_2^-
5	trigonal bipyramid	5	0	trigonal bipyramid	no examples known
		4	1	irregular tetrahedron	$IF_2O_2^-$
6	octahedron	6	0	octahedron	$I(OH)_5O$

* Some of the formulas shown represent only one of several possible canonical forms.

of molecules of the non-transitional elements. It should be pointed out that the maximum number of single normal covalent bonds formed by any non-transitional element is seven, since this is the maximum number of electrons in the outer quantum level of a chemically reactive atom. Therefore, we will not expect to find any examples of eight or nine electron pairs in a valency level except among certain of the transition elements wherein at least some of the electron-pair bonds will arise from coordinate covalence and the penultimate d shell will necessarily be involved in the bonding. For example, TaF_8^{3-} and thorium acetylacetonate, $Th(C_5H_7O_2)_4$, have the square antiprism structure shown in Figure 6–3. One other structure has been observed for an atom with eight bond pairs and this is the dodecahedron found for the ion $Mo(CN)_8^{4-}$. However, as was pointed out earlier, the molybdenum actually has nine valence shell electron pairs, one of these being a lone pair. Nine electron pairs apparently adopt a tripyramid configuration, an arrangement which has been observed with several crystalline compounds such as UCl_3, $LaCl_3$, and $Nd(H_2O)_9(BrO_3)_3$.

Molecules Containing Multiple Bonds

Thus far we have primarily been concerned with valency shells in which all electron pairs are engaged in forming single bonds to identical atoms or groups. For molecules which contain double and triple bonds the shapes may be predicted on the assumption that the two or three pairs of electrons in the multiple bond together occupy only one of the positions in the various arrangements given in Table 6–2.[27] In Table 6–3 are given the shapes of molecules which contain multiple bonds along with some examples. Thus it appears, at least as a first approximation, that the stereochemistry of a molecule forming double bonds can be assumed to be determined only by the number of σ-bonding and lone electron pairs, and the π-bonding pairs can be neglected. However, a more detailed consideration, even qualitative, would predict that the coulombic repulsion between two double bonds would exceed that between two single bonds. The expected effect of this order of repulsions upon the detailed bond angles in molecules containing multiple bonds is generally found to be true. For example, the bond angles in the molecules POX_3 and PSX_3 ($X = $ F or Cl) have approximately the expected tetrahedral value, but the XPX angles are found to be less than 109.5° (Table 6–4). Similarly in the molecules COX_2 ($X = $ H, Cl, CH_3) and $CSCl_2$ the XCX angles are all slightly less than 120°, the angle expected for three σ-bonding pairs (Table 6–4).

DEVIATIONS FROM REGULAR GEOMETRIES

Except for the foregoing discussion of the deviations expected from regular shapes caused by multiple bonding, we have thus far considered only molecules with regular geometries. For example, we have stated that three pairs of electrons will always be found in the triangular-planar

TABLE 6-4. / **XAX Bond Angles for Some Molecules Containing Double Bonds.**

Molecule	XAX Angle	Molecule	XAX Angle
$O{=}PF_3$	102.5 ± 2	$O{=}S(CH_3)_2$	100 ± 5
$O{=}PCl_3$	103.5 ± 2	$O{=}S(C_6H_5)_2$	97.3 ± 1
$S{=}PF_3$	100.3 ± 2	$O{=}SCl_2$	$114 \pm 2*$
			(95.8 ± 3.5)
$S{=}PCl_3$	100.5 ± 2	$O{=}SBr_2$	96 ± 2
		$O{=}SF_2$	92.8
$O{=}CH_2$	118 ± 2	$O{=}SF_2$	96.1
		$\quad\quad \parallel$	
		$\quad\quad O$	
$O{=}CCl_2$	111.3 ± 0.1		
$O{=}C(CH_3)_2$	119.6 ± 3	$O{=}SCl_2$	$111 \pm 3*$
		$\quad\quad \parallel$	(96.6 ± 3)
		$\quad\quad O$	
$S{=}CCl_2$	116		

* These values, greater than the tetrahedral angle, appear to be incorrect and the molecules deserve reinvestigation. The parenthetical values, predicted by an electrostatic model for covalent molecules, would appear to be more in line with expectation.[28]

arrangement, which requires 120° angles at the nucleus between the points of maximum electron density. This is borne out in the structures of BX_3 (X = F, Cl, Br), and GaX_3 and InX_3 (X = Cl, Br, I). Four pairs of electrons will dispose themselves with maximum probability at the tetrahedral angle from each other. The perfectly regular structures of CH_4, NH_4^+, $SiCl_4$, GeF_4, etc., support this prediction. Now we shall turn to the question of deviations from regular shapes caused by the presence of both bonding electron pairs (B) and lone electron pairs (L) in the valency level of the polycovalent atom.

Deviations from regular shapes may arise in at least two ways. Firstly, if the groups attached to the central atom are not all identical, we expect and we find deviations from the regular structures. For example, the HCH angles in the series CH_3F, CH_3Cl, CH_3Br, and CH_3I are 110.0°, 110.3°, 110.8°, and 111°, respectively. All of these are greater than the tetrahedral angle of 109.5° found for CH_4 and CX_4 (X = F, Cl, Br, I). However, it is apparent from the data that the deviations from regular symmetry are not very large, and we shall see later why this is so. Secondly, whenever there are both bond pairs and lone pairs present together in a valency shell we again expect and we observe deviations from regular symmetry. Deviations arising in this way may become somewhat larger. For example, in the series NH_4^+, NH_3, NH_2^-, the HNH angles decrease regularly from 109.5° to 104°. Similarly, in the isoelectronic series CH_4, NH_3, OH_2, we find a systematic decrease in bond angles from 109.5° to 107.3° to 104.5°. In each series we go from 0 to 1 to 2 lone electron pairs, which in the latter two cases are presumed to occupy approximately tetrahedral corners, as required by the Pauli principle. Additionally, the values of the angles suggest that the lone-pair electrons exert a greater repulsion upon each other and upon the bond pairs than the bond pairs, or even the bonded atoms, do upon each other. In fact, Gillespie and Nyholm[27] have found that the qualitative picture of stereochemistry is considerably improved for most inorganic molecules by the assumption that electrostatic repulsions between electron pairs in a given valency shell decrease in the order: lone-pair:lone-pair $(L-L)$ > lone-pair:bond-pair $(L-B)$ > bond-pair:bond-pair $(B-B)$. This can be attributed to the fact that since the lone pairs are under the influence of a single positive center, they are closer-in toward the central atom than the bond pairs which, under the influence also of the nucleus of a bonded atom, may be pulled out farther from the central atom. Hence the lone pairs, because of their greater proximity to each other and to the bond pairs, will exert a greater repulsion effect.

There is also another explanation[24] for the greater repulsion of lone pairs. The orbital containing the bonding electron pair, because it is under the influence of two positive centers, is more localized or smaller; whereas the orbital containing the lone pair is capable of spreading out and occupying more of the available space than the bond pairs. This assumption allows at least a qualitative understanding of the observed decrease of the bond angles from methane to ammonia to water.

Five or More Electron Pairs

Valency shells which contain five or more electron pairs, one or more of which may be lone pairs, require a more detailed examination. Let us first consider the case of five electron pairs. We have seen that five pairs will adopt a trigonal bipyramidal configuration and, therefore, AX_5 molecules should have this stereochemistry. Molecules AX_4L, where L represents a lone pair, have two possible arrangements or isomeric forms, assuming that the trigonal bipyramidal geometry of the five electron pairs is maintained. This situation arises because of the nonequivalence of the polar and equatorial positions of the trigonal bipyramid. Hence a lone pair occupying a polar position makes a 90° angle with each of the three equatorial bond pairs and a 180° angle with the polar bond pair. If the lone pair occupies an equatorial position, it makes a 120° angle with each of the other two equatorial positions and a 90° angle with each of the two polar positions. If the Pauli forces which we have been considering are in fact the most important in the determination of electron correlation, and if these forces fall off rapidly with distance, it would seem reasonable to consider only the interactions between a given electron pair and its nearest neighbors in predicting the shapes of molecules.[24] Therefore, in the foregoing situation involving the molecule AX_4L, the structure which has L in an equatorial position at 90° to only two bond pairs should be favored over the structure which has L in a polar position at 90° to three bond pairs. This prediction is borne out by the structures of the known AX_4L molecules (Table 6–5).

For AX_3L_2 molecules three possible lone-pair:bond-pair arrangements arise from the trigonal bipyramid. These are given in Table 6–5, where it is seen that the only structure observed is the one which has both of the lone pairs in equatorial positions. This is predicted by again assuming that only interactions of electron pairs making angles of 90° with the nucleus need be considered and that L-L > L-B > B-B. Then, for the three arrangements as they appear in Table 6–5, we have, respectively, (1) six L-B repulsions; (2) one L-L repulsion, three L-B repulsions, and two B-B repulsions; and (3) four L-B repulsions and two B-B repulsions. It is evident that the last involves the least total amount of interelectronic repul-

TABLE 6–5. / **Possible Structures Arising from Five Valency Shell Electron Pairs for Molecules** AX_5, AX_4L, AX_3L_2, and AX_2L_3.

No. of σ-Bonding Pairs	No. of Lone Pairs	ELECTRON PAIR DISTRIBUTION*		Molecular Shape	Examples
		Polar	Equatorial		
AX_5 5	0	2 B	3 B	trigonal bipyramid	PCl_5, PF_5, PF_3Cl_2
AX_4L 4	1	1 L 1 B	3 B	trigonal bipyramid	none
		2 B	1 L 2 B	distorted tetrahedron	$TeCl_4$, SbF_4^- $Cl_2Se(C_6H_4 \cdot Me)_2$ $IO_2F_2^-$ (one π-pair)
AX_3L_2 3	2	2 L	3 B	triangular plane	none
		1 L 1 B	1 L 2 B	trigonal pyramid	none
		2 B	2 L 1 B	T-shape	ClF_3, BrF_3, $C_6H_5ICl_2$
AX_2L_3 2	3	2 L	1 L 2 B	angular ($\sim 120°$)	none
		1 L 1 B	2 L 1 B	angular ($\sim 90°$)	none
		2 B	3 L	linear	ICl_2^-, I_3^-, $IBrCl^-$

* B = bond pair, L = lone pair.

sion. Analogous reasoning applied to AX_2L_3 molecules leads to the prediction that these molecules should be linear (Table 6–5).

Six valency shell electron pairs are always disposed at the corners of an octahedron, so it is not surprising to find that all known non-transitional element molecules of the form AX_6 have a regular octahedral configuration. Since all six positions on the octahedron are equivalent, AX_5L molecules have only one possible configuration, the square pyramid. This is the structure found for the several compounds of this type which have been studied (Table 6–6). The square planar arrangement for AX_4L_2 molecules, with the L in *trans* positions to each other (i.e., at 180°) rather than *cis* (90°), is readily predicted and the known examples are indeed planar (Table 6–6).

TABLE 6–6. / **Possible Structures Arising from Six Valency Shell Electron Pairs for Molecules AX_6, AX_5L, and AX_4L_2.**

Molecular Type	No. of σ-Bonding Pairs	No. of Lone Pairs	Molecular Shape	Examples
AX_6	6	0	octahedron	AlF_6^{3-}, $PbCl_6^{2-}$, PCl_6^{-} SF_6, $Te(OH)_6$
AX_5L	5	1	square pyramid	SbF_5^{2-}, $SbCl_5^{2-}$ IF_5, BrF_5
AX_4L_2	4	2	square plane (2 L *trans*)	ICl_4^{-}, BrF_4^{-}

An Alternative Electrostatic Model for Covalent Molecules

It should be pointed out that while the foregoing qualitative predictions concerning the stereochemistries of covalent molecules are all correct, the simple, intuitively attractive theory by which they are arrived at has been questioned by Searcy.[29] In 1958, he proposed[28] an electrostatic model for the prediction of the shapes of covalent molecules and ions which he has shown to be useful in the quantitative prediction of bond angles.[28–30] By means of his model, he is able to show that the total electrostatic repulsion energies between electron pairs in molecules of the types we have just considered are highly insensitive to a choice of structural forms where isomeric forms are possible. He suggests, as an alternative, that the gain in stability achieved in one structure relative to other structures is realized through placement of the lone-pair electrons at positions which leave free the widest possible solid angle adjacent to the central atom.[29] He arrives at this conclusion by reasoning that the two electrons of a lone pair are restricted in space by their occupancy of the same molecular orbital, but that within this limitation they will remain as far apart as possible in order to minimize their repulsive interactions. However, bonding pairs are restrained to a relatively small solid angle about the central atom because they are in the field of two nuclei. Thus, whereas Gillespie and Nyholm predict stereochemical arrangements of molecules with lone pairs by deducing the arrangements of electron pairs which minimize the repulsive interactions among the several electron pairs, Searcy deduces the same arrangements by considering the repulsions between the paired electrons sharing the same orbital. In either picture, and by analogy with organic chemistry where the size of groups often plays an important stereochemical role, we may conclude that stereochemically the lone electron pair acts as though it were a very large, bulky group.

The electrostatic model proposed by Searcy[28] is based upon the major assumption that each bonded pair or lone pair has a characteristic electrostatic charge concentrated on the line between the central atom and the bonded atom or lone pair. Taking all of these characteristic charges to be equidistant from the central atom, he then deduces the molecular shape by determining the bond angles that minimize the repulsive interactions of these characteristic charges. The first step is therefore to evaluate the characteristic charges of various atoms by working backward from molecules whose experimental bond angles are known. The bond pairs are then assigned *electrostatic repulsion numbers* (ERN), which measure the electrostatic repulsion of electron pairs bonded to various atoms relative to the lone pair taken as unity. The ERN value is really a function of the characteristic charge density located at some arbitrary point along the bond line. He finds that only two parameters are generally needed, and these depend primarily upon the period of the central atom and the family of the attached atom. For example, a value of 0.94 for the ERN of oxygen is obtained regardless of the period in the periodic table of the central atom, and this value is found to be successful in predicting bond angles if used also for sulfur. All halogen atoms when bonded to an atom of an element of the third or higher period all have an ERN of 0.52 ± 0.04. For bonding to a second period central atom the ERN for fluorine is 0.63 ± 0.04, whereas that for chlorine is 0.72 ± 0.06. A value of 0.81 is found for the ERN of hydrogen bonded to a second-period atom. This value reproduces experimental bond angles to within $0.7°$ on the average for four widely different kinds of molecules. An ERN of 0.38 for hydrogen attached to a third or higher-period element reproduces experimental bond angles for six molecules to within $3.1°$ in the least favorable case.

BOND LENGTHS

For linear molecules or ions AX_2, triangular planar ones AX_3, tetrahedral ones AX_4, octahedral ones AX_6, and square antiprismatic ones AX_8, where all of the bond pairs are to identical atoms or groups, perfectly regular geometries and equal *A-X* bond lengths are expected and found. In each of the foregoing molecules the bond pairs occupy equivalent geometric sites around the central atom. However, the same is not true if there are five or seven electron pairs in the valency shell. For example, in the trigonal-bipyramidal arrangement adopted by five electron pairs, the two polar positions are not equivalent to the three equatorial positions. An electron pair in a polar position makes an angle at the nucleus of 90° with three equatorial pairs and 180° with the other polar pair, whereas an equatorial pair makes two 90° angles and two 120° angles with the other electron pairs. We have seen that the Pauli forces, which operate to keep the electron pairs as far apart as the space will allow, are very short-range forces. Therefore, they increase greatly when orbitals begin to show appreciable overlap. Consequently, repulsions between nearest neighbor pairs will be much more important than those between more distant pairs. According to this reasoning, the total repulsion experienced by an axial electron pair will be greater than that experienced by an equatorial pair. Thus, we predict that the polar electron pairs will seek an equilibrium position at a greater distance from the nucleus than the equatorial pairs, since this will equalize the repulsions between any pair of electrons.[24,34] Experimental support for this model is found although the data is rather sparse. Equatorial and polar bond lengths (in angstroms), respectively, for the following AX_5 and AX_3L_2 molecules are: PCl_5, 2.04, 2.19; $SbCl_5$, 2.31, 2.43; ClF_3, 1.60, 1.70; BrF_3, 1.72, 1.81.

It is interesting to note that the hybrid orbital set sp^3d of the valence bond theory are directed toward the vertices of the trigonal bipyramid and they are not equivalent orbitals as, for example, the sp^3 set are. In fact it has been shown[32] for this hybridization that maximum overlap of a bonded atom orbital with a central atom equatorial orbital occurs at a slightly smaller internuclear distance than for a polar orbital. However, we should again emphasize that this is merely a convenient description and not an explanation of the difference in bond length between polar and equatorial bonds.

Analogous reasoning applied to the pentagonal bipyramidal arrangement of seven electron pairs leads to the prediction of longer polar than equatorial bonds for this case. Support for this comes from the sole compound studied, IF_7, for which the equatorial bond length is reported to be 1.83 Å, and the polar bond length is reported to be 1.94 Å.

For molecules in which the central atom has six electron pairs, one of which is a lone-pair, AX_5L, the square pyramidal shape is found and the lone pair might be expected to cause a lengthening of the equatorial bonds due to increased repulsion. This is found to be the case with, for example, $SbCl_5^{2-}$, where the equatorial bond length is reported as 2.62 Å compared to 2.36 Å for the polar bond length. However, in the two other molecules of this type for which data are available, the reverse situation is found. The equatorial and polar bond lengths for BrF_5 and SbF_5^{2-}, respectively, are 1.68, 1.79, and 2.02 and 2.08. Hence, it appears at the present time that there is no way of predicting the effect on bond length of a single lone pair in this type of molecule. For molecules of the AX_4L_2 type we have already seen that the square planar structure is predicted and found, with all bond lengths and bond angles equal.

TABLE 6-7. / **Effect of Atom Hybridization on the C—C Bond Length.**[33]

	C—C Hybridization	% of s Character in the σ-Bond	Valence-Bond Structure	Characteristic C—C Bond Length, Å
1	$sp^3\text{-}sp^3$	25	—C—C—	1.54
2	$sp^3\text{-}sp^2$	29	—C—C	1.50
3	$sp^3\text{-}sp$	33	—C—C≡	1.46
4	$sp^2\text{-}sp^2$	33	C—C	1.46
5	$sp^2\text{-}sp$	40	C—C≡	1.42
6	$sp\text{-}sp$	50	≡C—C≡	1.38
7	$sp^2\text{-}sp^2 + \pi$	33	C=C	1.34
8	$sp^2\text{-}sp + \pi$	40	C=C=	1.31
9	$sp\text{-}sp + \pi$	50	=C=C=	1.28
10	$sp\text{-}sp + 2\pi$	50	—C≡C—	1.20
11	$sp^2\text{-}sp^2 + 1/2\pi$	33	benzene	1.40*
12	$sp^2\text{-}sp^2 + 1/3\pi$	33	graphite	1.42*

* These values, obtained by linear interpolation between 4 and 7 are to be compared with the actual values for benzene and graphite of 1.397 Å and 1.421 Å, respectively.

Variations in Internuclear Distances

What we have been considering thus far are the ways in which trends in bond lengths may be predicted from a prior assumption of the stereochemistry of bond pairs and lone pairs. We have not discussed how actual internuclear distances vary with the nature of the bonded atom and the order of the covalent bond which it forms. In fact the stereochemical theory we have been using is of no value in these matters. Ideally we can assign a covalent radius to an atom which will remain nearly constant in all covalent molecules formed by that atom (see Chapter 4). Furthermore, if the bond order changes for a given atom from molecule to molecule, we can estimate the corresponding change in its radius, and in certain cases we can describe the change in terms of the degree of hybridization which is occurring. To illustrate, let us consider the effect of atom hybridization on the carbon-carbon distances found in the various types of aliphatic compounds.[33] This is shown in Table 6–7, where the characteristic bond length listed for each type reproduces the reported bond length for virtually all representatives of that type to within $\pm$ 0.01Å. This table illustrates the usefulness of the valence bond theory of hybridization in the classification of bond types and the estimation of bond lengths.[33] It may be seen from the values listed in the table that as the amount of s-character in the hybridized orbitals increases, the bond length correspondingly decreases. Furthermore, the superposition of one or two π-bonds on a σ-bond effects still further reduction in the bond length. The latter observation may be verified for many other atoms besides carbon which are known to form π-bonds. Values for multiple bond covalent radii are listed for several elements in Table 6–8.[34] The general conclusion can be drawn from the values listed in the table that superposition of a second π-bond causes a further, but smaller, decrease in a given radius.

TABLE 6–8. / **Multiple Bond Covalent Radii (Å).**[34]

Atom	Single Bond	Double Bond	Triple Bond	Atom	Single Bond	Double Bond
C	0.771	0.665	0.602	Ge	1.223	1.12
N	0.74	0.60	0.55	As	1.21	1.11
O	0.74	0.55	0.50	Se	1.17	1.07
Si	1.173	1.07	1.00	Sn	1.412	1.30
P	1.10	1.00	0.93	Sb	1.41	1.31
S	1.04	0.94	0.87	Te	1.37	1.27

BOND ANGLES

In considering the geometry of any molecule, the most important factor is the set of bond angles. The valence bond theory of hybridized orbitals provides a convenient description of many of the observed bond angles, particularly when a clear-cut choice of the contributing orbitals can be made. However, the theory does not offer an explanation for the observed bond angles. In fact, where the predicted bond angles differ from the experimental ones, the recourse has generally been the artificial one of determining the degree of hybridization, or amount of s-character or p-character,[33] etc., in the bond. As we shall show, at least a start has been made[31,35] toward a better understanding and explanation of the variations in bond angles which are observed in many formally analogous molecules. And the model which we will use is once again the one based primarily on the spatial correlation of valency shell electron pairs which arises from the operation of the Pauli exclusion principle.

We have already noted that for central atoms with two valency shell electron pairs the molecules or ions are linear (Table 6–2). This is also the shape if there are additional electron pairs in the valency shell which are π-bonding (Table 6–3). Three electron pairs which are all σ-bonding produce the expected triangular (120° bond angles) shape (Tables 6–2, 6–3). If one of the three electron pairs is a lone pair an angular molecule results (Tables 6–2, 6–3) and the angle is expected to fall below 120°. This is due to greater lone-pair:bond-pair repulsion than bond-pair:bond-pair repulsion. For example, the decrease in bond angle in the series

$$O=\overset{+}{N}=O \qquad \qquad \qquad$$

$$180° \qquad\qquad\qquad 134° \qquad\qquad\qquad 115°$$

illustrates this effect and, at the same time, points out that a lone pair has a greater repulsion effect than a single nonbonding electron.

Deviations from Regular Bond Angles — Four Electron Pairs

Now when we come to four valency shell electron pairs, all of which are either σ-bonding or lone pairs, we have a wealth of experimental data and many apparent anomalies. For example, (1) reference to Tables 6–9 and 6–10 will reveal that NH_3 and H_2O have bond angles close to the tetrahedral angle of 109.5°, while the hydrides of the remaining members of the nitrogen and oxygen families have bond angles very near 90°; (2) it may be seen that the bond angles in NF_3 and OF_2 are smaller than in the corresponding hydrides, whereas for the fluorides and hydrides of phosphorus and arsenic, the reverse is true; (3) there is an unexpected decrease in bond angles as the larger chlorine replaces fluorine in the phosphorus or arsenic compound; (4) finally, the decrease in bond angles as we pass from a Group V hydride to the Group VI hydride of the same period should be noted.

TABLE 6–9. / **Bond Angles for Some Group V Molecules.**[35,36]

N(CH₃)₃ 109	NH₃ 107.3	NF₃ 102.1			
P(CH₃)₃ 102.5	PH₃ 93.3	PF₃ 104	PCl₃ 100.0	PBr₃ 101.5	PI₃ 102
As(CH₃)₃ 96	AsH₃ 91.8	AsF₃ 102	AsCl₃ 98.4	AsBr₃ 100.5	AsI₃ 101
	SbH₃ 91.3		SbCl₃ 99.5	SbBr₃ 97	SbI₃ 99

To explain the above observations,[1-4] we need only to make certain simple assumptions, some of which we have made and justified earlier. Thus, a lone pair of electrons, which occupies a rather large, diffuse orbital, will exert greater repulsions on other electron pairs than will the bonding pairs which occupy more restricted two-center orbitals (Figure 6–4). The valency shell of the first short-period elements (Li-Ne) is complete when it contains four electron pairs, whereas the valency shell of the second and subsequent row elements can accommodate more than four electron pairs. We may interpret this to mean that the space surrounding a small first short period element is essentially completely filled by four electron pairs.

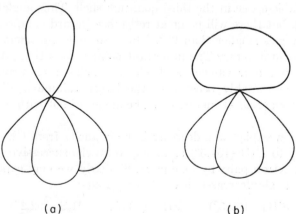

(a)   (b)

FIGURE 6–4. Orbitals for **(a)** Four Bonding Electron Pairs, and **(b)** for Three Bonding Pairs and One Lone Pair.

TABLE 6-10. / **Bond Angles for Some Group VI Molecules.**[35,36]

O(CH$_3$)$_2$ 110	OH(CH$_3$) 109	OH$_2$ 104.5	OF$_2$ 103.2	OCl$_2$ 110.8	
	SH(CH$_3$) 100	SH$_2$ 92.2		SCl$_2$ 102	
		SeH$_2$ 91.0			
		TeH$_2$ 89.5			TeBr$_2$ 98

As the occupied orbitals come into close contact, the Pauli forces increase very rapidly, since they appear to vary inversely as some large power of the interelectron distance.[26] Therefore, in a filled valency shell of a first short period element we should expect great resistance to large distortions of the bond angles from the preferred tetrahedral angle. This is found to be true experimentally in a large number of molecules of the first short period elements with completed valency shells,[35,36] where bond angles rarely deviate more than a few degrees from 109.5°. On the other hand, in the elements of the second and later periods, the valency shell may be expanded and, in fact, can theoretically contain up to nine electron pairs. However, the second short period elements (Na-Ar) are never found to possess more than six electron pairs. We have seen earlier that these electron pairs will have a maximum probability of being found at the corners of an octahedron and it may be reasonably presumed that they will effectively fill the available space in the third quantum shell. Thus angles of 90° are now allowed, but there will be great resistance toward compression of the orbitals to angles smaller than 90°. This also finds considerable support from experimental data.[36] The important point here is that when such an element has but four valency shell electron pairs, their orbitals can be compressed, presumably because of the larger volume available in the second or later period elements, to make angles of 90° with each other at the nucleus.

We can now explain the decrease in bond angles from CH$_4$ (109.5°) to NH$_3$ (107.3°) to H$_2$O (104.5°) as arising from the successive replacement of bonding electron pairs by lone pairs. Similarly we may explain the following bond angle decreases in the later periods:

SiH$_4$ (109.5°)   PH$_3$ (93.3°)   H$_2$S (92.2°)
GeH$_4$ (109.5°)   AsH$_3$ (91.8°)   H$_2$Se (91.0°)
SnH$_4$ (109.5°)   SbH$_3$ (91.3°)   H$_2$Te (89.5°)

The relatively small deviation from the tetrahedral angle caused by the lone pair in NH_3 compared to the large deviation caused by the lone pair in the heavier element hydrides is also now understandable. Thus, the lone pair:bond-pair repulsions in these heavier hydrides reduce the bond angles until bond-pair:bond-pair repulsions become large, but this occurs at 90°. Hence, the clustering of bond angles for all of the heavier Group V and VI hydrides around 90° is expected.

Turning now to the halides, the seemingly anomalous bond angle decreases from NH_3 (107.3°) to NF_3 (102.1°) and from H_2O (104.5°) to OF_2 (103.2°) are explained as follows: The highly electronegative fluorine atom contracts the bonding orbitals to a greater extent than the hydrogen atom, thereby drawing the electron pairs farther away from the central atom. Therefore, these orbitals repel each other to a lesser extent and move closer together under the strong repulsion from the lone pairs.

The bond angle trends from hydride to fluoride for phosphorus and arsenic are just the reverse of the trend for the nitrogen compounds, i.e., PH_3 (93.3°) to PF_3 (104°) and AsH_3 (91.8°) to AsF_3 (102°). In order to account for this reversal, Gillespie[35] assumes that the strong repulsions between the nonbonding electron pairs located on the small fluorine atoms causes them to be partially delocalized into an empty shell of the atom of the second or subsequent period element. This creates a partial double bonding which gives rise to resonance structures such as

$$\overset{\displaystyle\ddot{P}{}^{-}}{\underset{\displaystyle F}{{}^{+}F\diagup\ \big|\ \diagdown F}}$$

The increased repulsions between the bonding pairs resulting from such increased electron density in the bonding region opens up the angle in comparison with the hydride molecule where such bonding is impossible. The tendency for the heavier halogens to delocalize their nonbonding pairs for partial double bonding will be considerably reduced, since their valency shells are spatially much larger and therefore not as crowded with electrons.

The large angle (110.8°) in Cl_2O, compared to F_2O (103.2°) and H_2O (104.5°), may also be attributed[35] to the above type of delocalization of oxygen nonbonding electrons, giving rise to contributing structures such as

$$\overset{\displaystyle\ddot{O}{}^{+}}{{}^{-}Cl\diagup\diagdown Cl}$$

The decrease in bond angle to 102° for SCl_2 lends support to this postulation, since the larger sulfur atom will not have the same tendency to delocalize its nonbonding electrons. Further support for this tendency of oxygen toward partial double-bonding to atoms with unfilled shells or to aromatic conjugated systems comes from the experimental data on a large number of molecules[35,36] of the X-O-X type. For example, where X is an aliphatic group, the C-O-C angles fall in the narrow range from 108° to 110°. However, when X is an aromatic group or any of the second short period or later elements, we find that the X-O-X angles are invariably much larger than the tetrahedral angle. For example,[35] the Si-O-Si angles appear to fall in the range 130° to 140°. When the central oxygen atom is replaced by the larger S, Se, or Te atom, the bond angles drop to the tetrahedral angle or more commonly below this angle but approaching 90°.

Deviations from Regular Bond Angles — Five or More Electron Pairs

We move now to a consideration of molecules wherein the central atom has five electron pairs in its valency shell. Here the Pauli forces require the electrons to be at the corners of a trigonal bipyramid. For the AX_5 molecules, either with five identical bound groups (PCl_5, $SbCl_5$) or with three like equatorial groups and two like polar groups (PF_3Cl_2), all bond angles are expected and found to be either 90° or 120°. In the AX_4L molecules in which the lone pair is in an equatorial position, the lone-pair: bond-pair repulsions would be expected to reduce all bond angles. Experimentally it is found for several molecules that the equatorial bond angles are reduced[31] well below the ideal 120° to the approximate range of 96° to 110°. However the angle between the polar groups is not altered significantly from the ideal 180°. This is not surprising since the angle between the equatorial electron pairs (one lone pair and two bond pairs) and the polar groups is already 90°. In light of the earlier discussion, we would not expect this angle to deviate to any great extent. For the AX_3L_2 molecules, in which the lone pairs are in equatorial positions, the added repulsions caused by two lone pairs would be expected to decrease the angles between polar and equatorial bond pairs[31] to slightly below the ideal 90°. This is observed with, for example, ClF_3, (87.5°), BrF_3 (86.2°) and $(C_6H_5)ICl_2$ (86°).

Six electron pairs in molecules of the AX_6 type will occupy orbitals making 90° and 180° angles at the nucleus. These angles are not expected to show much deviation from these values regardless of any lowering of the molecular symmetry by the presence of lone pairs (e.g., AX_5L or AX_4L_2) or nonidentical bound groups.

REFERENCES

1. Clark, G., "Applied X-Rays," 4th ed., McGraw-Hill Book Co., New York, N.Y., 1955.
2. Bijvoet, J., Kolkmeyer, N., and Macgillavry, C., "X-Ray Analysis of Crystals," Butterworths, London, 1951.
3. Buerger, M., "Crystal-Structure Analysis," John Wiley & Sons, Inc., New York, N.Y., 1960.

4. Pinsker, Z., "Electron Diffraction," Butterworths, London, 1953.
5. Bacon, G., "Neutron Diffraction," Clarendon Press, Oxford, 1955.
6. Herzberg, G., "Molecular Spectra and Molecular Structure. II. Infrared and Raman Spectra of Polyatomic Molecules," D. Van Nostrand Co., Inc., Princeton, N.J., 1945.
7. Bellamy, L., "Infrared Spectra of Complex Molecules," 2nd ed., John Wiley & Sons, Inc., New York, N.Y., 1960.
8. Hackforth, H., "Infrared Radiation," McGraw-Hill Book Co., Inc., New York, N.Y., 1960.
9. Gordy, W., Smith, W., and Trambarulo, R., "Microwave Spectroscopy," John Wiley & Sons, Inc., New York, N.Y., 1953.
10. Townes, C. and Schawlow, A., "Microwave Spectroscopy," McGraw-Hill Book Co., New York, N.Y., 1955.
11. Gutowsky, H., *Ann. Rev. Phys. Chem.*, **5**, 333 (1954).
12. Rogers, N., *Record Chem. Progr.*, **21**, 197 (1960).
13. Roberts, J., "Nuclear Magnetic Resonance," McGraw-Hill Book Co., New York, N.Y., 1959.
14. Pople, J., Schneider, W., and Bernstein, H., "High Resolution Nuclear Magnetic Resonance," McGraw-Hill Book Co., New York, N.Y., 1959.
15. Bleaney, B. and Stevens, K., *Repts. Progr. in Phys.*, **16**, 108 (1953).
16. Fraenkel, G., "Paramagnetic Resonance Absorption," *in* "Physical Methods of Organic Chemistry," A. Weissberger, Ed., Vol. I, Part IV, 3rd ed., Interscience Publishers, Inc., New York, N.Y., 1960.
17. Pauling, L., *J. Am. Chem. Soc.*, **53**, 1367 (1931).
18. Slater, J., *Phys. Rev.*, **37**, 481 (1931).
19. Dickens, P. and Linnett, J., *Quart. Revs.*, **11**, 291 (1957).
20. Sidgwick, N. and Powell, H., *Proc. Roy. Soc., A.*, **176**, 153 (1940).
21. Lennard-Jones, J., *Adv. Sci.*, **11**, 136 (1954).
22. Linnett, J., "Wave Mechanics and Valency," John Wiley & Sons, Inc., New York, N.Y., 1960; *J. Am. Chem. Soc.*, **83**, 2643 (1961).
23. Zimmerman, H. and Van Rysselberghe, P., *J. Chem. Phys.*, **17**, 598 (1949).
24. Gillespie, R., *Can. J. Chem.*, **38**, 818 (1960).
25. Linnett, J. and Mellish, C., *Trans. Faraday Soc.*, **50**, 657 (1954).
26. Pitzer, K., "Quantum Chemistry," Prentice-Hall, Inc., New York, N.Y., 1953, p. 319.
27. Gillespie, R. and Nyholm, R., *Quart Revs.*, **11**, 339 (1957); "Progress in Stereochemistry," Vol. 2, Chap. 8, Academic Press, Inc., New York, N.Y., 1958.
28. Searcy, A., *J. Chem. Phys.*, **28**, 1237 (1958).
29. Searcy, A., *J. Chem. Phys.*, **31**, 1 (1959).
30. Parsons, A. and Searcy, A., *J. Chem. Phys.*, **30**, 1635 (1959).
31. Gillespie, R., *Can. J. Chem.*, **39**, 318 (1961).
32. Craig, D., Maccoll, A., Nyholm, R., Orgel, L., and Sutton, L., *J. Chem. Soc.*, **1954**, 332.
33. Bent, H., *J. Chem. Ed.*, **37**, 616 (1960); *Chem. Revs.*, **61**, 275 (1961).
34. Kleinberg, J., Argersinger, W., Jr., and Griswold, E., "Inorganic Chemistry," D. C. Heath & Co., Boston, Mass., 1960.
35. Gillespie, R., *J. Am. Chem. Soc.*, **82**, 5978 (1960).
36. Sutton, L., "Interatomic Distances," *Special Publication No. 11*, Chemical Society (London), 1958.

7 / *Electromotive Force*

The driving force of a chemical reaction results from a tendency for the system to approach equilibrium, and from thermodynamics we recall that this tendency is expressed by means of the free energy change, ΔF, in going from the initial to the final state of the system. For this reason it is of interest to determine ΔF, and as it turns out, one way of determining it for a redox system is by means of the relation between the free energy change and the electromotive force of a galvanic cell.

To appreciate this relationship between the free energy change and the cell emf, we can consider a reaction such as that of zinc metal with dilute sulfuric acid,

$$Zn + H_2SO_4 \rightarrow ZnSO_4 + H_2$$

If this reaction is allowed, for instance, to take place in a calorimeter, an amount of heat, q', will be evolved and an amount of work, w', will be done by the hydrogen gas against the atmosphere and other volume changes. According to the first law of thermodynamics, the change in internal energy of the system will be given by

$$\Delta E = E_f - E_i = q' - w' \qquad (7-1)$$

If a galvanic cell, such as that shown schematically in Figure 7–1, is now set up, the same net reaction can be made to take place in such a manner as to force the flow of electrons through an external circuit, and the resultant electrical energy can be harnessed to do useful work. In this particular cell, one electrode is made of zinc metal and the other is of some inert metallic conductor such as platinum. These are placed in a solution containing $ZnSO_4$ and H_2SO_4 and are then connected externally by means of an electrical conductor. The same basic reaction will take place as before,

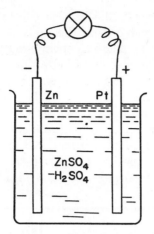

FIGURE 7–1. Schematic Diagram of a Galvanic Cell.

but we now note that the hydrogen gas is evolved from the surface of the platinum electrode rather than from the zinc. The current flow in the external circuit results from the oxidation reaction

$$Zn = Zn^{++} + 2e^-$$

which occurs at the zinc electrode-solution interface, and the reduction reaction

$$2\,H^+ + 2e^- = H_2$$

which occurs at the platinum electrode-solution interface. The electrons released at the zinc electrode proceed through the external circuit to the platinum electrode where they participate in the reduction of the H^+. This, then, gives the total cell reaction

$$Zn + 2H^+ = Zn^{++} + H_2$$

which can be considered to be made up of the two half-cell reactions shown.

Again, it can be said that

$$\Delta E = q - w$$

but the w we now have is made up of two parts, the work done against the atmosphere and the electrical work done in the external circuit. Consequently, ΔE can be expressed as

$$\Delta E = q - (w_e + P\Delta V) \tag{7–2}$$

Although the change in internal energy is independent of the path, the same is not true of the heat, q, and the work, w. If a large current flow is permitted, considerable heating effects will be observed as a result of electrical resistance in the cell. On the other hand, if the current flow can be made imperceptibly small, the heating effects will become negligible. The great advantage of such cells in the study of free energy changes lies in the fact that they can be made to operate very nearly reversibly. This is accomplished by placing a source of electrical potential in the external circuit in such a manner as to give an emf in opposition to that of the galvanic cell. The opposing emf is varied by means of a potentiometer until the current flow from the cell is essentially zero. Under these conditions, the cell may very well approach reversibility. This is readily tested by changing the direction of the current and allowing an infinitesimally small current flow in the opposite direction. If the cell is reversible, the cell reaction will proceed in the reverse direction with the same efficiency as it did in the forward direction.

For a reversible reaction

$$\Delta F = -w_{net} = -w_{max} + P\Delta V \tag{7-3}$$

and for our system, w_{net} is the same as w_e, the electrical work done by the cell. Thus, it is seen that a relationship does exist between the free energy change of the system and the electrical work done by the reversible cell. This relationship becomes more useful when it is recognized that the available electrical energy for a mole of reactants is

$$w_e = n\text{FE} \tag{7-4}$$

where E is the emf of the cell, F is Faraday's constant, and n is the number of electrons changed per atom or ion. This, then, leads to the fundamental relation

$$\Delta F = -n\text{FE} \tag{7-5}$$

and we now find that it is possible to express the thermodynamic driving force of a reaction in terms of the cell emf as well as in terms of the free energy change.

THE NERNST EQUATION

To give a thermodynamic description of a system in which a chemical reaction is taking place, it is usually not sufficient that the temperature, pressure, and volume be specified. It is also necessary to specify the composition of the system in terms of the concentrations of the various components present. This leads to the free energy expression

$$dF = -SdT + VdP + \sum_i \mu_i \, dn_i \tag{7-6}$$

where S, V, T, and P have their usual significance, n_i is the number of moles of the ith component, and μ_i is the chemical potential of the ith component and may be defined as

$$\mu_i = \left(\frac{\partial F}{\partial n_i}\right)_{T,P,n_j} \tag{7-7}$$

If the conditions of constant temperature and pressure are imposed, the free energy expression will then become

$$(dF)_{T,P} = \mu_1 dn_1 + \mu_2 dn_2 + \cdots . \tag{7-8}$$

If we consider the reaction in the galvanic cell to be

$$n_a A + n_b B = n_c C + n_d D$$

we can be more explicit and say that

$$(dF)_{T,P} = \mu_c dn_c + \mu_D dn_d - \mu_A dn_a - \mu_B dn_b \tag{7-9}$$

which on integration gives

$$\Delta F = \mu_c n_c + \mu_D n_d - \mu_A n_a - \mu_B n_b \tag{7-10}$$

assuming that the chemical potentials of the reactants and products remain constant. Now, since the chemical potential in terms of the activity is given by

$$\mu_i = \mu_i{}^0 + RT \ln a_i \tag{7-11}$$

it is possible to combine Eq. (7–10) and Eq. (7–11) to give

$$\Delta F = n_c \left(\mu_c{}^0 + RT \ln a_c\right) + n_d \left(\mu_D{}^0 + RT \ln a_D\right) \\ - n_a \left(\mu_A{}^0 + RT \ln a_A\right) - n_b \left(\mu_B{}^0 + RT \ln a_B\right) \tag{7-12}$$

or on rearrangement

$$\Delta F = n_c \, \mu_c{}^0 + n_d \, \mu_D{}^0 - n_a \, \mu_A{}^0 - n_b \, \mu_B{}^0 + RT \ln \frac{(a_c)^{n_c} (a_D)^{n_d}}{(a_A)^{n_a} (a_B)^{n_b}} \tag{7-13}$$

Finally, we can say that

$$\Delta F = \Delta F^0 + RT \ln \frac{(a_c)^{n_c} (a_D)^{n_d}}{(a_A)^{n_a} (a_B)^{n_b}} \tag{7-14}$$

where ΔF^0 is the *standard state* free energy change.

The transition to the reversible emf of a galvanic cell is now quite straightforward. Combining Eq. (7–14) with Eq. (7–5), we obtain the Nernst equation

$$E = E^0 - \frac{RT}{nF} \ln \frac{(a_c)^{n_c} (a_D)^{n_d}}{(a_A)^{n_a} (a_B)^{n_b}} \tag{7-15}$$

This now permits us to evaluate the thermodynamic driving force of a redox reaction in terms of a measurable cell emf. And going further, it is possible to utilize the relationship between the standard state potential and the standard state free energy to derive an expression for the equilibrium constant of a redox reaction in terms of the emf. Thus,

$$E^0 = \frac{RT}{n\mathrm{F}} \ln K_{eq} \qquad (7\text{-}16)$$

STANDARD ELECTRODE POTENTIALS

The relationship between a standard half-cell emf and the corresponding standard free energy change is given by the equation

$$\Delta F^0 = -n\mathrm{F}E^0 \qquad (7\text{-}17)$$

Just as is conventional with other thermodynamic functions, the choice of standard states used to determine E^0 is completely arbitrary and is left to the discretion of the experimenter. For pure substances, this is usually quite routine. Ordinarily, gases at pressures of 1 atm or less are chosen to have an activity equal to their partial pressures, and for pure solids or liquids, it is customary to choose the standard state such that the activity is unity at any specified temperature. On the other hand, when we consider ionic solutions, it is most advantageous to choose the standard state of the solute in such a manner that the activity is equal to the concentration in regions where the concentration is very low. That is, as the concentration approaches zero, the activity approaches the concentration.

Such a choice of the standard state of an electrolyte has several advantages. To begin with, it permits the determination of the standard state potential by means of a rather straightforward extrapolation procedure. And secondly, it allows one to make an interpretation of the activity coefficients in terms of a reasonable theoretical model. With respect to this last point, it can be recognized that at very high dilution, the only interactions of the ions are those with the solvent. However, as the ionic concentration is increased, the average distance of separation of the ions becomes less and ion-ion interactions become significant. By defining the standard state in such a manner that the activity equals the concentration at infinite dilution, we are essentially saying that the solution is ideal when the only interactions of the ions are those with the solvent. Therefore, it is then possible to attribute to ion-ion interactions any deviations from this ideal behavior that are observed with an increase in ionic concentration.

The Activity Coefficient

Deviations from this ideal state where the activity of the solute is equal to the concentration of the solute are expressed in terms of the *activity coefficient*. This is defined as

$$\gamma = \frac{a}{m} \qquad (7\text{-}18)$$

where a represents the activity and m the molal concentration of the solute.* Now, it can be seen that as the system deviates from the defined ideality, the activity coefficient reflects this deviation by showing a corresponding deviation from unity. Thus, according to our chosen standard state, as $m \to 0$, $a \to m$ and $\gamma \to 1$. And we can further say that, in the case of electrolytes, the activity coefficient will be a measure of the nonideality of the system due primarily to ion-ion interactions.

Determination of the Standard Electrode Potential

In studying thermodynamic properties of electrolytic solutions, both the standard state potential and the activity coefficients of the solute are of fundamental importance. From Eq. (7–15), it should be evident that if the value of the standard electrode potential is known, it is possible to determine the activities and, therefore, the activity coefficients of the electrolyte used in the cell. Consequently, our first endeavor will be to determine the standard potential, and to illustrate the general procedure we can consider a simple type of cell without liquid junction. In order to study the thermodynamic properties of a solute such as hydrochloric acid, such a cell can be represented as

$$\text{Pt, H}_{2(1 \text{ atm})} \mid \text{HCl}_{(m)} \mid \text{AgCl,Ag}$$

This involves simply the immersion of a hydrogen electrode and a silver-silver chloride electrode in a solution of hydrochloric acid. The half-cell reactions will be

$$\tfrac{1}{2}\text{H}_2 = \text{H}^+ + e^-$$

and

$$\text{AgCl} + e^- = \text{Ag} + \text{Cl}^-$$

This gives the over-all cell reaction

$$\text{AgCl} + \tfrac{1}{2}\text{H}_2 = \text{H}^+ + \text{Cl}^- + \text{Ag}$$

With this cell reaction, the emf is given by

$$E = E^0 - \frac{RT}{F} \ln \frac{(a_{\text{Ag}})\,(a_{\text{H}^+})\,(a_{\text{Cl}^-})}{(a_{\text{AgCl}})\,(a_{\text{H}_2})^{\frac{1}{2}}} \tag{7–19}$$

Now, if we use the conventional standard states, the activities of the silver, silver chloride, and the hydrogen can be set equal to unity, and the cell emf can then be expressed as

$$E = E^0 - \frac{RT}{F} \ln a_{\text{H}^+}\, a_{\text{Cl}^-} \tag{7–20}$$

---

* It is not necessary that the concentration be expressed in terms of the molal scale; mole fraction or molarity could be used equally well. Accordingly, the activity coefficient on these latter two scales is respectively, $f = a/N$ and $y = a/c$.

As it turns out, there is no way to measure the activity of a single ion. We must always measure the two together. Consequently, it is necessary to speak of a *mean* ionic activity, and this leads to the expression

$$E = E^0 - \frac{RT}{F} \ln a_{\pm}^2 \tag{7-21}$$

and this can be changed further to give

$$E = E^0 - \frac{2RT}{F} \ln a_{\pm}$$

In terms of the activity coefficient, this becomes

$$E = E^0 - \frac{2RT}{F} \ln \gamma_{\pm} m \tag{7-22}$$

At this point, several different approaches can be used to determine the E^0 value.[1] The most common of these utilize some form of the Debye-Huckel theory. If we have confidence in the theory, it is possible to supplement our experimental data with the theoretical treatment in regions of very great dilution. However, an experimental method for the determination of E^0 was developed by Lewis and Randall before the advent of the Debye-Huckel theory, and it will suffice to show the basic principles involved in addition to giving, in many instances, quite acceptable values for the standard emf.

In order to illustrate the method of Lewis and Randall for the determination of the standard half-cell emf, we can rearrange Eq. (7–22) to the form

$$E = E^0 - \frac{2RT}{F} \ln \gamma_{\pm} - \frac{2RT}{F} \ln m \tag{7-23}$$

or

$$E + \frac{2RT}{F} \ln m = E^0 - \frac{2RT}{F} \ln \gamma_{\pm} \tag{7-24}$$

Since the standard state has been defined in such a manner that $\gamma_{\pm} \to 1$ as $m \to 0$, it can be seen that the term containing the activity coefficient disappears as we approach infinite dilution. Thus, if a plot is made of the left side of Eq. (7–24) against some function of the concentration, the left side of the equation approaches E^0 as $m \to 0$. Such a plot is shown in Figure 7–2, where potential measurements have been made with the cell

$$\text{Pt, H}_{2\,(1\ \text{atm})} \mid \text{HCl}_{(m)} \mid \text{AgCl,Ag}$$

at various concentrations of hydrochloric acid. The extrapolation to infinite dilution yields a standard half-cell emf for the AgCl,Ag half-cell of -0.2234 v when measured with respect to a defined potential of zero for the standard hydrogen electrode. This is in fair agreement with the value of -0.2225 v determined by the more modern methods of extrapolation.

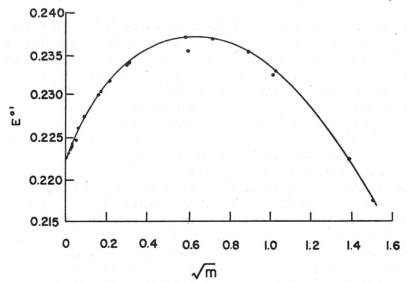

FIGURE 7-2. Determination of the Standard Electrode Potential of the Ag,AgCl Electrode by the Extrapolation Procedure of Lewis and Randall. (After Lewis, G. N. and Randall, M., "Thermodynamics," McGraw-Hill Book Co., New York, N. Y., 1923.)

SIGN CONVENTIONS

For years, two different sign conventions for electrode potentials have been in common use. Without real justification, they are usually referred to as the *European convention* and the *American convention*. The latter of these was originated by Lewis and Randall and has found quite general favor among the physical chemists. Unfortunately, the difference in the two conventions has been quite generally misunderstood, for the difference is not merely that of a sign as usually supposed, but rather lies in a basic difference in meaning.[2,3]

To illustrate the two conventions, we can consider the Zn,Zn^{++} electrode at which the reaction

$$Zn = Zn^{++} + 2e^-$$

takes place. According to the European convention, we would assign a value of -0.763 v for the standard potential of this electrode with respect to the standard hydrogen electrode. On the other hand, the value according to the American convention would be taken as $+0.763$ v. Thus, it would appear that the difference is merely that of a sign. However, if we now would consider the same electrode with the half-cell reaction

$$Zn^{++} + 2e^- = Zn$$

the standard potential would still be -0.763 v according to the European convention, but it would now be -0.763 v rather than $+0.763$ v according to the American convention. That is, according to the latter, if we express the reaction as an oxidation, the standard potential of this half-cell is positive, but if we express it as a reduction, the standard potential is negative. Here we see a significant difference in the two conventions. In the American convention the standard potential is a *bivariant* quantity, whereas in the European convention it is an *invariant* quantity.

Primarily, the misunderstanding between the two conventions results from a failure to recognize the difference between the potential of an actual electrode and the emf of a half-cell reaction. If we measure the standard potential of the zinc electrode in the presence of Zn^{++}, we will find that it has an experimental potential of -0.763 v with respect to the standard hydrogen electrode. That is, its actual potential will be negative with respect to the standard hydrogen electrode, and this is true regardless of whether we write the reaction as a reduction or as an oxidation. It is for this reason that the European convention assigns an invariant value of -0.763 v to its standard potential. On the other hand, from a thermodynamic standpoint, it is known that the reaction of zinc going to zinc ions tends to take place spontaneously in the presence of acid, and ΔF^0 is therefore negative. Since

$$\Delta F^0 = -n\mathrm{FE}^0 \qquad (7\text{--}17)$$

it can be seen that E^0 should be positive for the Zn,Zn^{++} half-cell expressed as an oxidation potential. It is for this reason that the American convention assigns a positive sign to the emf of the cell if it is expressed as an oxidation, but a negative sign if it is expressed as a reduction. Herein lies the difference between the two conventions. The European convention is referring to an experimentally observed *electrostatic potential* of an electrode with respect to the hydrogen electrode, whereas the American convention is referring to the *thermodynamic tendency* of a particular reaction to take place. And it might be pointed out that the problem is not solved by stating that

$$\Delta F^0 = +n\mathrm{FE}^0$$

This would lead to agreement in sign between the two conventions as long as we continue the usual convention of expressing the cell emf as an oxidation potential. Nevertheless, the American convention would still lead to a bivariant potential and the European convention would still lead to an invariant potential.

In an attempt to reconcile the two conventions, several authors as well as the IUPAC have recommended changes in terminology.[4,5] Basically, it is recommended that the term "electrode potential" be reserved for the European convention, and that the American convention refer to the "electromotive force" of a half-cell.

OXIDATION POTENTIALS

We have seen that it is possible to consider a cell reaction to be made up of two half-cell reactions, one of which may be the reaction associated with the hydrogen electrode as a primary reference. In the instance of the zinc electrode, the half-cell reactions can be expressed as

$$\frac{1}{2} Zn = \frac{1}{2} Zn^{++} + e^- \qquad\qquad E^0 = 0.763 \text{ v}$$
$$H^+ + e^- = \frac{1}{2} H_2 \qquad\qquad E^0 = 0.000 \text{ v}$$

Thus it can be said that with respect to the standard hydrogen electrode, the standard zinc electrode potential is -0.763 v, or the half-cell emf is $+0.763$ v, expressed as an oxidation. Now, if we compare a large number of half-cell reactions to the standard hydrogen half-cell reaction, it is possible to set up a table of relative oxidation potentials. From the relationship between ΔF and the cell emf, it follows that the more positive the oxidation potential of a half reaction, the greater will be its thermodynamic tendency to take place. Since the emf is being expressed as an oxidation potential, it can also be said that the more positive potentials are associated with the better reductants and the more negative potentials are associated with the better oxidants; those with potentials above hydrogen are better reducing agents than hydrogen and those with potentials below hydrogen are better oxidizing agents than the hydrogen ion. The standard potentials of a collection of inorganic couples as given by Latimer[6] are shown in Table 7-1. The most positive potentials, and therefore, the best reducing agents in their standard states are placed at the top of the table.

Now the algebraic difference between two such couples will give the emf for the total cell reaction if all species are at unit activity. If the resultant emf is positive, the reaction will be expected to proceed spontaneously in the direction written, but if the emf is negative, the reverse reaction would be favored. As an example, let us consider the reaction

$$Fe + Cd^{++} = Cd + Fe^{++}$$

The two half-cell reactions with their standard state potentials are

$$Fe = Fe^{++} + 2e^- \qquad\qquad E^0 = 0.440 \text{ v}$$
$$Cd = Cd^{++} + 2e^- \qquad\qquad E^0 = 0.403 \text{ v}$$

and by combining these we can obtain the standard state emf of the cell

$$E^0_{cell} = E^0_{Fe} - E^0_{Cd}$$

or

$$E^0_{cell} = 0.440 \text{ v} - 0.403 \text{ v} = 0.037 \text{ v}$$

The emf for the cell reaction is seen to be positive, so the reaction would be expected to proceed spontaneously as written.

TABLE 7-1. / **Oxidation-Reduction Couples in Acid and Basic Solutions**

ACID SOLUTIONS

Couple	E^0 (volts)	Couple	E^0 (volts)
$HN_3 = \frac{3}{2} N_2 + H^+ + e^-$	3.09	$2Ta + 5H_2O = Ta_2O_5$	
$Li = Li^+ + e^-$	3.045	$+ 10H^+ + 10\ e^-$	0.81
$K = K^+ + e^-$	2.925	$Zn = Zn^{2+} + 2e^-$	0.763
$Rb = Rb^+ + e^-$	2.925	$Tl + I^- = TlI + e^-$	0.753
$Cs = Cs^+ + e^-$	2.923	$Cr = Cr^{3+} + 3e^-$	0.74
$Ra = Ra^{2+} + 2e^-$	2.92	$H_2Te = Te + 2H^+ + 2e^-$	0.72
$Ba = Ba^{2+} + 2e^-$	2.90	$Tl + Br^- = TlBr + e^-$	0.658
$Sr = Sr^{2+} + 2e^-$	2.89	$2Nb + 5H_2O = Nb_2O_5$	
$Ca = Ca^{2+} + 2e^-$	2.87	$+ 10H^+ + 10e^-$	0.65
$Na = Na^+ + e^-$	2.714	$U^{3+} = U^{4+} + e^-$	0.61
$La = La^{3+} + 3e^-$	2.52	$AsH_3 = As + 3H^+ + 3e^-$	0.60
$Ce = Ce^{3+} + 3e^-$	2.48	$Tl + Cl^- = TlCl + e^-$	0.557
$Nd = Nd^{3+} + 3e^-$	2.44	$Ga = Ga^{3+} + 3e^-$	0.53
$Sm = Sm^{3+} + 3e^-$	2.41	$SbH_3(g) = Sb + 3H^+$	
$Gd = Gd^{3+} + 3e^-$	2.40	$+ 3e^-$	0.51
$Mg = Mg^{2+} + 2e^-$	2.37	$P + 2H_2O = H_3PO_2 + H^+$	
$Y = Y^{3+} + 3e^-$	2.37	$+ e^-$	0.51
$Am = Am^{3+} + 3e^-$	2.32	$H_3PO_2 + H_2O = H_3PO_3$	
$Lu = Lu^{3+} + 3e^-$	2.25	$+ 2H^+ + 2e^-$	0.50
$H^- = \frac{1}{2} H_2 + e^-$	2.25	$Fe = Fe^{2+} + 2e^-$	0.440
$H(g) = H^+ + e^-$	2.10	$Eu^{2+} = Eu^{3+} + e^-$	0.43
$Sc = Sc^{3+} + 3e^-$	2.08	$Cr^{2+} = Cr^{3+} + e^-$	0.41
$Pu = Pu^{3+} + 3e^-$	2.07	$Cd = Cd^{2+} + 2e^-$	0.403
$Al + 6F^- = AlF_6^{3-} + 3e^-$	2.07	$H_2Se = Se + 2H^+ + 2e^-$	0.40
$Th = Th^{4+} + 4e^-$	1.90	$Ti^{2+} = Ti^{3+} + e^-$	0.37 $ca.$
$Np = Np^{3+} + 3e^-$	1.86	$Pb + 2I^- = PbI_2 + 2e^-$	0.365
$Be = Be^{2+} + 2e^-$	1.85	$Pb + SO_4^{2-} = PbSO_4$	
$U = U^{3+} + 3e^-$	1.80	$+ 2e^-$	0.356
$Hf = Hf^{4+} + 4e^-$	1.70	$In = In^{3+} + 3e^-$	0.342
$Al = Al^{3+} + 3e^-$	1.66	$Tl = Tl^+ + e^-$	0.3363
$Ti = Ti^{2+} + 2e^-$	1.63	$\frac{1}{2} C_2N_2 + H_2O = HCNO$	
$Zr = Zr^{4+} + 4e^-$	1.53	$+ H^+ + e^-$	0.33
$Si + 6F^- = SiF_6^{2-} + 4e^-$	1.2	$Pt + H_2S = PtS + 2H^+$	
$Ti + 6F^- = TiF_6^{2-} + 4e^-$	1.19	$+ 2e^-$	0.30
$Mn = Mn^{2+} + 2e^-$	1.18	$Pb + 2Br^- = PbBr_2 + 2e^-$	0.280
$V = V^{2+} + 2e^-$	1.18 $ca.$	$Co = Co^{2+} + 2e^-$	0.277
$Nb = Nb^{3+} + 3e^-$	1.1 $ca.$	$H_3PO_3 + H_2O = H_3PO_4$	
$Ti + H_2O = TiO^{2+} + 2H^+$		$+ 2H^+ + 2e^-$	0.276
$+ 4e^-$	0.89	$Pb + 2Cl^- = PbCl_2 + 2e^-$	0.268
$B + 3H_2O = H_3BO_3$		$V^{2+} = V^{3+} + e^-$	0.255
$+ 3H^+ + 3e^-$	0.87	$V + 4H_2O = V(OH)_4^+$	
$Si + 2H_2O = SiO_2 + 4H^+$		$+ 4H^+ + 5e^-$	0.253
$+ 4e^-$	0.86	$Sn + 6F^- = SnF_6^{2-} + 4e^-$	0.25

TABLE 7–1 (Continued)

ACID SOLUTIONS — (Continued)			
Couple	E^0 (volts)	Couple	E^0 (volts)
$Ni = Ni^{2+} + 2e^-$	0.250	$Hg + 4Br^- = HgBr_4^{2-}$	
$N_2H_5^+ = N_2 + 5H^+ + 4e^-$	0.23	$+ 2e^-$	−0.21
$S_2O_6^{2-} + 2H_2O = 2SO_4^{2-}$		$Ag + Cl^- = AgCl + e^-$	−0.222
$+ 4H^+ + 2e^-$	0.22	$(CH_3)_2SO + H_2O$	
$Mo = Mo^{3+} + 3e^-$	0.2 *ca.*	$= (CH_3)_2SO_2$	
$HCOOH(aq) = CO_2$		$+ 2H^+ + 2e^-$	−0.23
$+ 2H^+ + 2e^-$	0.196	$As + 2H_2O = HAsO_2(aq)$	
$Cu + I^- = CuI + e^-$	0.185	$+ 3H^+ + 3e^-$	−0.247
$Ag + I^- = AgI + e^-$	0.151	$Re + 2H_2O = ReO_2$	
$Ge + 2H_2O = GeO_2$		$+ 4H^+ + 4e^-$	−0.252
$+ 4H^+ + 4e^-$	0.15	$Bi + H_2O = BiO^+ + 2H^+$	
$Sn = Sn^{2+} + 2e^-$	0.136	$+ 3e^-$	−0.32
$HO_2 = O_2 + H^+ + e^-$	0.13	$U^{4+} + 2H_2O = UO_2^{2+}$	
$Pb = Pb^{2+} + 2e^-$	0.126	$+ 4H^+ + 2e^-$	−0.334
$W + 3H_2O = WO_3(c) \mid 6H^+$		$Cu = Cu^{2+} + 2e^-$	−0.337
$+ 6e^-$	0.09	$Ag + IO_3^- = AgIO_3 + e^-$	−0.35
$HS_2O_4^- + 2H_2O = 2H_2SO_3$		$Fe(CN)_6^{4-} = Fe(CN)_6^{3-}$	
$+ H^+ + 2e^-$	0.08	$+ e^-$	−0.36
$Hg + 4I^- = HgI_4^{2-} + 2e^-$	0.04	$V^{3+} + H_2O = VO^{2+}$	
$H_2 = 2H^+ + 2e^-$	0.00	$+ 2H^+ + e^-$	−0.361
$Ag + 2S_2O_3^{2-}$		$Re + 4H_2O = ReO_4^-$	
$= Ag(S_2O_3)_2^{3-} + e^-$	−0.01	$+ 8H^+ + 7e^-$	−0.363
$Cu + Br^- = CuBr + e$	−0.033	$HCN(aq) = \frac{1}{2} C_2N_2 + H^+$	
$UO_2^+ = UO_2^{2+} + e^-$	−0.05	$+ e^-$	−0.37
$HCHO(aq) + H_2O$		$S_2O_3^{2-} + 3H_2O = 2H_2SO_3$	
$= HCOOH(aq) + 2H^+$		$+ 2H^+ + 4e^-$	−0.40
$+ 2e^-$	−0.056	$Rh + 6Cl^- = RhCl_6^{3-}$	
$PH_3(g) = P + 3H^+ + 3e^-$	−0.06	$+ 3e^-$	−0.44
$Ag + Br^- = AgBr + e^-$	−0.095	$2Ag + CrO_4^{2-} = Ag_2CrO_4$	
$Ti^{3+} + H_2O = TiO^{2+}$		$+ 2e^-$	−0.446
$+ 2H^+ + e^-$	−0.1	$S + 3H_2O = H_2SO_3 + 4H^+$	
$SiH_4 = Si + 4H^+ + 4e^-$	−0.102	$+ 4e^-$	−0.45
$CH_4 = C + 4H^+ + 4e^-$	−0.13	$Sb_2O_4 + H_2O = Sb_2O_5$	
$Cu + Cl^- = CuCl + e^-$	−0.137	$+ 2H^+ + 2e^-$	−0.48
$H_2S = S + 2H^+ + 2e^-$	−0.141	$2Ag + MoO_4^{2-}$	
$Np^{3+} = Np^{4+} + e^-$	−0.147	$= Ag_2MoO_4 + 2e^-$	−0.49
$Sn^{2+} = Sn^{4+} + 2e^-$	−0.15	$2NH_3OH^+ = H_2N_2O_2$	
$2Sb + 3H_2O = Sb_2O_3$		$+ 6H^+ + 4e^-$	−0.496
$+ 6H^+ + 6e^-$	−0.152	$ReO_2 + 2H_2O = ReO_4^-$	
$Cu^+ = Cu^{2+} + e^-$	−0.153	$+ 4H^+ + 3e^-$	−0.51
$Bi + H_2O + Cl^- = BiOCl$		$S_4O_6^{2-} + 6H_2O = 4H_2SO_3$	
$+ 2H^+ + 3e^-$	−0.16	$+ 4H^+ + 6e^-$	−0.51
$H_2SO_3 + H_2O = SO_4^{2-}$		$C_2H_6 = C_2H_4 + 2H^+$	
$+ 4H^+ + 2e^-$	−0.17	$+ 2e^-$	−0.52
$CH_3OH(aq) = HCHO(aq)$		$Cu = Cu^+ + e^-$	−0.521
$+ 2H^+ + 2e^-$	−0.19		

TABLE 7–1 (Continued)

ACID SOLUTIONS — (Continued)			
Couple	E^0 (volts)	Couple	E^0 (volts)
$Te + 2H_2O = TeO_2(c)$ $+ 4H^+ + 4e^-$	-0.529	$Pt + 4Cl^- = PtCl_4^{2-} + 2e^-$	-0.73
$2I^- = I_2 + 2e^-$	-0.5355	$C_2H_4 = C_2H_2 + 2H^+ + 2e^-$	-0.73
$3I^- = I_3^- + 2e^-$	-0.536	$Se + 3H_2O = H_2SeO_3$ $+ 4H^+ + 4e^-$	-0.74
$CuCl = Cu^{2+} + Cl^- + e^-$	-0.538	$Np^{4+} + 2H_2O = NpO_2^+$ $+ 4H^+ + e^-$	-0.75
$Ag + BrO_3^- = AgBrO_3$ $+ e^-$	-0.55	$2CNS^- = (CNS)_2 + 2e^-$	-0.77
$Te + 2H_2O = TeOOH^+$ $+ 3H^+ + 4e^-$	-0.559	$Ir + 6Cl^- = IrCl_6^{3-} + 3e^-$	-0.77
$HAsO_2 + 2H_2O = H_3AsO_4$ $+ 2H^+ + 2e^-$	-0.559	$Fe^{2+} = Fe^{3+} + e^-$	-0.771
$Ag + NO_2^- = AgNO_2 + e^-$	-0.564	$2Hg = Hg_2^{2+} + 2e^-$	-0.789
$MnO_4^{2-} = MnO_4^- + e^-$	-0.564	$Ag = Ag^+ + e^-$	-0.7991
$2H_2SO_3 = S_2O_6^{2-} + 4H^+$ $+ 2e^-$	-0.57	$N_2O_4 + 2H_2O = 2NO_3^-$ $+ 4H^+ + 2e^-$	-0.80
$Pt + 4Br^- = PtBr_4^{2-}$ $+ 2e^-$	-0.58	$Rh = Rh^{3+} + 3e^-$	-0.8 *ca.*
$2SbO^+ + 3H_2O = Sb_2O_5$ $+ 6H^+ + 4e^-$	-0.581	$Os + 4H_2O = OsO_4(c) +$ $8H^+ + 8e^-$	-0.85
$CH_4 + H_2O = CH_3OH(aq)$ $+ 2H^+ + 2e^-$	-0.586	$H_2N_2O_2 + 2H_2O = 2HNO_2$ $+ 4H^+ + 4e^-$	-0.86
$Pd + 4Br^- = PdBr_4^{2-}$ $+ 2e^-$	-0.6	$CuI = Cu^{2+} + I^- + e^-$	-0.86
$Ru + 5Cl^- = RuCl_5^{2-}$ $+ 3e^-$	-0.60	$Au + 4Br^- = AuBr_4^-$ $+ 3e^-$	-0.87
$U^{4+} + 2H_2O = UO_2^+$ $+ 4H^+ + e^-$	-0.62	$Hg_2^{2+} = 2Hg^{2+} + 2e^-$	-0.920
$Pd + 4Cl^- = PdCl_4^{2-}$ $+ 2e^-$	-0.62	$PuO_2^+ = PuO_2^{2+} + e^-$	-0.93
$CuBr = Cu^{2+} + Br^- + e^-$	-0.640	$HNO_2 + H_2O = NO_3^-$ $+ 3H^+ + 2e^-$	-0.94
$Ag + C_2H_3O_2^-$ $= AgC_2H_3O_2 + e^-$	-0.643	$NO + 2H_2O = NO_3^-$ $+ 4H^+ + 4e^-$	-0.96
$2Ag + SO_4^{2-} = Ag_2SO_4$ $+ 2e^-$	-0.653	$Au + 2Br^- = AuBr_2^- + e^-$	-0.96
$Au + 4CNS^-$ $= Au(CNS)_4^- + 3e^-$	-0.66	$Pu^{3+} + Pu^{4+} + e^-$	-0.97
$PtCl_4^{2-} + 2Cl^- = PtCl_6^{2-}$ $+ 2e^-$	-0.68	$Pt + 2H_2O = Pt(OH)_2$ $+ 2H^+ + 2e^-$	-0.98
$H_2O_2 = O_2 + 2H^+ + 2e^-$	-0.682	$Pd = Pd^{2+} + 2e^-$	-0.987
$2NH_4^+ = HN_3 + 11H^+$ $+ 8e^-$	-0.69	$IrBr_6^{4-} = IrBr_6^{3-} + e^-$	-0.99
$H_2Te = Te + 2H^+ + 2e^-$	-0.70	$NO + H_2O = HNO_2 + H^+$ $+ e^-$	-1.00
$H_2N_2O_2 = 2NO + 2H^+$ $+ 2e^-$	-0.71	$Au + 4Cl^- = AuCl_4^-$ $+ 3e^-$	-1.00
$OH + H_2O = H_2O_2 + H^+$ $+ e^-$	-0.72	$VO^{2+} + 3H_2O = V(OH)_4^+$ $+ 2H^+ + e^-$	-1.00
		$IrCl_6^{3-} = IrCl_6^{2-} + e^-$	-1.017
		$TeO_2 + 4H_2O = H_6TeO_6$ (c) $+ 2H^+ + 2e^-$	-1.02
		$2NO + 2H_2O = N_2O_4$ $+ 4H^+ + 4e^-$	-1.03
		$Pu^{4+} + 2H_2O = PuO_2^{2+}$ $+ 4H^+ + 2e^-$	-1.04

TABLE 7–1 (Continued)

ACID SOLUTIONS — (Continued)			
Couple	E^0 (volts)	Couple	E^0 (volts)
$2Cl^- + \frac{1}{2}I_2 = ICl_2^- + e^-$	-1.06	$Au = Au^{3+} + 3e^-$	-1.50
$2Br^- = Br_2(1) + 2e^-$	-1.0652	$H_2O_2 = HO_2 + H^+ + e^-$	-1.5
$2HNO_2 = N_2O_4 + 2H^+$		$Mn^{2+} = Mn^{3+} + e^-$	-1.51
$\quad + 2e^-$	-1.07	$Mn^{2+} + 4H_2O = MnO_4^-$	
$Cu(CN)_2^- = Cu^{2+}$		$\quad + 8H^+ + 5e^-$	-1.51
$\quad + 2CN^- + e^-$	-1.12	$\frac{1}{2}Br_2 + 3H_2O = BrO_3^-$	
$Pu^{4+} + 2H_2O = PuO_2^+$		$\quad + 6H^+ + 5e^-$	-1.52
$\quad + 4H^+ + e^-$	-1.15	$\frac{1}{2}Br_2 + H_2O = HBrO$	
$H_2SeO_3 + H_2O = SeO_4^{2-}$		$\quad + H^+ + e^-$	-1.59
$\quad \mid 4H^+ \mid 2e^-$	1.15	$2BiO^+ + 2H_2O - Bi_2O_4$	
$NpO_2^+ = NpO_2^{2+} + e^-$	-1.15	$\quad + 4H^+ + 2e^-$	-1.59
$4Cl^- + C + 4H^+ = CCl_4$		$IO_3^- + 3H_2O = H_5IO_6$	
$\quad + 4H^+ + 4e^-$	-1.18	$\quad + H^+ + 2e^-$	-1.6
$ClO_3^- + H_2O = ClO_4^-$		$Bk^{3+} - Bk^{4+} + e^-$	-1.6
$\quad + 2H^+ + 2e^-$	-1.19	$Ce^{3+} = Ce^{4+} + e^-$	-1.61
$\frac{1}{2}I_2 + 3H_2O = IO_3^-$		$\frac{1}{2}Cl_2 + H_2O = HClO$	
$\quad + 6H^+ + 5e^-$	-1.195	$\quad + H^+ + e^-$	-1.63
$HClO_2 + H_2O = ClO_3^-$		$AmO_2^+ = AmO_2^{2+} + e^-$	-1.64
$\quad + 3H^+ + 2e^-$	-1.21	$HClO + H_2O = HClO_2$	
$2H_2O - O_2 + 4H^+ + 4e^-$	-1.229	$\quad + 2H^+ + 2e^-$	-1.64
$2S + 2Cl^- = S_2Cl_2 + 2e^-$	-1.23	$Au = Au^+ + e^-$	-1.68 *ca.*
$Mn^{2+} + 2H_2O = MnO_2$		$Ni^{2+} + 2H_2O = NiO_2$	
$\quad + 4H^+ + 2e^-$	-1.23	$\quad + 4H^+ + 2e^-$	-1.68
$Tl^+ = Tl^{3+} + 2e^-$	-1.25	$PbSO_4 + 2H_2O = PbO_2$	
$Am^{4+} + 2H_2O = AmO_2^+$		$\quad + SO_4^{2-} + 4H^+ + 2e^-$	-1.685
$\quad + 4H^+ + e^-$	-1.26	$Am^{3+} + 2H_2O = AmO_2^{2+}$	
$2NH_4^+ = N_2H_5^+ + 3H^+$		$\quad + 4H^+ + 3e^-$	-1.69
$\quad + 2e^-$	-1.275	$MnO_2 + 2H_2O = MnO_4^-$	
$HClO_2 = ClO_2 + H^+ + e^-$	-1.275	$\quad + 4H^+ + 3e^-$	-1.695
$PdCl_4^{2-} + 2Cl^- = PdCl_6^{2-}$		$Am^{3+} + 2H_2O = AmO_2^+$	
$\quad + 2e^-$	-1.288	$\quad + 4H^+ + 2e^-$	-1.725
$N_2O + 3H_2O = 2HNO_2$		$2H_2O = H_2O_2 + 2H^+$	
$\quad + 4H^+ + 4e^-$	-1.29	$\quad + 2e^-$	-1.77
$2Cr^{3+} + 7H_2O = Cr_2O_7^{2-}$		$Co^{2+} = Co^{3+} + e^-$	-1.82
$\quad + 14H^+ + 6e^-$	-1.33	$Fe^{3+} + 4H_2O = FeO_4^{2-}$	
$NH_4^+ + H_2O = NH_3OH^+$		$\quad + 8H^+ + 3e^-$	-1.9
$\quad + 2H^+ + 2e^-$	-1.35	$NH_4^+ + N_2 = HN_3 + 3H^+$	
$2Cl^- = Cl_2 + 2e^-$	-1.3595	$\quad + 2e^-$	-1.96
$N_2H_5^+ + 2H_2O$		$Ag^+ = Ag^{2+} + e^-$	-1.98
$\quad = 2NH_3OH^+ + H^+ + 2e^-$	-1.42	$2SO_4^{2-} = S_2O_8^{2-} + 2e^-$	-2.01
$Au + 3H_2O = Au(OH)_3$		$O_2 + H_2O = O_3 + 2H^+$	
$\quad + 3H^+ + 3e^-$	-1.45	$\quad + 2e^-$	-2.07
$\frac{1}{2}I_2 + H_2O = HIO + H^+$		$H_2O + 2F^- = F_2O + 2H^+$	
$\quad + e^-$	-1.45	$\quad + 4e^-$	-2.1
$Pb^{2+} + 2H_2O = PbO_2$		$Am^{3+} = Am^{4+} + e^-$	-2.18
$\quad + 4H^+ + 2e^-$	-1.455	$H_2O = O(g) + 2H^+ + 2e^-$	-2.42

TABLE 7–1 (Continued)

ACID SOLUTIONS — (Continued)			
Couple	E^0 (volts)	Couple	E^0 (volts)
$H_2O = OH + H^+ + e^-$	-2.8	$2F^- = F_2 + 2e^-$	-2.87
$N_2 + 2H_2O = H_2N_2O_2$ $+ 2H^+ + 2e^-$	-2.85	$2HF(aq) = F_2 + 2H^+$ $+ 2e^-$	-3.06

BASIC SOLUTIONS			
Couple	E^0 (volts)	Couple	E^0 (volts)
$Ca + 2OH^- = Ca(OH)_2$ $+ 2e^-$	3.03	$= Na_2UO_4 + 4H_2O + 2e^-$	1.61
$Sr + 2OH^- + 8H_2O$ $= Sr(OH)_2 \cdot 8H_2O + 2e^-$	2.99	$H_2PO_2^- + 3OH^- = HPO_3^{2-}$ $+ 2H_2O + 2e^-$	1.57
$Ba + 2OH^- + 8H_2O$ $= Ba(OH)_2 \cdot 8H_2O + 2e^-$	2.97	$Mn + 2OH^- = Mn(OH)_2$ $+ 2e^-$	1.55
$H(g) + OH^- = H_2O + e^-$	2.93	$Mn + CO_3^{2-} = MnCO_3$ $+ 2e^-$	1.48
$La + 3OH^- = La(OH)_3$ $+ 3e^-$	2.90	$Zn + S^{2-} = ZnS + 2e^-$	1.44
$Lu + 3OH^- = Lu(OH)_3$ $+ 3e^-$	2.72	$Cr + 3OH^- = Cr(OH)_3$ $+ 3e^-$	1.3
$Mg + 2OH^- = Mg(OH)_2$ $+ 2e^-$	2.69	$Zn + 4CN^- = Zn(CN)_4^{2-}$ $+ 2e^-$	1.26
$2Be + 6OH^- = Be_2O_3^{2-}$ $+ 3H_2O + 4e^-$	2.62	$Zn + 2OH^- = Zn(OH)_2$ $+ 2e^-$	1.245
$Sc + 3OH^- = Sc(OH)_3$ $+ 3e^-$	2.6 $ca.$	$Ga + 4OH^- = H_2GaO_3^-$ $+ H_2O + 3e^-$	1.22
$Hf + 4OH^- = HfO(OH)_2$ $+ H_2O + 4e^-$	2.50	$Zn + 4OH^- = ZnO_2^{2-}$ $+ 2H_2O + 2e^-$	1.216
$Th + 4OH^- = Th(OH)_4$ $+ 4e^-$	2.48	$Cr + 4OH^- = CrO_2^-$ $+ 2H_2O + 3e^-$	1.2
$Pu + 3OH^- = Pu(OH)_3$ $+ 3e^-$	2.42	$Cd + S^{2-} = CdS + 2e^-$	1.21
$U + 4OH^- = UO_2 + 2H_2O$ $+ 4e^-$	2.39	$6V + 33OH^- = 16H_2O$ $+ HV_6O_{17}^{3-} + 30e^-$	1.15
$Zr + 4OH^- = H_2ZrO_3$ $+ H_2O + 4e^-$	2.36	$Te^{2-} = Te + 2e^-$	1.14
$Al + 4OH^- = H_2AlO_3^-$ $+ H_2O + 3e^-$	2.35	$HPO_3^{2-} + 3OH^- = PO_4^{3-}$ $+ 2H_2O + 2e^-$	1.12
$U(OH)_3 + OH^- = U(OH)_4$ $+ e^-$	2.2	$S_2O_4^{2-} + 4OH^- = 2SO_3^{2-}$ $+ 2H_2O + 2e^-$	1.12
$U + 3OH^- = U(OH)_3$ $+ 3e^-$	2.17	$Zn + CO_3^{2-} = ZnCO_3$ $+ 2e^-$	1.06
$P + 2OH^- = H_2PO_2^- + e^-$	2.05	$W + 8OH^- = WO_4^{2-}$ $+ 4H_2O + 6e^-$	1.05
$B + 4OH^- = H_2BO_3^-$ $+ 3e^-$	1.79	$Mo + 8OH^- = MoO_4^{2-}$ $4H_2O + 6e^-$	1.05
$Si + 6OH^- = SiO_3^{2-}$ $+ 3H_2O + 4e^-$	1.70	$Cd + 4CN^- = Cd(CN)_4^{2-}$ $+ 2e^-$	1.03
$U(OH)_4 = 2Na^+ + 4OH^-$		$Zn + 4NH_3 = Zn(NH_3)_4^{2+}$ $+ 2e^-$	1.03
		$Fe + S^{2-} = FeS_{(\alpha +)} 2e^-$	1.01

TABLE 7–1 (Continued)

BASIC SOLUTIONS — (Continued)

Couple	E^0 (volts)	Couple	E^0 (volts)
$In + 3OH^- = In(OH)_3 + 3e^-$	1.0	$Cd + 4NH_3 = Cd(NH_3)_4^{2+} + 2e^-$	0.597
$CN^- + 2OH^- = CNO^- + H_2O + 2e^-$	0.97	$ReO_2 + 4OH^- = ReO_4^- + 2H_2O + 3e^-$	0.594
$2Tl + S^{2-} = Tl_2S + 2e^-$	0.96	$Re + 8OH^- = ReO_4^- + 4H_2O + 7e^-$	0.584
$Pb + S^{2-} = PbS + 2e^-$	0.95	$S_2O_3^{2-} + 6OH^- = 2SO_3^{2-} + 3H_2O + 4e^-$	0.58
$Pu(OH)_3 + OH^- = Pu(OH)_4 + e^-$	0.95	$Re + 4OH^- = ReO_2 + 2H_2O + 4e^-$	0.576
$Sn + S^{2-} = SnS + 2e^-$	0.94	$Te + 6OH^- = TeO_3^{2-} + 3H_2O + 4e^-$	0.57
$SO_3^{2-} + 2OH^- = SO_4^{2-} + H_2O + 2e^-$	0.93	$Fe(OH)_2 + OH^- = Fe(OH)_3 + e^-$	0.56
$Se^{2-} = Se + 2e^-$	0.92	$O_2^- = O_2 + e^-$	0.56
$Sn + 3OH^- = HSnO_2^- + H_2O + 2e^-$	0.91	$2Cu + S^{2-} = Cu_2S + 2e^-$	0.54
$Ge + 5OH^- = HGeO_3^- + 2H_2O + 4e^-$	0.9	$Pb + 3OH^- = HPbO_2^- + H_2O + 2e^-$	0.54
$HSnO_2^- + H_2O + 3OH^- = Sn(OH)_6^{2-} + 2e^-$	0.90	$Pb + CO_3^{2-} = PbCO_3 + 2e^-$	0.506
$PH_3 + 3OH^- = P + 3H_2O + 3e^-$	0.89	$S^{2-} = S + 2e^-$	0.48
$Fe + 2OH^- = Fe(OH)_2 + 2e^-$	0.877	$Ni + 6NH_3(aq) = Ni(NH_3)_6^{2+} + 2e^-$	0.47
$Ni + S^{2-} = NiS_{(\alpha)} + 2e^-$	0.83	$Ni + CO_3^{2-} = NiCO_3 + 2e^-$	0.45
$H_2 + 2OH^- = 2H_2O + 2e^-$	0.828	$2Bi + 6OH^- = Bi_2O_3 + 3H_2O + 6e^-$	0.44
$Cd + 2OH^- = Cd(OH)_2 + 2e^-$	0.809	$Cu + 2CN^- = Cu(CN)_2^- + e^-$	0.43
$Fe + CO_3^{2-} = FeCO_3 + 2e^-$	0.756	$Hg + 4CN^- = Hg(CN)_4^{2-} + 2e^-$	0.37
$Cd + CO_3^{2-} = CdCO_3 + 2e^-$	0.74	$Se + 6OH^- = SeO_3^{2-} + 3H_2O + 4e^-$	0.366
$Co + 2OH^- = Co(OH)_2 + 2e^-$	0.73	$2Cu + 2OH^- = Cu_2O + H_2O + 2e^-$	0.358
$Hg + S^{2-} = HgS + 2e^-$	0.72	$Tl + OH^- = Tl(OH) + e^-$	0.3445
$Ni + 2OH^- = Ni(OH)_2 + 2e^-$	0.72	$Ag + 2CN^- = Ag(CN)_2^- + e^-$	0.31
$2Ag + S^{2-} = Ag_2S + 2e^-$	0.69	$Cu + CNS^- = Cu(CNS) + e^-$	0.27
$As + 4OH^- = AsO_2^- + 2H_2O + 3e^-$	0.68	$OH + 2OH^- = HO_2^- + H_2O + e^-$	0.24
$AsO_2^- + 4OH^- = AsO_4^{3-} + 2H_2O + 2e^-$	0.67	$Cr(OH)_3 + 5OH^- = CrO_4^{2-} + 4H_2O + 3e^-$	0.13
$2FeS + S^{2-} = Fe_2S_3 + 2e^-$	0.67		
$Sb + 4OH^- = SbO_2^- + 2H_2O + 3e^-$	0.66	$Cu + 2NH_3 = Cu(NH_3)_2^+ + e^-$	0.12
$Co + CO_3^{2-} = CoCO_3 + 2e^-$	0.64		

TABLE 7–1 (Continued)

Basic Solutions — (Continued)			
Couple	E^0 (volts)	Couple	E^0 (volts)
$Cu_2O + 2OH^- + H_2O$ $= 2Cu(OH)_2 + 2e^-$	0.080	$2Ag + 2OH^- = Ag_2O$ $+ H_2O + 2e^-$	-0.344
$HO_2^- + OH^- = O_2 + H_2O$ $+ 2e^-$	0.076	$ClO_3^- + 2OH^- = ClO_4^-$ $+ H_2O + 2e^-$	-0.36
$TlOH + 2OH^- = Tl(OH)_3$ $+ 2e^-$	0.05	$Ag + 2NH_3 = Ag(NH_3)_2^+$ $+ e^-$	-0.373
$Ag + CN^- = AgCN + e^-$	0.017	$TeO_3^{2-} + 2OH^- = TeO_4^{2-}$ $+ H_2O + 2e^-$	-0.4
$Mn(OH)_2 + 2OH^-$ $= MnO_2 + 2H_2O + 2e^-$	0.05	$OH^- + HO_2^- = O_2^-$ $+ H_2O + e^-$	-0.4
$NO_2^- + 2OH^- = NO_3^-$ $+ H_2O + 2e^-$	-0.01	$4OH^- = O_2 + 2H_2O + 4e^-$	-0.401
$Os + 9OH^- = HOsO_5^-$ $+ 4H_2O + 8e^-$	-0.02	$2Ag + CO_3^{2-} = Ag_2CO_3$ $+ 2e^-$	-0.47
$2Rh + 6OH^- = Rh_2O_3$ $+ 3H_2O + 6e^-$	-0.04	$Ni(OH)_2 + 2OH^- = NiO_2$ $+ 2H_2O + 2e^-$	-0.49
$SeO_3^{2-} + 2OH^- = SeO_4^{2-}$ $+ H_2O + 2e^-$	-0.05	$I^- + 2OH^- = IO^- + H_2O$ $+ 2e^-$	-0.49
$Pd + 2OH^- = Pd(OH)_2$ $+ 2e^-$	-0.07	$Ag_2O + 2OH^- = 2AgO$ $+ H_2O + 2e^-$	-0.57
$2S_2O_3^{2-} = S_4O_6^{2-} + 2e^-$	-0.08	$MnO_2 + 4OH^- = MnO_4^{2-}$ $+ 2H_2O + 2e^-$	-0.60
$Hg + 2OH^- = HgO(r)$ $+ H_2O + 2e^-$	-0.098	$RuO_4^{2-} = RuO_4^- + e^-$	-0.60
$2NH_4OH + 2OH^- = N_2H_4$ $+ 4H_2O + 2e^-$	-0.1	$Br^- + 6OH^- = BrO_3^-$ $+ 3H_2O + 6e^-$	-0.61
$2Ir + 6OH^- = Ir_2O_3$ $+ 3H_2O + 6e^-$	-0.1	$ClO^- + 2OH^- = ClO_2^-$ $+ H_2O + 2e^-$	-0.66
$Co(NH_3)_6^{2+} = Co(NH_3)_6^{3+}$ $+ e^-$	-0.1	$IO_3^- + 3OH^- = H_3IO_6^{2-}$ $+ 2e^-$	-0.7
$Mn(OH)_2 + OH^-$ $= Mn(OH)_3 + e^-$	-0.1	$N_2H_4 + 2OH^- = 2NH_2OH$ $+ 2e^-$	-0.73
$Pt + 2OH^- = Pt(OH)_2$ $+ 2e^-$	-0.15	$2AgO + 2OH^- = Ag_2O_3$ $+ H_2O + 2e^-$	-0.74
$Co(OH)_2 + OH^-$ $= Co(OH)_3 + e^-$	-0.17	$Br^- + 2OH^- = BrO^-$ $+ H_2O + 2e^-$	-0.76
$PbO(r) + 2OH^- = PbO_2$ $+ H_2O + 2e^-$	-0.248	$3OH^- = HO_2^- + H_2O$ $+ 2e^-$	-0.88
$I^- + 6OH^- = IO_3^-$ $+ 3H_2O + 6e^-$	-0.26	$Cl^- + 2OH^- = ClO^-$ $+ H_2O + 2e^-$	-0.89
$PuO_2OH + OH^-$ $= PuO_2(OH)_2 + 2e^-$	-0.26	$FeO_2^- + 4OH^- = FeO_4^{2-}$ $+ 2H_2O + 3e^-$	-0.9
$Ag + 2SO_3^{2-} = Ag(SO_3)_2^{3-}$ $+ e^-$	-0.30	$ClO_2^- = ClO_2 + e^-$	-1.16
$ClO_2^- + 2OH^- = ClO_3^-$ $+ H_2O + 2e^-$	-0.33	$O_2 + 2OH^- = O_3 + H_2O$ $+ 2e^-$	-1.24
		$OH^- = OH + e^-$	-2.0

* The values reported in this table were taken directly from Latimer, "The Oxidation States of the Elements and Their Potentials in Aqueous Solutions," 2nd ed., Prentice-Hall, Inc., New York, N.Y., 1952.

There are two important limitations to this argument. Firstly, we are neglecting the kinetics of the reaction, and secondly, we are using standard state potentials and these are valid at unit activity only. With respect to the first point, it should be recognized that thermodynamics considers the initial and the final state of a system, but it does not consider what takes place between these two states. There are numerous examples of reactions with negative free energy changes that apparently do not occur spontaneously. This can result from such factors as a mechanism involving an intermediate step which has a positive free energy change, the formation of a surface coating, alternative reaction paths that are more probable than those proposed, and so on. With respect to the second point, we should recognize that it is not likely that a reaction would be carried out at such specific activities and in fact it would be coincidental if such were possible. So it can be seen that the actual experimental situation is only approximated by the use of the standard oxidation potentials. To be more nearly correct, it would be necessary to calculate the cell emf under the specific conditions of the experiment. For this particular reaction,

$$ E = E^0 - \frac{RT}{2F} \ln \frac{a_{Fe^{++}}}{a_{Cd^{++}}} $$

or, at 25°C,

$$ E = 0.037 - \frac{0.059}{2} \log \frac{a_{Fe^{++}}}{a_{Cd^{++}}} $$

It follows from the above that, although from the standard potentials we would predict that iron would reduce cadmium ion, if the ratio of $a_{Fe^{++}}$ to $a_{Cd^{++}}$ is sufficiently large, the cell emf may actually be negative and, under these conditions, iron would not reduce cadmium ion. It might be mentioned that the activities are not usually used since the activity coefficients of each ion type are not ordinarily known in a system of this complexity. However, if the concentrations are not too great, it is possible to substitute concentration for activity and still obtain a good first-order approximation of the cell emf.

APPLICATIONS OF OXIDATION POTENTIALS

We have seen that, once the standard state emf values for the various half-cell reactions have been determined, it is possible to combine these to determine the over-all cell emf and therefore, the thermodynamic tendency for the reaction to proceed as written. In combining half-cell potentials it is not necessary to consider the number of electrons involved in the change since the half-cell potentials are evaluated for a one-electron change. Thus, in adding two half-cell potentials, we can directly add the listed potentials from the tables. This point can be appreciated if we consider a reaction where the half cells do not involve the same number of electrons, such as in the reaction

$$3 \text{ Ag}^+ + \text{Al} = 3 \text{ Ag} + \text{Al}^{+++}$$

The half-cell reactions are

$$\text{Ag} = \text{Ag}^+ + e^- \qquad\qquad E^0 = -0.7991 \text{ v}$$
$$\text{Al} = \text{Al}^{+++} + 3e^- \qquad\qquad E^0 = 1.66 \text{ v}$$

This, then, gives an over-all cell potential of $E^0 = 2.46$ v, and we therefore conclude that if all species are at unit activity at 25°C, aluminum will reduce silver ion.

The situation is somewhat different when two half-cell reactions are added to obtain a third half-cell reaction. Ordinarily, it is necessary to evaluate the free energy change for each half reaction in order to take into consideration the number of electrons involved. These are then additive. Once the free energy change is evaluated for the desired half-cell reaction, it is possible to convert back to the half-cell emf. As an example, we can consider the half-cell

$$\text{Tl} = \text{Tl}^{+++} + 3e^-$$

From the table of oxidation potentials, it can be seen that

$$\text{Tl} = \text{Tl}^+ + e^- \qquad\qquad E^0 = 0.3363 \text{ v}$$
and
$$\text{Tl}^+ = \text{Tl}^{+++} + 2e^- \qquad\qquad E^0 = -1.250 \text{ v}$$

Converting these to standard free energies according to Eq. (7–17), we obtain $\Delta F^0 = -1 \times (0.3363)\text{F}$ and $\Delta F^0 = -2 \times (-1.250)\text{F} = 2.50\text{F}$, respectively. Adding these, we find that ΔF^0 for the half-cell reaction

$$\text{Tl} = \text{Tl}^{+++} + 3e^-$$

is equal to $(-0.3363 + 2.50)\text{F}$ or 2.16F, from which we obtain the value $-(2.16\text{F}/3\text{F})$ or -0.720 v for E^0.

Stabilization of Oxidation States of Metals

One of the important applications of half-cell potentials is that of predicting the relative stabilities of different oxidation states of a given element. As an example of such a calculation, the disproportionation of Au(I) can be considered. For the reaction

$$3 \text{ Au}^+ = 2 \text{ Au} + \text{Au}^{+++}$$

the two half-cell reactions

$$\text{Au}^+ = \text{Au}^{+++} + 2e^- \qquad\qquad E^0 = -1.41 \text{ v}$$
and
$$\text{Au}^+ + e^- = \text{Au} \qquad\qquad E^0 = 1.68 \text{ v}$$

can be written. This yields a positive emf of 0.27 v for the total cell reaction, and therefore it would be expected that gold(I) would disproportionate to gold(0) and gold(III) if all species are at unit activity.

It should be pointed out that in every reaction we have written thus far and in those that will follow, all ionic species are written as if only the simple ion were involved. This, of course, is not the case, since all ions are hydrated to some extent in an aqueous solution. Thus, each ion may be considered to be surrounded by a number of water molecules, the number, firmness of attachment, and the distance of closest approach being determined primarily by the size, charge, and electronic nature of the ion. With this in mind, it is interesting to note that the standard potential for either of these half-cell reactions can be changed merely by changing the environment of the gold(I) species, that is, by replacing the water molecules which surround the metal ion by other molecules or ions. We can illustrate this effect of environment on the central ion by considering the ions Br^-, NCS^-, I^-, and CN^- with respect to the standard potential of the following half cells:

$$
\begin{aligned}
Au + H_2O &= Au_{(aq)}^+ + e^- & E^0 &= -1.68 \text{ v} \\
Au + 2\, Br^- &= [AuBr_2]^- + e^- & &-0.96 \text{ v} \\
Au + 2\, NCS^- &= [Au(SCN)_2]^- + e^- & &-0.69 \text{ v} \\
Au + I^- &= AuI + e^- & &-0.50 \text{ v} \\
Au + CN^- &= [Au(CN)_2]^- + e^- & &+0.60 \text{ v}
\end{aligned}
$$

Here we note that the various ions have effected a stabilization of the gold(I) toward reduction, with the CN^- giving the greatest stabilization. This is an example of the stabilization toward reduction of an oxidation state through the formation of either an insoluble compound or a complex ion which is more stable than the simple hydrated ion.

As an example of the stabilization of a given oxidation state toward oxidation, we can consider the iron(II)-iron(III) system for which we have the following half-cell potentials:

$$
\begin{aligned}
2FeS + S^{2-} &= Fe_2S_3 + 2e^- & E^0 &= +0.7 \text{ v} \\
Fe(OH)_2 + OH^- &= Fe(OH)_3 + e^- & &+0.56 \text{ v} \\
Fe(CN)_6^{4-} &= Fe(CN)_6^{3-} + e^- & &-0.36 \text{ v} \\
Fe^{2+} + 6F^- &= FeF_6^{3-} + e^- & &-0.40 \text{ v} \\
Fe^{2+} + 2PO_4^{3-} &= [Fe(PO_4)_2]^{3-} + e^- & &-0.61 \text{ v} \\
Fe^{2+} &= Fe^{3+} + e^- & &-0.771 \text{ v} \\
[Fe(dipy)_3]^{2+} &= [Fe(dipy)_3]^{3+} + e^- & &-1.10 \text{ v} \\
[Fe(o\text{-phen})_3]^{2+} &= [Fe(o\text{-phen})_3]^{3+} + e^- & &-1.14 \text{ v} \\
[Fe(NO_2)\text{-}o\text{-phen})_3]^{2+} &= [Fe(NO_2\text{-}o\text{-phen})_3]^{3+} + e^- & &-1.25 \text{ v}
\end{aligned}
$$

(where dipy ≡ dipyridyl, o-phen ≡ *ortho*phenanthroline, and NO_2-o-phen ≡ nitro-*ortho*phenanthroline). From these values it is concluded that sulfide, hydroxide, cyanide, fluoride, and phosphate ions all stabilize iron(III) against reduction to a greater degree than does water. Likewise, the organic complexing agents stabilize iron(II) against oxidation to a greater degree than water.

Many examples are known of the stabilization of particular oxidation states for the large number of multivalent metals. However, it should again be emphasized that the standard potentials give the thermodynamic tendency of a particular reaction to proceed when all components are at unit activity, and the actual rate of a reaction is dependent on the kinetics of the reaction. So, for example, while the above values predict $Fe(CN)_6{}^{4-}$ to be less stable toward oxidation than the aquated Fe^{2+}, the cyano complex shows greater chemical stability. This is attributed to the slow rate of oxidation under ordinary conditions.

Equilibrium Constants from Half-Cell Potentials

Recalling the two basic relationships

$$\Delta F^\circ = -RT \ln K_{eq}$$

and

$$\Delta F^\circ = -n\mathrm{F}\mathrm{E}^0$$

it can be seen that the equilibrium constant of a reaction can readily be related to the standard-cell potential by the expression

$$\mathrm{E}^0 = \frac{RT}{n\mathrm{F}} \ln K_{eq} \tag{7-16}$$

As an example of the calculation of a simple equilibrium constant, let us consider the reduction of selenous acid with stannous chloride. The over-all reaction can be represented as

$$H_2SeO_3 + 2\ Sn^{2+} + 4\ H^+ = 2\ Sn^{4+} + Se + 3\ H_2O$$

and this can be broken down into the two half reactions

$$H_2SeO_3 + 4\ H^+ + 4e^- = Se + 3\ H_2O \qquad\qquad \mathrm{E}^0 = 0.74\ \mathrm{v}$$

and

$$Sn^{2+} = Sn^{4+} + 2e^- \qquad\qquad \mathrm{E}^0 = -0.15\ \mathrm{v}$$

This leads to an over-all cell potential of $\mathrm{E}^0 = +0.59$ v. Solving Eq. (7–16) for $\log K$, we obtain for 25°C

$$\log K = \frac{n\mathrm{E}^0}{0.059} = \frac{(4)\ (0.59)}{0.059} = 40$$

or $K = 10^{40}$.

It is also possible to calculate solubility products for relatively insoluble substances by the same general means. For instance, the solubility of silver chloride can be determined by considering the reaction

$$AgCl = Ag^+ + Cl^-$$

to be made up of the two half-cell reactions

$$AgCl + e^- = Ag + Cl^- \qquad\qquad E^0 = 0.222 \text{ v}$$

and

$$Ag = Ag^+ + e^- \qquad\qquad E^0 = -0.799 \text{ v}$$

The standard potential for a cell composed of these two half reactions is $E^0 = -0.577$ v, and log K at 25°C is given by the following equation:

$$\log K = \frac{(1)\,(-0.577)}{0.059} = -9.78$$

or $K = 10^{-9.78} = 1.7 \times 10^{-10}$.

In solutions of this dilution it is permissible to substitute concentrations for activities, and therefore, calculation of the solubilities of silver chloride in aqueous solutions having a low ionic strength is straightforward.

BIBLIOGRAPHY

1. Harned, H. and Owen, B., "The Physical Chemistry of Electrolytic Solutions," 3rd ed., Reinhold Publishing Corp., New York, N.Y., 1958.
2. Lingane, J., "Electroanalytical Chemistry," Interscience Publishers, New York, N.Y., 1953.
3. Anson, F., *J. Chem. Ed.*, **36, 396** (1959).
4. Christiansen, J. and Pourbaix, M., "Conventions Concerning the Signs of Electromotive Forces and Electrode Potentials," *Comptes Rendus of the 17th Conference of the IUPAC*, Maison de la Chimie, Paris, 1954.
5. Licht, T. and de Béthune, A., *J. Chem. Ed.*, **34,** 433 (1957).
6. Latimer, W., "Oxidation Potentials," 2nd ed., Prentice-Hall, Inc., New York, N.Y., 1952.

SUGGESTED SUPPLEMENTARY READING

Lewis, G. and Randall, M., "Thermodynamics," 2nd ed., McGraw-Hill Book Co., New York, N.Y., 1961.

MacInnes, D., "The Principles of Electrochemistry," Reinhold Publishing Corp., New York, N.Y., 1939.

Kleinberg, J., Argersinger, W., Jr., and Griswold, E., "Inorganic Chemistry," D. C. Heath & Co., Boston, Mass., 1960.

8 / Acids and Bases

The realization that an acid is a unique type of compound existed long before its properties were first systematized by Robert Boyle. Yet, after almost three centuries of experience with definitions and theories of acid behavior, we still lack a unanimity of opinion. Of necessity, the first concepts of an acid were empirical in character. The fact that the particular species of compounds known as acids has certain observable properties characteristic only of that species, led to the original setting apart of these compounds. It had very early been observed that calcareous earths such as limestone effervesced when dissolved in certain solvents of which vinegar was typical. In addition, dilute solutions of such solvents were observed to have a characteristic sour taste. Because of this property, they were termed "acids" from the Latin *acetum* for vinegar. And by the end of the seventeenth century, other properties were found that also proved to be characteristic of this class of compounds, such as their general solvent ability and their action on certain plant dyes.

Another class of compounds, that had properties quite different from those of acids, was early recognized. These compounds were first derived from the ashes of various plants and were, for this reason, given the name of *alkali* from the Arabic term for ashes of a plant. Just as acids had certain characteristic properties, the alkalies could be recognized by their unique properties. These consisted of the ability to dissolve sulfur and oils, to affect the colors of certain plant dyes, and in particular, to neutralize the effects of acids.

It should be noted that the designation of a substance as an acid or an alkali depended on the unique observable properties of the substance. This idea was emphasized by Robert Boyle when he recognized the properties of an acid to consist of its solvent action on many substances, its ability

238

to precipitate sulfur from alkali solutions, and its ability to turn certain blue plant dyes to red. Along the same lines, Rouelle extended the concept of an alkali in 1744, by introducing the more general class of compounds known as *bases*. Rouelle maintained that a salt resulted from the combination of an acid and a base, and a base, therefore, could be defined as any species that reacts with an acid to form a salt. According to Rouelle, the group of compounds known as bases included the alkalies, the alkaline earth equivalents of the alkalies, metals, and certain oils.

The first deviation from a strictly experimental definition of an acid came as a result of Lavoisier's studies on oxidation. During this work, Lavoisier observed that many of the more common acids resulted from the union of oxygen with nonmetals such as sulfur and phosphorous. This led him to conclude that the peculiar properties of an acid could be attributed to the presence of oxygen. Such a view was not necessarily intended to displace the experimental definition of an acid, but rather, it represented a first attempt to understand this characteristic behavior.

The breakdown of Lavoisier's theory came as a result of studies on *muriatic acid* (HCl). There could be no question that muriatic acid was an acid by all experimental criteria. Thus, according to Lavoisier, it must contain oxygen as all acids must. At that time, an acid was thought to be the oxide of the nonmetal, and the compound we now know to have the formula H_2SO_4, for instance, was considered to be the acid plus water of crystallization. In a similar fashion, muriatic acid would be represented as XO,HO where XO was the anhydrous acid and HO was the water of crystallization written in the characteristic form of that time. Such a structure for muriatic acid seemed to receive support from the studies of neutralization reactions. If we consider the reaction of sulfuric acid with lime, we find that it would have been expressed at that time as

$$CaO + SO_3,HO \rightarrow CaO,SO_3 + HO$$

An analogous reaction for muriatic acid would be expressed as

$$NaO + XO,HO \rightarrow NaO,XO + HO$$

Just as the reaction of sulfuric acid had resulted in a salt plus water, the reaction of muriatic acid had also resulted in a salt plus water. Thus, it would appear that the two acids were similar insofar as they both contained the so-called water of crystallization. Consequently, if the anhydrous form of sulfuric acid could be obtained, it seemed reasonable that the anhydrous form of muriatic acid could also be obtained. All attempts to make the anhydrous form, however, either resulted in what appeared to be the hydrated form of the acid or in a substance that apparently contained no oxygen. Many experiments were carried out along these lines by Sir Humphrey Davy in an attempt to show that muriatic acid contained the required oxygen of the Lavoisier theory, but they always met with failure.

Finally, Davy concluded that there was no oxygen in muriatic acid, but rather, it contained the *dephlogisticated* muriatic acid gas discovered by Scheele. Davy maintained that this was an element, and he named it chlorine.

Shortly after he had shown that muriatic acid contained no oxygen, Davy proposed that acidity could not be attributed to any particular element, but rather, it was due to particular arrangements of various substances. However, in 1816, he finally expressed the opinion that hydrogen was peculiar to all acidic species. This idea did not meet with immediate approval. In particular, Gay-Lussac was not convinced that muriatic acid contained no oxygen until he, himself, showed that there was none in HI and HCN. Still refusing to make a complete break with the oxygen theory of Lavoisier, Gay-Lussac proposed that those acids which did not contain oxygen should be considered as a new class of compounds known as *hydracides*. This view lasted for a short while but was thrown out when Liebig presented a rather convincing argument that it was much simpler to consider an acid to be a compound containing a hydrogen atom that could be replaced by a metal. This brought all of the then recognized acids into a common classification.

THE ARRHENIUS DEFINITION

Before the Arrhenius theory of electrolytic dissociation, which was developed between 1880 and 1890, we have seen that acids were classified either in terms of their observable properties or in terms of some acidifying species such as hydrogen. Actually, these two approaches were not independent. The search for an acidifying species was a search for the source of the particular properties of this class of compounds known as acids. Thus, an acid was ultimately recognized by its properties. This can be appreciated when we recall that the oxygen theory of Lavoisier was discarded because it failed to give complete agreement with experiment. The subsequent hydrogen theory of Davy was acceptable only because all substances that could then be classified as acids by virtue of their properties also contained a replaceable hydrogen atom.

The proposal of an acidifying species to explain the properties of an acid represents a rather crude but first attempt to find a model for acid character. Such a model offered little to the understanding of acid properties and was of absolutely no value from a quantitative point of view. Yet, with the extremely limited knowledge of solutions at that time, little more could reasonably be expected. The door was opened, however, with the Arrhenius theory of electrolytic dissociation. The new concept of ionization processes made possible the Arrhenius model of acid behavior which was the first model to approach the somewhat more sophisticated views of the present day on acid-base character. According to the Arrhenius model, *an acid is any hydrogen-containing compound which gives hydrogen ions in aqueous solution, and a base is any hydroxyl-containing compound which gives hydroxyl ions in aqueous solution.* The process of neutralization of an acid by a base can be represented by the reaction

$$H^+ + OH^- = H_2O$$

With the Arrhenius definition, many of the aspects of acid-base behavior were now understandable in terms of a mechanistic picture, and for the first time quantitative relationships could be determined. This is the kind of model that leads to great advances in any phase of science. For instance, the constant heat of neutralization of a strong acid by a strong base can readily be understood in terms of the Arrhenius picture. Since the reaction involves only the combination of a hydrogen ion and a hydroxyl ion in all such neutralization reactions, the approximately constant molar heat of neutralization would be expected. The theory also leads to quantitative determinations of acid or base strengths from the evaluation of an equilibrium relation such as

$$K_i = \frac{a_{H^+}\, a_{B^-}}{a_{HB}} \tag{8--1}$$

One of the more significant correlations of the Arrhenius model with experiment lay in the catalytic properties of acids. It had been found quite early that along with the other acid properties, catalytic character was also fundamental, and the Arrhenius theory of electrolytic dissociation offered a means of correlating this character with the concentration of the hydrogen ion. Due to the high mobility of the hydrogen ion and the relatively low mobilities of the various anions, the conductivity of a solution should parallel the catalytic activity of the solution if the hydrogen ion is truly the source of the catalytic properties. One of the more outstanding examples of such a correlation is shown in Table 8–1, where the relative conductivities and catalytic effects are compared for a series of acids in anhydrous ethanol as determined by Goldschmidt.

TABLE 8–1. / **Catalytic Effects of Various Acids in Anhydrous Ethanol Relative to HCl = 100.**

Acid	Conductivity	Catalytic Effect on the Esterification of Formic Acid
Hydrochloric	100	100
Picric	10.4	10.3
Trichloroacetic	1.00	1.04
Trichlorobutyric	0.35	0.30
Dichloroacetic	0.22	0.18

In spite of the obvious successes of the Arrhenius definition, several serious shortcomings were soon apparent. It was only natural that a serious complaint should arise with regard to the limitation of all acid-base reactions to aqueous media. It is certainly true that the large majority of chemical reactions are carried out in aqueous systems, but it must be admitted that other solvents exist and their chemistry is also important. This was particularly true for liquid ammonia at that time. Unfortunately, the Arrhenius theory would deny the use of acid-base concepts in these nonaqueous solvents. Equally important, reactions in the gas phase where no solvent is present were also excluded from the acid-base concept. Another serious weakness of the definition lay in the restriction of bases to hydroxyl compounds. Although chemists had come to think of acids as hydrogen-containing compounds, they were not yet convinced that a base had to be a hydroxyl compound. Many organic substances as well as ammonia were known to show basic properties insofar as their chemistry was concerned, and it was difficult to ignore these. By analogy, it would seem that if some acidic compounds that did not contain hydrogen had been known at that time, a corresponding feeling would undoubtedly have existed with regard to the restriction of acids to hydrogen-containing compounds. This, however, was not the case, and the hydrogen concept of an acid was greatly strengthened by the Arrhenius definition.

THE PROTONIC DEFINITION

The climax to the hydrogenic concept of an acid came in 1923, when Bronsted[1] in Denmark and Lowry[2] in England independently proposed that *an acid is a species that tends to give up a proton, and a base is a species that tends to accept a proton.* It is readily apparent that such a definition does not change the status of an Arrhenius acid or base. A hydroxyl-containing compound that yields hydroxide ions in aqueous solution is still a base, and a hydrogen-containing compound that yields hydrogen ions in aqueous solution is still an acid. Yet, the scope of acid-base reactions has been greatly extended with the corresponding removal of many of the shortcomings that were found in the Arrhenius definition.

The protonic definition of a base is obviously far different from that proposed by Arrhenius. Whereas the Arrhenius model restricted a base to a hydroxyl compound that gives a hydroxyl ion in aqueous solution, the protonic definition requires no particular type of ion or any particular solvent. Although they are still bases, the hydroxyl bases are no more so than molecules such as pyridine or ammonia or a multitude of other molecules or ions. The protonic definition of an acid, on the other hand, is not quite so radically removed from that of Arrhenius. The most significant difference is the inherent acid character of a Bronsted acid in the absence or presence of any solvent. Thus, HCl is an acid by virtue of the fact that it can donate a hydrogen ion, not because it might have already done so in an aqueous solution. The restriction of an acid-base reaction to an aqueous medium has, therefore, been removed, and we see that it is possible to have such reactions in any medium or in the absence of a medium.

In the light of the protonic definition, an acid-base reaction can be considered to involve a competition for a proton by two different bases. If we consider the ionization of an acid such as HCl, it is obvious that the resultant chloride ion is a base, inasmuch as it can accept a proton. Such an acid-base pair is referred to as a *conjugate pair*, the chloride ion being the conjugate base of the acid HCl. In order for the acid to donate its proton, it is necessary that there be a base to accept the proton. For the simple ionization of an acid, the solvent will act as that base. For instance,

$$HCl + H_2O = H_3O^+ + Cl^-$$

Here we see that the water accepts the proton from the HCl and is, therefore, a base. The reverse reaction that expresses the competition for the proton is represented by the reaction of the chloride ion with the hydronium ion. Since this particular reaction proceeds essentially 100 per cent to the right, it is quite apparent that the chloride ion is a much weaker base than the water molecule. In general, we can say that the conjugate base of a strong acid is a weak base, and the conjugate base of a weak acid is a strong base.

In the instance of an aqueous solution of HCl, we have seen that the water acts as a base. This is not always the case. If a solute that is more basic than water had been used, the water would have donated the proton and would, itself, be the acid. Thus, we can say that water is an amphiprotic solvent. Actually, we find that the acidity or basicity of a particular substance may vary with the basicity or acidity of the medium in which it is placed. Towards a sufficiently strong acid, such as anhydrous perchloric acid, even nitric acid behaves as a base.

Although the meaning is somewhat different in the protonic definition, the relative strengths of acids and bases can be determined in much the same manner as in the Arrhenius definition. If we consider the general acid-base reaction to be expressable as

$$acid_1 + base_1 = acid_2 + base_2$$

the thermodynamic equilibrium constant for the reaction will be given by

$$K' = \frac{a_{A2}\, a_{B2}}{a_{A1}\, a_{B1}} \tag{8-2}$$

Here we have an expression that will give the relative acidity of $acid_1$ with respect to any $base_1$. Ordinarily, $base_1$ will be a solvent, such as water. This is not necessarily the case. However, under such circumstances, the strength of an acid, HA, can be expressed in terms of the ionization constant

$$K = K' \, a_{H_2O} = \frac{a_{H^+} \, a_{A^-}}{a_{HA}} \qquad (8\text{--}3)$$

which is the same as the expression for the acid strength in the Arrhenius theory.

The success of the protonic definition in handling acid-base systems has been more than impressive, and as a result, we might be prone to forget the original criteria of acid-base character. Yet, if a definition is adequate, it should be consistent with the experimental data. If acid-base character can truly be attributed to the proton, then it should be possible to correlate all acid-base reactions in terms of this definition. If, on the other hand, there are acid-base reactions that cannot be described by the protonic definition, then we must admit that the Bronsted-Lowry approach is not sufficient and seek a new definition.

THE SOLVENT SYSTEM DEFINITION

One of the more important weaknesses of the Arrhenius model of acid-base behavior is its undue restriction of acid-base reactions to aqueous media. This very early led to some conflicts, primarily as the result of solvent studies in liquid ammonia. On the basis of the experimental criteria, similarities could be pointed out between acid-base reactions in aqueous media and certain types of reactions in ammonia. If we consider the auto-ionization of water to form the hydronium and the hydroxyl ions, we can note an analogous autoionization of ammonia to form the ammonium and the amide ions,

$$2 \, H_2O = H_3O^+ + OH^-$$
$$2 \, NH_3 = NH_4^+ + NH_2^-$$

If, further, we consider an ordinary neutralization reaction between a strong acid and a strong base in aqueous media, we can again recognize an exact analog in liquid ammonia. This similarity is apparent from the reactions

$$H_3OCl + NaOH \rightarrow NaCl + 2H_2O$$
$$NH_4Cl + NaNH_2 \rightarrow NaCl + 2NH_3$$
$$\text{acid} \quad + \text{base} \quad \rightarrow \text{salt} \quad + \text{solvent}$$

Such reactions as these are typical of a wide variety of acid-base type reactions which were recognized by Franklin[3] at the turn of the century.

The ammono and the aquo systems of acids and bases are formally very similar. This becomes apparent when we realize that the ammonium ion and the hydronium ion can both be considered to be solvated protons. Although, historically, a solvent system definition of acid-base behavior existed before the protonic definition, it is apparent that the latter will, in general, suffice for protonic solvents. The protonic definition, however, does not satisfy the needs for non-protonic solvents. Researches on such solvents as $COCl_2$, $SeOCl_2$, and SO_2 indicate that acid-base type behavior can be observed in systems where a proton plays no part in the reactions at all, and it would be desirable to talk in terms of acid-base concepts here as well as in protonic solvents.

In an attempt to apply the acid-base concept to the various nonprotonic solvents, several definitions of acids and bases have been proposed.[4,5] Using the definition of Cady and Elsey, we can say that *an acid is a solute that, either by direct dissociation or by reaction with the solvent, gives the cation characteristic of the solvent, and a base is a solute that, either by direct dissociation or by reaction with the solvent, gives the anion characteristic of the solvent.* If, for example, we consider the solvent SO_2, its characteristic cation and anion are seen to be

$$2\, SO_2 = SO^{++} + SO_3^{=}$$

A neutralization reaction would then result from the reaction of a substance such as $SOCl_2$, which should be an acid, and tetramethylammonium sulfite, which should be a base:

$$SOCl_2 + [(CH_3)_4N]_2SO_3 \rightarrow 2(CH_3)_4NCl + 2\, SO_2$$

Just as with the Arrhenius definition, the product of neutralization in the solvent system definition is a salt plus the solvent. This can be seen from Table 8–2, where examples of typical neutralization reactions along with the characteristic cations and anions are given for several solvents.

TABLE 8–2. / **Neutralization Reactions in Various Solvents.**

Solvent	Cation	Anion	Neutralization Reaction
H_2O	$H_3O^+(H^+)$	OH^-	$HCl + NaOH \rightarrow NaCl + H_2O$
NH_3	$NH_4^+(H^+)$	NH_2^-	$NH_4Cl + NaNH_2 \rightarrow NaCl + 2\, NH_3$
$HC_2H_3O_2$	$H_2C_2H_3O_2^+(H^+)$	$C_2H_3O_2^-$	$HCl + NaC_2H_3O_2 \rightarrow NaCl + HC_2H_3O_2$
SO_2	SO^{++}	$SO_3^{=}$	$SOCl_2 + Na_2SO_3 \rightarrow 2NaCl + 2\, SO_2$

There can be no question that an acid-base definition in terms of the parent solvent extends the realm of acid-base reactions to systems that previously had been ignored. But, it omits a large segment of typical acid-base reactions that had been included in the protonic definition, and for this reason, it can in no way be considered to displace the protonic definition. In actuality, the solvent-system approach differs little from a series of Arrhenius type models, one for each solvent. Consequently, virtually all of the complaints that were leveled against the Arrhenius definition can be repeated against the solvent-system approach, except for the Arrhenius restriction of all acid-base reactions to aqueous media. Nevertheless, we cannot help but see the desirability of devising an acid-base definition to cover these systems, and at the same time appreciate the need for a definition of sufficient generality to include all possible systems.

THE LEWIS DEFINITION

In the same year that the Bronsted-Lowry definition was published, G. N. Lewis[6] attacked the problem from a direction that has now led to the unification of virtually all of the existant acid-base definitions. Reemphasizing the experimental basis, Lewis proposed the following four necessary and sufficient criteria for acid-base classification:

(1) "When an acid and a base can combine, the process of combination, or neutralization, is a rapid one.

(2) "An acid or a base will replace a weaker acid or base from its compounds.

(3) "Acids and bases may be titrated against one another by the use of substances, usually colored, known as indicators.

(4) "Both acids and bases play an extremely important part in promoting chemical processes through their action as catalysts."

Going a step further, Lewis attributed these characteristic properties to the electronic structure of the acid or base along with the formation of a coordinate covalent bond. According to Lewis, *a base is any species that is capable of donating a pair of electrons to the formation of a covalent bond, and an acid is any species that is capable of accepting a pair of electrons to form a covalent bond*. Neutralization can then be attributed to the formation of the covalent bond. For instance, in the reaction

$$H^+ \ + \ :\overset{..}{O}:H^- \ = \ H:\overset{..}{O}:H$$

it is seen that the H^+ is capable of accepting a pair of electrons to form a covalent bond and is therefore an acid, whereas, the OH^- has an electron pair to donate to the formation of the covalent bond and is, therefore, a base.

It is invariably found that the most thorough understanding is obtained when a system is viewed in terms of the most fundamental concepts possible. In the instance of a base, it is found that, although a variety of compounds and ions are admitted under this classification, they all have one fundamental property in common. This, of course, is a pair of available electrons. In like manner, the properties of an acid might be attributed to the availability of an empty orbital for the acceptance of a pair of electrons. The hydrogen ion has this fundamental property. However, this property is not limited to the hydrogen ion, and we might, therefore, expect other species with this same fundamental property to also behave as acids. Here we see that the Lewis definition does not attribute acidity to any particular element, but rather, to a unique electronic arrangement. This is apparent when we consider the electron arrangements for the Lewis acid-base reaction

$$
\begin{array}{ccccc}
\text{F} & & \text{H} & & \text{F H} \\
\text{F} \ \overset{..}{\underset{..}{:}} \text{B} & + & :\overset{..}{\text{N}}: \text{H} & \to & \text{F} \ \overset{..}{\underset{..}{:}} \text{B} : \overset{..}{\text{N}} : \text{H} \\
\text{F} & & \text{H} & & \text{F H}
\end{array}
$$

$$\text{(acid)} \qquad \text{(base)}$$

The classification of a reaction such as this as an acid-base type reaction might appear to be rather extreme in the light of our experience with protonic acids. Yet, it is found that Lewis acid-base reactions of this type can actually be titrated to an end-point using a colored indicator in the same manner as can be done with a protonic acid.

Among the most extreme examples of a Lewis acid-base reaction is the formation of a coordination compound. As an example, the formation of the copper ammine complex involves the donation of a pair of electrons by each ammonia molecule to the copper ion, forming the complex $Cu(NH_3)_4{}^{2+}$. Such a broad applicability might be considered to be a weakness of the Lewis definition. This, however, will depend on one's own opinion of the purpose of the acid-base concept. If the purpose is to offer a

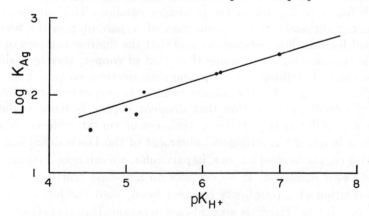

FIGURE 8–1. Stability of Silver Ammine Complexes as a Function of the Basicity of the Coordinating Ammines: Aniline, Quinoline, Hexamethylenetetramine, Pyridine, α-Picoline, γ-Picoline, and 2,4 Lutidine. (Based on data from Bjerrum, J., *Chem. Rev.*, **46**, 38 (1950).)

means of correlating data, then it must be admitted that the Lewis definition has a definite value in the study of coordination compounds. This
can be seen from Figure 8–1, where the relation between the basicity of
coordinating ammines and the stability constants of the corresponding
silver ammine complexes is given.

Along with a more fundamental understanding of the mechanism of
acid-base reactions, the Lewis approach obviously offers a much greater
generality than any previous approach. However, we do not obtain these
without making some serious sacrifices. In fact, these sacrifices are deemed
sufficiently serious by some that a definite opposition to the Lewis definition[7] has arisen. One of the more obvious weaknesses of this definition lies
in its treatment of the conventional protonic acids such as H_2SO_4 and HCl.
According to the Lewis approach, an acid must be able to accept a pair of
electrons to form a covalent bond. This, of course, does not take place with
the protonic acids. An attempt has been made to overcome this difficulty
by a rather indirect approach. It is considered that the acid-base reaction
between an acid, HX, and a base, B, is initiated by the formation of a
hydrogen bond, thereby giving an intermediate species represented by
X-H $\cdots$ B, which then breaks down to give the final neutralization products. It must be admitted that the necessity of using such an indirect
approach for the most common of the known acids is undesirable.

Although, the above weakness might be passed off as more or less
trivial, the question of relative acid strengths is not so trivial. One of
the strong points of the protonic definition lies in the quantitative determination of relative acid and base strengths that it permits. In terms of
the Lewis definition, this is no longer possible. The strength of an acid or
base is found to depend on the particular reaction. This can be seen by
comparing the stabilities of complexes of a pair of positive ions with
different ligands. For instance, we find that the fluoride complex of beryllium is considerably more stable than that of copper, thereby indicating
that divalent beryllium is more acidic than divalent copper. Yet, on the
other hand, we find that the ammine complex of copper is more stable than
that of beryllium, indicating that divalent copper is more acidic than
divalent beryllium. Herein lies a weakness of considerable consequence,
and in it is found the strongest indictment of the Lewis definition.

With regard to complex ions, in particular, we can note a contradiction
in the Lewis definition. If we consider an acid-base reaction in terms of
the formation of a coordinate covalent bond, then the formation of the
complex ion $Cr(NH_3)_6{}^{3+}$ is an acid-base reaction. However, this is not so
in terms of the phenomenological criteria of Lewis because the rate of
formation of the complex is slow. According to the phenomenological criteria, an acid-base reaction should be a rapid reaction. There are many

reactions that will fall into the acid-base category by virtue of electron donation and acceptance but, because of the kinetics of the reaction, they will be slow. Both this factor as well as the arbitrariness of our definition of a covalent bond, make quantitative comparisons among Lewis acids and bases rather difficult.

A third instance in which some question has arisen concerning the validity of the Lewis classification, is found in the catalytic ability of Lewis acids. It has been shown that in certain cases the apparent catalytic character of the Lewis acid can be attributed to impurities that lead to the formation of a hydrogen ion.[8] And, in general, it is found that the reactions catalyzed by Lewis acids are not catalyzed by the common protonic acids. This is of some concern inasmuch as Lewis considered catalytic behavior as one of the four criteria of acid character. However, more recently reactions have been found where Lewis acids were shown to serve as better catalysts than the protonic acids. Bell and Skinner[9] studied the catalytic depolymerisation of paraldehyde in ether using both protonic acids and Lewis acids, and the Lewis acids were found, in general, to be better catalysts for this reaction than the protonic acids. Nevertheless, Bell points out that this particular reaction is rather unique in that it requires only a rearrangement of electrons rather than the migration of atoms. Nevertheless, there can be no question that the Lewis acids do behave as catalysts in many reactions.

THE USANOVICH DEFINITION

Although, the definitions of Lewis and Bronsted are the most commonly used, there have been several additional classifications proposed for the interpretation of acid-base behavior. Of these, the most significant is the *positive-negative* definition of Usanovich[10], in which an acid is defined as *any species capable of giving up cations, combining with anions or electrons, or neutralizing a base to give a salt. A base is defined as any species capable of giving up anions or electrons, combining with cations, or neutralizing an acid to give a salt.* It is obvious that the Usanovich definition includes all previous acid-base definitions, as well as including oxidation-reduction reactions as a special class of acid-base reactions.

In accounting for the acid-base character of a substance, Usanovich places considerable emphasis on the degree of coordination unsaturation of the central atom in the compound as well as emphasizing the general trends of the periodic table. If we consider the coordination unsaturation of an electropositive ion, we note that it can exhibit its acid function by adding an anion, and if an electronegative ion is coordinatively unsaturated, it can exhibit its basic function by adding a cation. For instance, in sulfur dioxide the central atom can be considered to be sulfur, and it is coordinatively unsaturated. Thus, it is capable of accepting an anion such as $O^=$, thereby acting as an acid. It is in terms of such qualitative arguments as these, along with the general periodic trends, that the Usanovich definition is capable of correlating a vast number of reactions under the classification of acid-base.

In support of the Usanovich definition, it must be admitted that it is the most general of all the acid-base definitions thus far proposed. In addition, it appears to satisfy the phenomenological criteria of Lewis about as well as does the Lewis definition. From this latter standpoint, it would appear that the Usanovich definition should certainly be accepted as a legitimate acid-base definition. On the other hand, one wonders how far this can go. If we accept the Usanovich definition, we find that virtually all chemical reactions fall into the acid-base category, and one begins to wonder at the purpose of using any name other than chemical reaction.

There have been several other acid-base definitions proposed, but they add little to the fundamental principles embodied in the ideas already discussed. The Ebert-Konopik *donor-acceptor* acids and bases[11] amount to little more than a new nomenclature for the Usanovich system, and the Lux-Flood definition[12] for oxide reactions can be handled by either the Lewis or the Usanovich definition. Bjerrum[13] has made an attempt at reconciling the protonic and Lewis approaches, in which he proposes that an acid be defined as a *proton donor* while a conventional Lewis acid be referred to as an *antibase*. This contributes nothing but a change in terminology. Finally, it is of interest to note that a quantum mechanical treatment of acids and bases has been developed by Mulliken.[14] Although much more sophisticated, it is essentially as inclusive as the Usanovich definition.

All of the various definitions of acids and bases have a certain utility, and where it may be convenient to use one particular definition it may not be convenient to use another. From the basic nature of a definition, it is obvious that the question of validity does not enter. The problem is one of choosing which definition will be of the greatest value for the particular problems at hand.

ACID-BASE STRENGTHS

Although it is not possible to make a general determination of the relative strength of a Lewis acid, the strength of a protonic acid can be determined by its tendency to give up a proton. Quantitatively, this tendency can be expressed for the equilibrium

$$HA = H^+ + A^-$$

by means of the equilibrium constant

$$K = \frac{a_{H^+} \, a_{A^-}}{a_{HA}} \tag{8-1}$$

The actual direct measurement of such an equilibrium constant is not possible, since the hydrogen ion cannot be donated unless there is a base present to accept it. Thus, in practice, it is necessary to consider an equilibrium of the type

$$HA + B = BII + A$$

where B is some reference base. If we now choose the conjugate pair BH - B as a reference acid-base, we can measure the relative acidities of a series of acids with respect to this pair.

Most commonly, the base, B, is taken to be the solvent. If the solvent happens to be water, the reference acid-base pair is H_3O^+ - H_2O, and this leads to the equilibrium relation

$$K' = \frac{a_{H_3O^+} \, a_{A^-}}{a_{HA} \, a_{H_2O}} \tag{8-4}$$

Since the activity of the water can be treated as a constant, its value can be included in the equilibrium constant, thereby giving

$$K = \frac{a_{H_3O^+} \, a_{A^-}}{a_{HA}} \tag{8-5}$$

Several methods can be used to determine the ionization constant of an acid. The simplest of these would be to assume that concentrations could be substituted for the activities of the various species in the equation. Such an approach would give a good first-order approximation of the ionization constant if the measurements were made in a sufficiently dilute solution using a solvent of relatively high dielectric constant. The most valid method for the determination of a thermodynamic ionization constant is based on emf measurements[15], using a cell of the type

$$\text{Pt, } H_2 \mid HA_{(m1)}, \text{ NaA}_{(m2)}, \text{ NaCl}_{(m3)} \mid \text{AgCl,Ag}$$

where HA represents the weak acid and NaA represents its sodium salt. The use of such a cell can be understood from a thermodynamic standpoint by recognizing that the potential of this cell is given by

$$E = E^0 - \frac{RT}{F} \ln m_{H^+} \, \gamma_{H^+} \, m_{Cl^-} \, \gamma_{Cl^-} \tag{8-6}$$

and that the ionization constant for the acid can be expressed as

$$K = \frac{m_{H^+} \, \gamma_{H^+} \, m_{A^-} \, \gamma_{A^-}}{m_{HA} \, \gamma_{HA}} \tag{8-7}$$

If we now solve Eq. (8–7) for m_{H^+} and substitute for this term in Eq. (8–6), we obtain on rearrangement,

$$\mathrm{E} - \mathrm{E}^0 + \frac{RT}{\mathrm{F}} \ln \frac{m_{HA}\, m_{Cl^-}}{m_{A^-}} = -\frac{RT}{\mathrm{F}} \ln \frac{\gamma_{HA}\, \gamma_{Cl^-}}{\gamma_{A^-}} - RT \ln K \qquad (8\text{--}8)$$

If measurements are made as a function of the ionic strength of the system, the right hand side of the equation will approach $(- RT \ln K)$ as the ionic strength approaches zero. Thus, an extrapolation to infinite dilution would lead to the value of the ionization constant of the weak acid.

In determining relative strengths of the stronger acids such as HCl or H_2SO_4 in an aqueous system, the equilibrium constants are all found to be indeterminately large. This is due to the basicity of the water molecule. If we consider the reaction

$$\mathrm{HA} + \mathrm{H_2O} \rightarrow \mathrm{H_3O^+} + \mathrm{A^-}$$

it is found to go essentially 100 per cent to the right for all of these so-called strong acids. This property of the solvent is known as the *leveling effect*, and it would, of course, be expected to become more pronounced if a more basic solvent were used. This point can be illustrated by considering the extent of ionization of acids in liquid ammonia. For instance, benzoic acid, which is only slightly ionized in water turns out to be quite highly ionized in ammonia due to the fact that the basicity of the ammonia molecule is sufficiently great to cause the reaction

$$\mathrm{HA} + \mathrm{NH_3} = \mathrm{NH_4^+} + \mathrm{A^-}$$

to go essentially to completion. Thus, if we define acid strength in terms of the magnitude of a pK, benzoic acid would appear to be a strong acid in ammonia. However, it is not really possible to compare the strength of an acid in one solvent to its strength in another solvent, and from a phenomenological basis it is not possible to consider an acid such as benzoic acid to be a strong one in any solvent.

Nevertheless, in order to determine the relative strengths of the stronger acids, it is obviously necessary to overcome the leveling effect of the solvent. This can be done by either going to a more acidic solvent such as acetic or sulfuric acid, or by going to an aprotic solvent such as benzene. In principal, both of these approaches should lead to a differentiation of acid strengths. However, in practice, serious difficulties are likely to be encountered in either type of solvent.

One might think that an aprotic solvent would be quite ideally suited as a medium for studying relative acid-base strengths, since the solvent itself is completely inert and will not enter in the determination by accepting or donating a proton. This, of course, would require the addition of some reference acid or base. Measurements along these lines have been made, but considerable question exists as to their interpretation. Primarily, the difficulty with the use of such solvents arises from their low dielectric constant, which is usually around 2 or 3. Consequently, if charged species are present in solution, ion pair formation and higher-order association effects will be large. Under these circumstances, the usual methods for studying acid strengths are of questionable validity, and the equilibrium relationships are not of the simple form that are found in solvents of higher dielectric constant. For these reasons, very little worthwhile information has been obtained on relative acid-base strengths in these solvents.

In spite of the fact that acidic solvents are in some ways as difficult to use as aprotic solvents, they do offer some advantages and have been much more intensively studied. Although the problem of low dielectric constant exists with acetic acid, most of the other acid solvents have quite high values for their dielectric constant. This can be considered as a distinct advantage over the aprotic solvents. Unfortunately, it is found that many of these solvents react with the solute to give more complicated products than would be obtained from a simple proton transfer. Nevertheless, relative strengths of numerous acids have been determined in acidic solvents and the order of decreasing strengths of the stronger mineral acids has been found to be

$$HClO_4 > HBr > H_2SO_4 > HCl > HNO_3$$

This order of decreasing acid strengths was determined by Kolthoff and Willman[16] using conductivity measurements in acetic acid. As can be seen from the conductivity curves in Figure 8–2, $HClO_4$ is considerably stronger than the other acids. However, it is interesting to note that all of the acids have conductivity curves typical of weak electrolytes. This behavior, of course, can be attributed to the low dielectric constant of acetic acid.

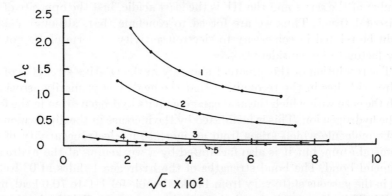

FIGURE 8–2. Relative Strengths of Mineral Acids, (1) $HClO_4$, (2) HBr, (3) H_2SO_4, (4) HCl, and (5) HNO_3 from Conductivity Measurements in Anhydrous Acetic Acid. (After Kolthoff, I., and Willman, A., *J. Am. Chem. Soc.*, **56**, 1007 (1934).)

GENERAL TRENDS IN ACID STRENGTH

As might be expected, various trends in acid strengths are readily apparent, and it would be desirable to understand these trends in terms of some fundamental concepts or a simple theoretical picture of the system. In answer to this problem, several approaches have been offered. However, due to the complexity of the systems involved, these can give only a qualitative correlation with experiment.

TABLE 8–3. / **Approximate pK Values of Some Hydrides.**

H_3N	35	H_2O	16	HF	3
H_3P	27	H_2S	7	HCl	−7
		H_2Se	4	HBr	−9
		H_2Te	3	HI	−10

Strengths of Hydro Acids

As can be seen from Table 8–3, very definite trends in acidity exist in the hydro acids. These are obvious in going across the periodic table in a given period or in going down in a given family. In the first instance, a large increase in acidity can be noted in going from left to right across the periodic table. The apparent explanation of this trend would be in terms of the electronegativities of the nonmetals concerned. Thus, the fluorine atom is more electronegative than the nitrogen atom. Although this argument is consistent with the observed horizontal trends, we find that it does not hold for the vertical trends. Here we find that the acidity in a given family increases with a decrease in electronegativity of the nonmetal. For instance, in the series HF, HCl, HBr, and HI, the HI is the most acidic member of the series and the HF is the least acidic, just the opposite of the horizontal trend. Thus we are forced to conclude that, although acidity might be related in some way to electronegativity, it certainly is not the only factor to be considered.

The resolution of the apparent anomaly in the relative strengths of the hydro acids lies in the recognition that the acidity is primarily associated with the ease with which the acid can give up its hydrogen atom in the form of the hydrogen ion. This is facilitated by the increase in the dipole moment of the molecule which arises from an increase in electronegativity of the nonmetal atom, but it is also facilitated by a weakening of the hydrogen-nonmetal bond. The bond strengths of the hydrogen halides at 0° Kelvin and in the gaseous state vary from 141 kcal/mole for HF to 70.6 kcal/mole for HI. This decrease in bond strength is seen to parallel the increase in acidic character. On the other hand, in the series H_3N, H_2O, and HF the negative ions are all of about the same size, and the H—X bond strengths do not differ quite so radically.

General trends such as these are valuable rules of thumb, but a somewhat greater insight might be obtained by devising a path equivalent to the ionization process and considering each step individually. If the entropy and energy terms could be evaluated for each step, it would then be possible to calculate the pK value of an acid from thermodynamic considerations. Such a path can be represented by a cyclic process of the form

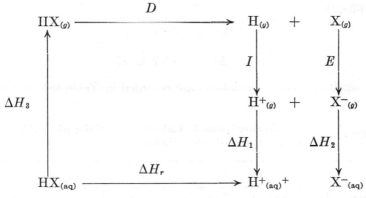

The dissociation energy of the gaseous HX molecule is represented by D, the ionization potential of the hydrogen atom by I, and the electron affinity of the nonmetal by E. The enthalpy of the reaction is given by ΔH_r, and the remaining ΔH terms represent enthalpies of hydration.

This treatment has been applied quite successfully to the halogen hydro acids.[17] ΔH_r can be expressed in terms of the other steps in the cycle giving

$$\Delta H_r = \Delta H_1 + \Delta H_2 - \Delta H_3 + \Delta H_g$$

where $\Delta H_g = D + I - E$. All of the necessary quantities for this calculation have been determined and their accepted values are listed in Table 8–4 along with the calculated values for the entropies.

TABLE 8–4. / **Ionization Data of the Hydrogen Halides.**

	HF	HCl	HBr	HI
D	134.6	103.2	87.5	71.4
E	82.2	87.3	82.0	75.7
I	315	315	315	315
ΔH_g	367	331	321	311
$\Delta H_1 + \Delta H_2$	−381.9	−348.8	−340.7	−330.3
ΔH_3	−11.5	−4.2	−5.0	−5.5
ΔS^0	−20.8	−13.4	−9.1	−3.2

The entropy term, $-\Delta S^0$, is determined from the expression

$$-\Delta S^0 = S^0_{HX_{aq}} - (S^0_{H^+_{aq}} + S^0_{X^-_{aq}}) \tag{8-9}$$

Several approximations are necessary in the evaluation of the entropy terms, but they are probably valid to within 2 or 3 eu.

Now that the enthalpy and entropy terms are known for the ionization of the acid, HX, the ionization constant of the acid can be calculated by recalling that

$$\Delta F^0 = \Delta H^0 - T\Delta S^0 \tag{8-10}$$

and

$$\Delta F^0 = -RT \ln K \tag{8-11}$$

The results of these calculations are recorded in Table 8–5 for 25°C. The

TABLE 8-5. / **Thermodynamic Calculation of the pK Values for the Hydrogen Halides.**

	ΔH_r^0	$T\Delta S_r^0$	ΔF_r^0	pK_{calc}	pK_{exp}
HF	−3.0	−6	3	2	3
HCl	−13.7	−4	−10	−7	−7
HBr	−15.2	−3	−12	−9	−9
HI	−14.1	−1	−13	−10	−10

agreement between the calculated and experimental pK values is seen to be quite striking. This would tend to give some credence to the proposed cyclic process, and in terms of the various steps it is possible to rationalize the general trends of the hydro acids.

Strengths of Inorganic Oxy Acids

Somewhat greater emphasis has been placed on the relative strengths of the inorganic oxy acids than those of the hydro acids and, just as with the hydro acids, various trends can be detected. From an experimental standpoint, it has been found that the pK values of these acids can be placed in four distinct groupings. These are given in Table 8–6, along with the general structures of the acids. Immediately, we can see that a correlation exists between the structure of the acid and its grouping. In this respect, it is to be noted that the oxygen atoms of acids in the first grouping are all bonded to a hydrogen atom. That is, they are all hydroxyl oxygens. However, in the second grouping there is one nonhydroxyl oxygen atom, and each successive grouping has an additional one. Corresponding to this increase in the number of nonhydroxyl oxygen atoms, we find a consistent

TABLE 8–6. / **pK Groupings of Some Inorganic Oxy Acids.**

FIRST GROUPING			SECOND GROUPING		
Class	Example	pK	Class	Example	pK
$X(OH)_m$	$Ge(OH)_4$	8.6	$XO(OH)_m$	$PO(OH)_3$	2.1
	$As(OH)_3$	9.2		$HPO(OH)_2$	1.8
	$Te(OH)_6$	(8.8)		$H_2PO(OH)$	2.0
	$Cl(OH)$	7.2		$AsO(OH)_3$	2.3
	$Br(OH)$	8.7		$SO(OH)_2$	1.9
	$I(OH)$	11.0		$SeO(OH)_2$	2.6
				$TeO(OH)_2$	2.7
				$ClO(OH)$	2.0
				$IO(OH)_5$	1.6

THIRD GROUPING			FOURTH GROUPING		
Class	Example	pK	Class	Example	pK
$XO_2(OH)_m$	$SO_2(OH)_2$	(−3)	$XO_3(OH)_m$	$ClO_3(OH)$	(−10)
	$SeO_2(OH)_2$	(−3)			
	$IO_2(OH)_2$	0.8			
	$ClO_2(OH)$	−1			
	$NO_2(OH)$	−1.4			

increase in acidity. At the same time, we note that the number of hydroxyl groups in the molecule apparently has little or no effect on the relative acidity. Thus, we conclude that a nonhydroxyl oxygen atom is in some way significant in the determination of the strength of an oxy acid.

It can also be seen from Table 8–6, that, for a given structure, the acid strength decreases with an increase in size of the central atom. This trend can be illustrated by the example of ClOH, BrOH, and IOH, where the pK values are 7.2, 8.7, and 11.0 respectively. This principle was utilized by Cartledge in an early attempt to find a correlation between structure and acid strength. By considering acids and bases to be hydroxides of non-metals and metals respectively, Cartledge pointed out that the *ionic potential* ϕ, defined as the charge to radius ratio of the central atom, could be used to determine if the hydroxide were acidic, basic, or amphoteric. According to Cartledge, for a value of $\sqrt{\phi} < 2.2$, the hydroxide is basic, $2.2 < \sqrt{\phi} < 3.2$, the hydroxide is amphoteric, and for $\sqrt{\phi} > 3.2$, the hydroxide is acidic.

An attempt to go beyond the simple correlation of the strengths of the oxy acids with some particular structural property of the acid was made by Kossiakoff and Harker.[18] They proposed a mechanism for the ionization process involving a series of steps, and, in essence, calculated the free energy change for each step. The final expression for the free energy change obtained by Kossiakoff and Harker was

$$\Delta F = \sum_i W_i - C + RT \ln n_O/n_H \qquad (8\text{--}12)$$

in which C is a constant characteristic of the solvent, n_O is the number of nonhydroxyl oxygen atoms in the resultant ion, n_H is the number of transferable hydrogen atoms in the acid, and W_i is the electrostatic energy involved in the transfer of a single ion. This latter quantity can be determined from the classical expression for the electrostatic energy

$$W_i = \sum_j \frac{m_j e}{\epsilon} \left(\frac{1}{r_j} - \frac{1}{r_j'} \right) \qquad (8\text{--}13)$$

The distance $(r_j' - r_j)$ is the displacement of the proton with respect to the j'th atom in the molecule, e is the electron charge, and ϵ is the solvent

TABLE 8–7. / **Classification of Inorganic Oxy Acids.**[*]

Class	Example	pK$_1$	pK$_2$	pK$_3$	pK$_4$
$m = 0$		$(n = 0)$	$(n = 1)$		
	H$_4$GeO$_4$	8.6	12.7		
	H$_3$AsO$_3$	9.2	—		
	H$_6$TeO$_6$	(6.2; 8.8)	10.4		
	HClO	7.2	—		
	HBrO	8.7	—		
	(HIO)	(11.0)	—		
$m = 1$		$(n = 1)$	$(n = 2)$	$(n = 3)$	
	H$_3$PO$_4$	2.1	7.2	12.0	
	H$_3$PO$_3$	1.8	6.2	—	
	H$_3$PO$_2$	2.0	—	—	
	H$_3$AsO$_4$	2.3	7.0	13.0	
	H$_2$SO$_3$	1.9	7.0	—	
	H$_2$SeO$_3$	2.6	8.3	—	
	H$_2$TeO$_3$	2.7	8.0	—	
	HClO$_2$	2.0	—	—	
	H$_5$IO$_6$	1.6	6.0	—	
$m = 2$		$(n = 2)$	$(n = 3)$	$(n = 4)$	$(n = 5)$
	H$_2$SO$_4$	—	1.9	—	—
	H$_2$SeO$_4$	—	2.0	—	—
	HIO$_3$	0.8	—	—	—
	H$_4$P$_2$O$_7$	0.9	2.0	6.7	9.4
	H$_4$P$_2$O$_6$	(2.2)	(2.8)	7.3	10.0
	H$_2$S$_2$O$_4$	0.3	2.5	—	—

* From Ricci, J. E., *J. Am. Chem. Soc.*, **70**, 109 (1948).

dielectric constant. The *formal charge* of the jth atom is represented by m_j, and is defined as the group number of the atom in the periodic table minus the number of electrons in its valence shell. In determining the formal charge of an atom, a shared pair of electrons is counted as one.

In terms of the treatment of Kossiakoff and Harker, the determination of the ionization constant of an acid involves an evaluation of ΣW_i and C, which should be a constant for all of the oxy acids in a given solvent. ΣW_i can be determined from a detailed knowledge of bond angles and bond distances of the molecules involved; however, the calculations are somewhat time-consuming. Once ΣW_i is known for a particular acid, C can be determined, using the free energy change based on the experimental evaluation of the pK of that acid. For this purpose, Kossiakoff and Harker used the first ionization constant of *ortho*phosphoric acid as a reference. Once the value of C has been determined, it is possible to calculate the ionization constants of the other oxy acids. Kossiakoff and Harker have carried out these calculations for 26 acids in addition to *ortho*phosphoric acid, and they found the over-all average deviation between the calculated and the observed log K values to be only 0.89.

Although, the results obtained by Kossiakoff and Harker appear to be quite encouraging, a critical review of this work by Ricci[19] has shown that it is far from conclusive. As shown by Ricci, the contributions of the various structural terms are less than the average deviation between the observed and their calculated pK values. This is not to say that the factors considered by Kossiakoff and Harker are not valid, but rather that the treatment does not give a legitimate test of their validity. Ricci points out, however, that a remarkable grouping of pK values is obtained if the acids are classified in terms of the formal charge of the central atom and the number of nonhydroxyl oxygen atoms in the acid. This grouping is illustrated in Table 8–7, where the acids in each group have the same value of m, the formal charge of the central atom, and n, the number of nonhydroxyl oxygen atoms in the acid. On this basis, Ricci proposes the empirical expression

$$\text{pK} = 8.0 - m\ (9.0) + n\ (4.0) \tag{8–14}$$

for the determination of the pK of an oxy acid. Accordingly, if the structure of H_3PO_4 can be represented as

$$\text{HO} : \overset{\displaystyle \text{OH}}{\underset{\displaystyle \text{OH}}{\overset{..}{\underset{..}{\text{P}}}}} : \text{O}$$

the pK will be $8 - 9 + 4 = 3$. The experimental value of the pK of H_3PO_4 is approximately 2.1. Using this equation, Ricci has calculated the pK values for 36 oxy acids with an average deviation of 0.91 between the observed and the calculated values. This agreement is comparable to that obtained by Kossiakoff and Harker, and the amount of calculation involved is considerably less.

There can be no question that an empirical relation such as that proposed by Ricci is valuable. Certainly, quite acceptable results can be obtained with a minimum of effort. However, such an approach contributes very little to our understanding of the mechanisms involved, and it is this that we are ultimately after. Consequently, if a calculation of a pK value could be made from a mechanistic picture, it would be of much greater significance, regardless of the amount of effort necessary for its determination.

BIBLIOGRAPHY

1. Bronsted, J., *Rec. Trav. Chim.*, **42,** 718 (1923).
2. Lowry, T., *Chem. & Ind.*, **42,** 43 (1923).
3. Franklin, E., *J. Am. Chem. Soc.*, **27,** 820 (1905).
4. Franklin, E., *J. Am. Chem. Soc.*, **46,** 2137 (1924).
5. Cady, H. and Elsey, H., *J. Chem. Ed.*, **5,** 1425 (1928).
6. Lewis, G., "Valence and the Structure of Atoms and Molecules," The Chemical Catalog Co., New York, N.Y., 1923.
7. Bell, R., "Acids and Bases," Methuen's Monographs on Chemical Subjects, New York, N.Y., 1952.
8. Norrish, R. and Russell, K., *Trans. Faraday Soc.*, **48,** 91 (1952).
9. Bell, R. and Skinner, B., *J. Chem. Soc.*, 2955 (1952).
10. Usanovich, M., *J. Gen. Chem.*, (USSR), **9,** 182 (1939).
11. Ebert, L. and Konopik, N., *Osterr. Chem. Ztg.*, **50,** 184 (1949).
12. Lux, H., *Z. Electrochem.*, **45,** 303 (1939).
13. Bjerrum, J., *Naturwissenschaften*, **38,** 46 (1951).
14. Mulliken, R., *J. Phys. Chem.*, **56,** 801 (1952).
15. MacInnes, D., "The Principles of Electrochemistry," Reinhold Publishing Corp., New York, N.Y., 1939.
16. Kolthoff, I. and Willman, A., *J. Am. Chem. Soc.*, **56,** 1007 (1934).
17. McCoubrey, J., *Trans. Faraday Soc.*, **51,** 743 (1955).
18. Kossiakoff, A. and Harker, D., *J. Am. Chem. Soc.*, **60,** 2047 (1938).
19. Ricci, J., *J. Am. Chem. Soc.*, **70,** 109 (1948).

SUGGESTED SUPPLEMENTAY READING

Hall, N., "Modern Conceptions of Acids and Bases," *J. Chem. Ed.*, **7,** 782 (1930).
Bell, R., "The Proton in Chemistry," Cornell University Press, Ithaca, N.Y., 1959.
Luder, W. and Zuffanti, S., "The Electronic Theory of Acids and Bases," John Wiley & Sons, New York, N.Y., 1946.
Bjerrum, N., "Acids, Salts, and Bases," *Chem. Revs.*, **16,** 287 (1935).
Moeller, T., "Inorganic Chemistry," John Wiley & Sons, New York, N.Y., 1952.

9 / *Coordination Chemistry*

The field of coordination chemistry has grown in a half-century from a readily defined and limited area into what is now the most active field of inorganic chemistry. And in recent years it has received not only a large amount of experimental study, but also a rather extensive theoretical treatment. The scope of this field has now become so broad and the number and kind of compounds with which it is concerned are so large that it is appropriate that we devote this chapter to simply introducing the subject and indicating the current theoretical approaches.

For over one hundred years the study of inorganic, metal-containing compounds was largely descriptive, as indeed was much of the whole field of chemistry. Real theoretical progress toward understanding the structure and behavior of these inorganic compounds was not possible until the discovery of the electron in 1897. This made possible the development of the electronic theory of valency. Since that time theoretical inorganic chemistry has made rapid progress. Primarily, this has been due to the pioneering work of Lewis, Kossel, Langmuir, Sidgwick, Fajans, Pauling, and many others who have extended and amplified their ideas.

Ordinarily, new terms will be defined as they arise, but there are several definitions which should be given at the outset. A *complex ion* will be understood to be a more or less stable, charged aggregate formed when a metal atom or ion becomes directly attached to a group of neutral molecules and/or ions. The latter are called *ligands* or *donor groups* and they are said to be *coordinated* or *complexed* to the *central* ion or *acceptor* in a *first coordination sphere*. The first coordination sphere of the complex ion is indicated by enclosing the formula for the ion in square brackets, for example: $[Cu(H_2O)_4]^{2+}$ or $[Co(NH_3)_4F_2]^+$. The number of ligand atoms arranged in a definite geometry and directly bonded to a central ion is called the *coordination number* of that ion. Whereas 4 and 6 are the most commonly encountered coordination numbers, 2, 3, 5, 7, and 8 have all been well established. A group which can attach to the same metal ion through more than one of its atoms is termed a *chelate* or *multidentate* ligand. Chelating agents are known which can attach to metal ions through two, three, four, five, six and even more donor atoms, with two being the most common. The terms applied to such polydentate ligands are bidentate, terdentate, quadridentate, quinquidentate, and sexidentate, respectively.

A *coordination compound* may be one of two types. Firstly, it may be a *neutral* complex which, by our definition, would make it identical to the above complex ion except that the aggregate has no net charge. This may be due to either a zero-valent central metal atom surrounded by neutral ligands, such as $[Fe(CO)_5]$ and $[Pt(RNC)_4]$, or a central metal ion surrounded by enough oppositely charged ligands to produce a neutral aggregate. The latter is more common and examples would be $[Co(NH_3)(NO_2)_3]$ and $[Fe(acac)_3]$, where *acac* = acetylacetonate ion, and $[Cr(gly)_3]$, where *gly* = glycinate ion. Secondly, the compound may be *ionic*, and then it must contain a complex ion as at least one of its ions. This is the most common type of complex compound.

One of the characteristics of the complex compound is that the complex ion or neutral complex of which it is composed will most often retain its identity in solution, although partial dissociation may occur. In fact, the extent of dissociation varies from very slight to very extensive. For example, the compound $2KBr \cdot HgBr_2$ contains the tetrahedral ion $[HgBr_4]^{2-}$ in the crystalline solid, and this same ion persists in solution with only very slight dissociation. On the other hand, the compound $2KCl \cdot CoCl_2$, shown to contain the tetrahedral ion $[CoCl_4]^{2-}$ in the crystalline solid, is found to dissociate extensively in aqueous solution into chloride ions, potassium ions, and hydrated cobalt(II) ions. These two examples illustrate the differences found in the relative thermodynamic stability of various bonds. Thus, from the preceding we would infer that the mercury(II)-bromide ion bond is more stable than the mercury(II)-water bond, whereas the cobalt(II)-water bond is more stable than the cobalt(II)-chloride ion bond.

Complexes which *exchange* ligands rapidly, that is, within mixing times, are generally referred to as *labile* complexes, while those which exchange ligands at a slower rate are called *nonlabile* or *inert* complexes. One must guard against confusing thermodynamic stability with kinetic stability when employing these terms.

Much of the chemistry of coordination compounds is determined by the electronic configuration of the central ion, by the donor and acceptor properties of the ligands, and by the nature of the linkage between the ligand and the central ion. For this reason, correspondingly more space will be devoted here to these aspects of the subject than to such items as stereochemistry, types of isomerism, substitution reactions, and redox reactions. Nor will the increasing importance of coordination compounds in the fields of analytical chemistry, biochemistry, and electrochemistry be discussed. Several excellent texts are available which may be consulted for detailed treatments of these and other aspects of coordination chemistry.[1-8]

WERNER'S COORDINATION THEORY

The early study of inorganic complex compounds consisted largely of a series of attempts to explain the existence and structure of hydrates, double salts, and metal ammonia compounds. These compounds were termed *molecular* or *addition* compounds because they are formed by the union of two or more already stable and apparently saturated molecules. Early theories and explanations offered by such men as Graham (1837), Claus (1854), Blomstrand (1869), and Jorgensen (1878), are of little more than historical interest now since the coordination theory proposed by Alfred Werner in 1893 proved to be so all-encompassing in its scope. This theory, which was extended and substantiated experimentally in the quarter century following its conception, was largely responsible for the renewed interest in, and rapid growth of inorganic chemistry around the turn of the century.

Like many great theories, Werner's coordination theory was fundamentally quite simple. The basic postulate in his own words is as follows: "Even when, to judge by the valence number, the combining power of certain atoms is exhausted, they still possess in most cases the power of participating further in the construction of complex molecules with the formation of very definite atomic linkages. The possibility of this action is to be traced back to the fact that, besides the affinity bonds designated as principal valencies, still other bonds on the atoms, called auxiliary valences, may be called into action."

The remainder of the theory is an elucidation of the number, nature, and spatial arrangement of these secondary or nonionizable valences. Thus every metal ion possesses a fixed number of secondary valences which must be satisfied in compound formation. For example, Werner recognized that platinum(IV), cobalt(III), iridium(III), and chromium(III) all have six such valences (i.e., a coordination number of 6), and platinum(II), palladium(II), copper(II), and zinc all have four such valences (i.e., a coordination number of 4). Whereas the primary valences must be satisfied by negative ions, the secondary valences may be satisfied by either negative ions or neutral molecules. Commonly we find a negative ion satisfying both a primary and a secondary valence. For example, in the complex $[Co(NH_3)_5Cl]Cl_2$, one chloride ion is different from the other two in that it has lost its ionic character and is spatially closer to the cobalt than the other two.

Werner's method for assigning groups to the first coordination sphere was based on their response in solution to various chemical and physical tests. To illustrate this we can consider the complex compounds of platinum(IV) and cobalt(III) shown in Table 9–1. From the corresponding

TABLE 9–1. / **Molar Conductances of Some Platinum(IV) and Cobalt(III) Complex Compounds.**

Werner Formula	Molar Conductance 0.001 N solution, 25°C	Number of Ions Indicated
$[Pt(NH_3)_6]$ Cl_4	523	5
$[Pt(NH_3)_5Cl]$ Cl_3	404	4
$[Pt(NH_3)_4Cl_2]$ Cl_2	228	3
$[Pt(NH_3)_3Cl_3]$ Cl	97	2
$[Pt(NH_3)_2Cl_4]$	0	0
K $[Pt(NH_3)Cl_5]$	108	2
K_2 $[PtCl_6]$	256	3
$[Co(NH_3)_6]$ Cl_3	432	4
$[Co(NH_3)_5NO_2]$ Cl_2	246	3
$[Co(NH_3)_4(NO_2)_2]$ Cl	98	2
$[Co(NH_3)_3(NO_2)_3]$	0	0
K $[Co(NH_3)_2(NO_2)_4]$	99	2

conductance data it can be seen that the indicated number of ions produced in solution substantiates the Werner formula shown. Further support is obtained from chemical evidence showing how many chlorine atoms are tightly bound to the platinum and how many are ionizable. Thus, the last three platinum complexes in the table give no test for ionic chloride while the first four precipitate $\frac{4}{4}$, $\frac{3}{4}$, $\frac{2}{4}$, and $\frac{1}{4}$, respectively, of their chlorine with silver nitrate. Furthermore, that the ammonia molecules are tightly bound to both the platinum and the cobalt is indicated by their inability to neutralize strong acids and the failure of strong alkali to drive off the ammonia from aqueous solutions of the complexes. The primary valence of 4 for the Pt(IV) and 3 for the Co(III), and the secondary valence of 6 for both of the metals are maintained throughout the series. Many other complex ions were studied in this manner, and a great mass of experimental data was accumulated by Werner and his students to substantiate the postulation of two kinds of valency. It should be pointed out, however, that Werner had no theoretical justification for his two types of valency, and widespread acceptance of the theory did not come until the electronic theory of valency was able to present a self-consistent explanation of valence types.

STEREOCHEMISTRY OF WERNER COMPLEXES

Equally as important as the postulation of two types of valency by Werner, was his fundamental postulate that the secondary valences are directed in space about the central ion, not only in the solid state, but also when the complex ion is dissolved in solution. Thus he postulated, and later obtained considerable experimental evidence to prove, that a grouping of six such valences are directed toward the apices of a *regular octahedron* which is imagined to be circumscribed about the metal ion. On the other hand, he was able to show that a grouping of four such valencies may be arranged in either a *square planar* configuration or a *tetrahedral* configuration. This postulation made possible the correlation of a large body of facts concerning complexes and the prediction of the structures and structural changes of many new and as yet unprepared inorganic compounds. Perhaps the most striking support for the directed valency ideas came from their ready explanation of both the various isomeric compounds which were known at that time as well as the new isomers prepared in the succeeding years.

Coordination Number Four

Werner demonstrated that in the case of tetracoordinated platinum(II) complexes, for compounds with the general formula $[Ma_2b_2]^{n+}$, *cis-trans* isomerism exists.* This is made possible if the four ligand atoms lie in or nearly in the same plane, as illustrated for $[Pt(NH_3)_2Cl_2]$ in Figure 9–1.

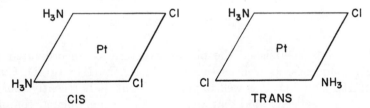

CIS   TRANS

FIGURE 9–1. *Cis* and *Trans* Isomers of the Planar Complex $[Pt(NH_3)_2Cl_2]$.

Cleverly devised chemical reactions were carried out to determine which of a pair of isomeric compounds was *cis* and which was *trans*, for a large variety of compounds of this basic structure. Werner pointed out that the isolation of two isomers of any compounds having this general formula is a good indication of a planar structure, since only one compound is possible if the configuration is a regular tetrahedron. Further proof of the planar structure of platinum(II) and palladium(II) complexes was obtained by the synthesis of two geometrical isomers of complexes of the general type

* M will often be used to represent a central metal ion, lower-case letters will stand for unidentate ligands, and capital letters will be used for multidentate ligands, e.g., AA will represent a symmetrical bidentate group; AB, an unsymmetrical one, etc.

$[M(AB)_2]$, neither of which could be resolved into optical isomers (see **(a)** below). A tetrahedral structure allows only one geometrical structure which is asymmetric and must give rise to optical isomers as shown here (see **(b)** below). Many different methods, both chemical and physical,

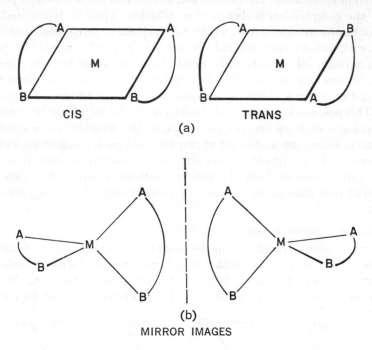

have now firmly established the planar structure of 4-coordinated platinum(II) complexes, as well as those of Pd(II), Ni(II), Ag(II), Cu(II), and Au(III). However, it is well to point out that quite recently considerable evidence has been found that most, if not all, square planar complexes should really be considered as *tetragonal*. That is, they can be considered to have a fifth and a sixth group coordinated, or perhaps we should say located, at a longer distance from the central ion than are the four planar ligands. For example, it is not unlikely that in solution, or in the solid obtained from a solution, that square planar ions may have solvent molecules or even other anions in a fifth and possibly sixth position completing a distorted octahedron about the central ion. The ions $[PdCl_5]^{3-}$ and $[Ni(CN)_5]^{3-}$ are examples of this for which spectroscopic evidence has been found. In addition, solid complexes of the type $[M(AA)_2X]ClO_4$, where M is Pd(II) or Ni(II) and X is Cl, Br, or I, have been isolated. These complexes exhibit the conductivity in nitrobenzene of uni-univalent electrolytes. Even Au(III), which is isoelectronic with Pt(II), has been observed to form 5- and 6-coordinated complexes of the type $[Au(AA)_2X]^{2+}$ and $[Au(AA)_2X_2]^+$.

There is now a considerable body of evidence available to show that the tetrahedral configuration is also important in 4-coordinate complexes. The existence of optical activity in compounds of the type $[M(AB)_2]$, where M is Be(II) or B(III), is direct chemical proof of this configuration, or more precisely, it is proof that the structure cannot be planar. Other complexes for which there is strong evidence for the tetrahedral structure are those of Cu(I), Ag(I), Au(I), Zn(II), Cd(II), Hg(II), Al(III), Ga(III), In(III), Fe(III), Co(II), and Ni(0). Most of the evidence on the structure of these complexes comes from X-ray crystallography. Recently there have been reports of the preparation of tetrahedral complexes of all of the first row transitional elements in the divalent oxidation state. However this configuration must still be considered rare for transition elements where octahedral and tetragonal configurations are most common. The reason for this will be made clear later in terms of modern theories. This last statement concerning configuration does not apply to the metals in their very high oxidation states in which they behave like nonmetals and form tetrahedral oxyanions, such as VO_4^{3-}, CrO_4^{2-}, FeO_4^{2-}, MnO_4^-, MnO_4^{2-}.

Coordination Number Six

Werner also demonstrated the existence of *cis-trans* and optical isomerism in hexa-coordinated complexes, thereby substantiating his prediction of an octahedral configuration for these compounds. Figure 9–2 illustrates the geometrical isomers for a typical complex having the general formula $[Ma_4b_2]^{n\pm}$. In Figure 9–3 an example of the complex type $[M(AA)a_2b_2]^{n\pm}$

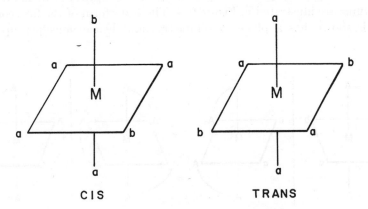

CIS   TRANS

FIGURE 9–2. *Cis* and *Trans* Isomers of the Octahedral Complexes Having the General Formula $[Ma_4b_2]^{n\pm}$.

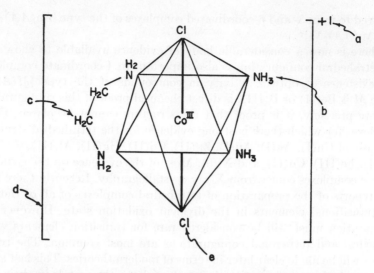

FIGURE 9–3. Example of the Complex Type $[M(AA)a_2b_2]^{n\pm}$, indicating (a) the charge on the entire complex ion, (b) a unidentate neutral ligand in a *cis* position to the other NH_3 and *cis* to both Cl ligands, (c) a bidentate neutral ligand (spans *cis* positions only), (d) square brackets, enclosing the metal ion and its first coordination sphere, and (e) a unidentate negative ligand in a *trans* position to the other Cl and *cis* to the remaining ligand atoms.

is given and several of the terms introduced thus far are illustrated. Werner's proof of the octahedral configuration also rested upon the demonstration of the existence of optical isomers for complexes with the general formulas *cis*-$[M(AA)_2ab]^{n\pm}$ and $[M(AA)_3]^{n\pm}$. The optical isomers for these structures are illustrated in Figure 9–4. The *trans* form of the first complex that is shown has a plane of symmetry, and hence nonsuperimposable

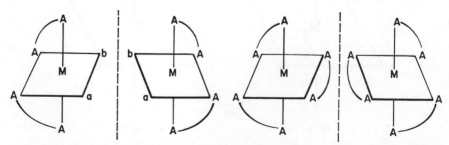

FIGURE 9–4. The Optical Isomers of the Complex Types $[M(AA)_2ab]^{n\pm}$ and $[M(AA)_3]^{n\pm}$

mirror image isomers cannot exist for this geometrical isomer. The *trans* form of the second complex is structurally impossible. The two other symmetrical six-cornered geometries, the planar hexagon and the trigonal prism, are clearly eliminated by the resolution of such complexes, since no asymmetric structures are possible if a equals b for the above complex types with these configurations.

Six-coordinated complexes of at least 16 different metals, some in more than one valence state, have been successfully resolved into their optical isomers. The rates and mechanisms of the racemization of many of these optically active complexes have been the subject of a considerable amount of recent research.[3,6]

Much of the effort of Werner and his students went into devising and carrying out experiments to substantiate the stereochemical implications of his theory. At that time, such proofs involved primarily chemical methods. Today there is ample X-ray diffraction data as well as other physical data providing unequivocal support for the structural ideas of the theory. In addition, both the stereochemical concepts and the two kinds of valency envisioned by Werner are now explainable in terms of our modern valency theories.

CLASSIFICATION OF COORDINATION COMPOUNDS

Because of the large variety of compounds which are properly considered to be coordination compounds, it is difficult to classify them, even for study purposes. In fact, no one method of classification will be completely satisfactory. However, we shall find it at least instructive to examine separately some possible methods of classification.

(1) If coordination number is chosen as the criterion for classification, then virtually all complexes will be found under the numbers 4 and 6, since all metal ions exhibit one or both of these coordination numbers in their complexes. Examples of complexes with other well-defined coordination numbers ranging from 2 to 10 are given in Table 9–2. It should be pointed out that after 4 and 6 the most common coordination numbers are 8 and 2. The number of metallic complexes with a true odd coordination number is relatively very small. Since most complexes have either four or six ligands attached to the central atom, a further breakdown is certainly desirable.

(2) It might be suggested that we classify complexes by the kind of central atom. However, there are about 84 elements whose atoms may be considered to act as central metal ions, and most of these display multiple oxidation states each of which must be considered as an entirely different acceptor.

(3) A classification of complexes according to the kind of ligand atom

TABLE 9–2. / **Complexes with Coordination Numbers Other Than Four or Six.**

Coordination Number	Examples*
2	$M(CN)_2^-$, $[M = Cu(I), Ag(I), Au(I)]$, $Hg(NH_3)_2^{2+}$, $AuCl_2^-$, $Ag(NH_3)_2^+$, $Cu(tu)_2^+$
3	$M(R_3Z)_2I$, $[M = Cu(I), Ag(I), Au(I); Z = P, As]$ $Ag(R_3P)_3^+$, $Ag(R_2S)_3^+$, $Ag(tu)_3^+$
5	$Fe(CO)_5$, $M(terpy)Cl_2$ $[M = Cu(II), Zn, Cd]$ $Ni(DMG)_2Br$, $Ni(tas)X_2$ $[X = Cl,Br]$, $Ni(Et_3P)_2Br_3$, $Zn(acac)_2(H_2O)$ $M(das)_2I$ $[M = Ni(II), Pd(II), Au(III)]$ $Co(CN)_5^{3-}$, $Co(CNR)_5$
7	ZrF_7^{3-}, MF_7^{2-} $[M = Nb, Ta]$ $UO_2F_5^{3-}$, UF_7^{3-}, $NbOF_6^{3-}$
8	$Mo(CN)_8^{4-}$, TaF_8^{3-} $M(acac)_4$ $[M(IV) = Ce, Zr, Hf, Th, U, Pu]$ $M(ox)_4^{4-}$ $[M(IV) = Zr, Hf, Th, U, Sn]$ $M(oxine)_4$ $[M(IV) = Th, Pu]$
9	$Nd(H_2O)_9^{3+}$
10	$M_2[M'(CN)_8X_2]\cdot 4H_2O$ $[M = Cd, Mn; M' = Mo, W; X = H_2O, NH_3, N_2H_4]$

*Symbols used are: tu = thiourea; $terpy$ = 2,2′,2″-terpyridine; DMG = dimethyl-glyoximate ion; tas = $(CH_3)_2As(CH_2)_3AsCH_3(CH_2)_2As(CH_3)_2$; Et = ethyl; das = o-phenyl-enebisdimethylarsine; $acac$ = acetylacetonate ion; ox = oxalate ion; $oxine$ = 8-hydroxy-quinolinate ion.

is much more realistic and indeed this is the approach taken by Bailar[2] in an excellent survey of complexes. The elements whose atoms, in appropriate molecules or ions, may attach directly to metal ions are shown below:

			H
C	N	O	F
	P	S	Cl
	As	Se	Br
	Sb	Te	I

It is seen that all of the true nonmetals, except boron, are included. Those to the right of the vertical line are simple donors coordinating always as the simple uninegative ion. The remainder usually coordinate when they are part of a molecule or polyatomic ion. However, we cannot exclude oxide, sulfide, and selenide simple ions from being called ligands. Table 9–3 gives some examples of commonly encountered ligands grouped according to the donor atom.

TABLE 9–3. / **Some Typical Ligands Grouped According to the Donor Atom.**

Donor Atom	Examples
C	CO, CN^-, RNC
N	NH_3, C_5H_5N, NO_2^-, RNH$_2$, $NH_2CH_2CH_2NH_2$
	, N_3^-, RCN, NCS^-,
P	R_3P, PX_3 $(X = F, Cl, Br)$
As	R_3As,
O	H_2O, OH^-, $CO_3^=$, $SO_4^=$, $S_2O_3^=$, RCOO$^-$, ONO^-, $C_2O_4^=$, $CH_3CCH_2CCH_3$ (with $\overset{\parallel}{O}$ $\overset{\parallel}{O}$)
S	R_2S, SCN^-
O and N	, $H_2NCH_2COO^-$

In general there is a very great difference between the coordinating affinities of the elements in the first short period and their respective congeners,[9] i.e., between N and P, O and S, and F and Cl. In fact it is possible to recognize two extreme classes of acceptor: Class A, those which form their most stable complexes with the first ligand atom of each group (N, O, and F), and class B, those which form their most stable complexes with the second or subsequent ligand atom of each group. However, it should be pointed out in this connection that each oxidation state of a metal must be regarded as a different acceptor. Most of the metals with empty or completely filled $(n - 1)d$ orbitals belong in class A, as do the transition elements with one, two, or three d electrons. Only a few metals

TABLE 9–4. / **Classification of Metals According to Their Coordinating Affinities for the Elements of the First Short Period or Their Respective Congeners.**

Class A	Intermediate		Class B
IA IIA IIIA IVA VA Al, Ga, In, Ge Sn, Cr, U	Mn, Fe, Co, Ni, Cu, Zn Mo, Tc, Ru, Rh W, Re, Os, Ir Tl, Pb, Bi, Te, Po	Cd	Pd, Ag Pt, Au, Hg

seem to belong solely to class B, whereas many transition metals fall into an intermediate range. This is shown in Table 9–4. Of course, more important than the classifications themselves are the reasons why the particular classes exist. Perhaps, as we shall see, the most important single determining factor is the electron configuration of the metal atom.

(4) A fourth method by which we may classify complexes is according to the type or nature of the coordinate bond which is formed. Since a given metal ion may form several different types of bonds, it will be convenient to consider the possible bond types in terms of the electronic makeup of the various ligands. Table 9–5 summarizes the electronic types of the

TABLE 9–5. / **Types of Unidentate Ligands.**

1. Those with one or more unshared pairs of electrons
   (a) Containing no vacant orbitals for receiving electrons from the metal; examples are H_2O, NH_3, F^-, OH^-, RNH_2 (restricted to negative ions and Lewis base molecules involving donor atoms of the first short period).
   (b) Containing vacant orbitals or orbitals that can be vacated for receiving π-bonding electrons from the metal; examples are: CN^-, CO, NO_2^-, R_3P, R_3As, R_2S (negative ions and generally very poor Lewis base molecules).
   (c) Containing two or more electron lone pairs, one of which may become π-bonding by donation to vacant metal orbitals; examples are: OH^-, NH_2^-, Cl^-, Br^- (evidence for this type of bonding is not as strong as for others).
2. Those without an unshared pair of electrons but with electrons already involved in π-bonds; examples are: olefins, benzene, cyclopentadienyl ion, alkynes.
3. Those that may act as bridging groups between two metal atoms; for example: OH^-, Cl^-, NH_2^-, $O_2^=$, CO.

unidentate ligands. Multidentate coordinating agents may have all ligand atoms alike whereby they will coincide with one of the types shown in the table, or one or more of the ligand atoms may be of a different type. Examples of both kinds of chelating agent are very numerous. It should be noted that in this classification all bonds are assumed to be covalent and that in each case donation of electron pairs, both to and from metal ions, is mentioned or implied. As we shall see later, it will not always be necessary to treat the coordinate bond as a covalent one, but rather we shall find it convenient in certain cases to consider it as arising from purely electrostatic interactions.

(5) Finally, it is possible to place all metallic complexes into one of four categories which have as their sole criterion the electronic makeup of the metal atom or ion in question.

Category I. This category includes metal ions which in their complexes have an inert gas configuration, i.e., $1s^2$ or ns^2np^6, where n is 2, 3, 4, 5, or 6 These ions are all spherically symmetrical. The two series of inner transition elements, the lanthanides and actinides, in their trivalent oxidation state can also be included here since the incomplete $4f$ or $5f$ electronic level is buried sufficiently far below the valency shell as to exert relatively little effect on the nature of the bonds.** The elements included in this category are shown in Figure 9–5(a). The Roman numerals give the oxidation state which, for this first category, coincides with the periodic group number.

Category II. Here we find the metal ions or atoms shown in Figure 9–5(b), which in their complexes have a pseudo-inert gas configuration,

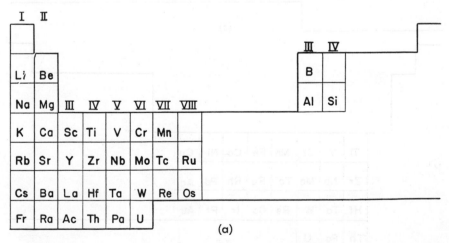

(a)

FIGURE 9–5 (Continued on p. 274).

** Recent theoretical work has, however, shown that $5f$ orbitals and electrons should be included in covalent bonding considerations.

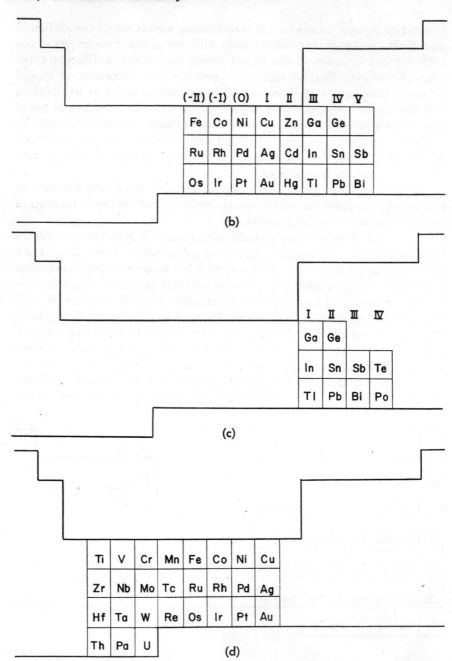

FIGURE 9–5. **(a)** Category I Metals; **(b)** Category II Metals; **(c)** Category III Metals; and **(d)** Category IV Metals. The Roman numerals represent the oxidation states.

i.e., $(n - 1)d^{10}$, where n is 4, 5, or 6. These are also spherically symmetrical species among which are included some metals in negative oxidation states.

Category III. These include metal ions or atoms which in the complex have a pseudo-inert gas plus two configuration, i.e., $(n - 1)d^{10}ns^2$, where n is 4, 5, or 6. These are shown in Figure 9–5(c).

Category IV. These include metal atoms or ions which in the complex have incompletely filled d orbitals, i.e., $(n - 1)d^{1-9}$. This group is by far the largest and most diverse, and it includes all the transition metals in all oxidation states other than those which would place them in one of the previous categories. These are listed in Figure 9–5(d). Because of the size of this group, as well as for more fundamental reasons, it will be desirable to divide this category still further according to the detailed configuration of the d-orbital electrons. In order to understand this subdivision we will have to introduce some additional ideas, particularly those of the crystal field theory. Suffice it to say at this point that the further subdivision of the category will depend primarily upon two things, the number of d electrons and the nature of the bond formed with a particular ligand. From the point of view of the symmetry of structure of the complex ion, the subdivisions will separate perfectly regular structures, slightly distorted structures, and grossly distorted structures. These matters will become clearer later in this chapter.

THEORIES OF THE COORDINATE BOND

We require of a theory that it be capable of doing at least two things. It should be able to explain experimental facts and it should be capable of predicting new experimental findings. For complexes, we wish to explain and predict their thermodynamic, kinetic, spectral, stereochemical, and magnetic properties. When we consider the wide variety of metal ions, ligands, and resultant complex types we can appreciate the magnitude of this task. We shall find, not unexpectedly, that there is no one all-encompassing theory but rather several partially successful theories each with its particular merits for dealing with selected complex systems. It is estimated that more than 95 per cent of the known complexes are either 4-coordinated and approximately planar or tetrahedral, or 6-coordinated and approximately octahedral in configuration. Hence we shall confine most of our further considerations to those complexes which have coordination numbers of 4 and 6.

Before discussing the several theories of the coordinate bond, it might be well to point out that a theory is no more than an approximation to reality. The more examples which can be found to conform to the theory the better the approximation. However, when a few exceptions to the theory arise, they do not necessarily invalidate the whole concept. More likely they point up our failure to give a satisfactory approximation. And this usually requires only that the theory be modified so as to include these exceptions. For example, this is the current position of the valence bond approach to the coordinate bond. Also, it often happens that two or more theories can explain the same phenomena, and then we must search for some more fundamental concept common to both theories, for this will likely be a better approximation to the truth. This is the situation now existing with the crystal field and molecular orbital theories of bonding as they are applied to complexes. Growing out of these at the present time is a broader approach known as the Ligand Field Theory.

The electronic theory of valency, clearly enunciated by Lewis in 1916 and interpreted and extended for many systems by Langmuir in 1919 and others in the succeeding decade, enabled chemists to express Werner's valence concepts in terms of electrons. Much credit for this particular application of the new theory of valence must go to Sidgwick[10,11] and to Lowry.[12] The primary valences of Werner were interpreted as arising from electrovalence or electron transfer and the secondary valencies were regarded as consisting of covalency or electron-pair sharing. A primary valency may or may not be ionic. Thus, if a negative ion is present in the first coordination sphere, as for example the chlorine in chloropentam-minechromium(III) nitrate, $[Cr(NH_3)_5Cl](NO_3)_2$, it is satisfying simul-taneously both a primary and a secondary valence. In this case the chlorine has lost its ionic character. The nitrate ions satisfy only primary valences and thereby retain their ionicity.

Sidgwick Model

Sidgwick accepted the Lewis concept of the two-electron covalent bond between two atoms in a molecule and introduced the coordinate bond for the case in which both electrons in the shared pair originate on the same atom. Noting that all molecules and ions which can attach to metal ions have at least one unshared pair of electrons, he suggested that this free electron pair is partially donated to the metal ion in the formation of the bond. The bond thus formed is also called a *dative* or *semipolar* bond, and it is sometimes represented with an arrow, $M \leftarrow L$, to indicate that the donor group, L, has supplied both electrons to the acceptor, M.

Sidgwick further suggested that metal ions will tend to accept electron pairs from donors until they have obtained a sufficient number of electrons such that the metal in the resulting complex ion has an *effective atomic number* (EAN) of the next inert gas.[11] This may be illustrated with hexammineplatinum(IV) chloride, $[Pt(NH_3)_6]Cl_4$:

Pt(IV) contains	74 electrons
6 NH₃ groups donate	12 electrons
The EAN of Pt(IV) in complex	86 electrons (AN of Rn)

While this rule is followed by many of the known complex ions, there are a large number of exceptions. For example, all of the metal ions which have more than one coordination number, depending upon the nature of the ligand, such as Ni(II), Co(II), Zn(II), Ag(I), etc., must violate the rule. In fact, complexes of some metal ions such as Fe(III), which is 4-coordinate in $[FeCl_4]^-$ and 6-coordinate in $[Fe(CN)_6]^{3-}$, never obey the rule. Whereas Sidgwick's effective atomic number concept has little more than historical significance now, it is noteworthy that almost all of the known metal carbonyls and many of their derivatives and related compounds obey this simple rule. The recently reported $V(CO)_6$ violates the rule, but it is interesting that its stability is much lower than that of any of the other carbonyls.

The concept of a coordinate bond between two atoms seems quite satisfactory for explaining the formation and stability of the ammonium ion (formed from $:NH_3$ and H^+), addition compounds such as $(CH_3)_3B:NH_3$, and other Lewis acid-base products. However, in the case of a hexacoordinated metal ion, the suggested donation of six pairs of electrons to the central ion poses the serious problem of the accumulation of very high negative charge on the metal. Although we would like to retain the simplicity of the Sidgwick model, we must recognize that modifications in the theory are required to remove not only the objection just cited but also other shortcomings which will become apparent later.

The Three Current Models

At the present time, three more or less distinct approaches to the theoretical treatment of the bonding in coordination compounds are recognized. Chronologically, and according to increasing complexity, they are (1) the *electrostatic* theory with its more recent *crystal field* modifications, (2) the *valence bond* theory, and (3) the *molecular orbital* theory. An even more comprehensive and sophisticated theory which is currently evolving from a combination of the crystal field and the molecular orbital theories is known as the *ligand field* theory. It should be realized, of course, that none of these theories (except the last-mentioned one) was specifically designed to explain only complex compounds, but they have achieved considerable success in this respect.

Before considering the various theories, it will be useful to first review some of the pertinent knowledge relating to the atomic orbitals belonging to the central ion as they would exist in the gaseous ion free of perturbing ligands. Figure 9–6 shows the conventional boundary surfaces of the s, p, and d atomic orbitals. It must be borne in mind that they only indicate the regions of space which will enclose most of the charge of the electron contained in them. The symbol ψ stands for a solution of the wave equation and $\int \psi^2 d\tau$ represents the probability that the electron will be

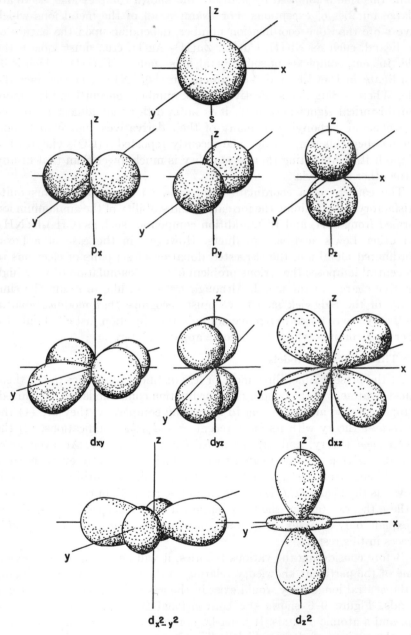

FIGURE 9–6. Conventional Boundary Surfaces of the *s*, *p*, and *d* Atomic Orbitals.

found in the volume element $d\tau$, and it is, therefore, ψ^2 which is physically significant, or to be technically correct, we should use $\psi\psi^*$ or $|\psi|^2$ rather than ψ^2.

The valence electrons in transition metal ions move primarily in the d orbitals and for this reason they will be of the most concern to us. The d_{xy}, d_{xz}, and d_{yz} orbitals are mutually perpendicular, and each has four alternating plus and minus lobes in the respective planes. The lobes are at 45° angles to the cartesian coordinates. Three other orbitals, designated as $d_{x^2-y^2}$, $d_{z^2-y^2}$, and $d_{x^2-z^2}$ are likewise mutually perpendicular, each having four lobes lying along the respective axes in one of the three perpendicular planes. However, of these three equivalent orbitals only two are independent, that is, mutually orthogonal, and we usually take a hybrid of the latter two and call it simply d_{z^2}. This orbital will have large positive lobes along the z axis and a doughnut-shaped negative belt around the z axis which is symmetric in the xy plane. For reasons which will become clear later, the first three d orbitals described above are grouped together and designated as t_{2g} or d_ϵ, whereas the latter two, the d_{z^2} and $d_{x^2-y^2}$ orbitals are termed e_g or d_γ orbitals. In the absence of a magnetic or electric field, the three p orbitals of a given principal quantum level are of equal energy, as are the five d orbitals. Two electrons are allowed per atomic orbital providing their spins are opposed, but if possible, they will tend to enter different orbitals of the same or slightly differing energies with their spins oriented in the same direction according to one of Hund's rules.

We may now proceed to examine the three theories. The valence bond theory will be considered first, since it is conceptually the simplest and has served admirably for the interpretation of several properties of complex molecules for more than a quarter of a century. Even today, with the many shortcomings of this theory clearly recognized, a large number of chemists still find it convenient to use the valence bond concept in interpreting and correlating their results. Next we shall discuss the electrostatic theory, emphasizing the crystal field approach. This approach has proved to be the most successful of the three in the satisfactory correlation of properties, as well as in the number of calculations and predictions it permits with regard to complexes. Finally, we shall discuss briefly the molecular orbital approximation. This theory has not been applied to metal complexes as often as the other theories because of the complexity involved in dealing with many-electron systems by this method.

THE VALENCE BOND THEORY

The application of the valence bond approximation to complexes is due mainly to Pauling.[13] It deals with the electronic structure of the ground state of the central metal ion and, as we shall see, is concerned primarily with the shapes and magnetic moments of complexes. The orbitals of the complex are designated only in terms of the central atom orbitals. Pauling has devised a very simple and satisfactory means for presenting the bonding picture which involves the following assumptions:

(1) The central metal atom will make available a number of orbitals equal to its coordination number for the formation of covalent bonds with ligand orbitals.

(2) A covalent σ-bond arises from the overlap of a vacant metal orbital and a filled orbital of the donor group. The donor group must, therefore, be a chemical species which contains at least one lone pair of electrons. This bond, called a *coordinate link*, is seen to be simply a covalent bond involving the characteristic overlap of two orbitals. However, it possesses a considerable amount of polarity because of the mode of its formation.

(3) In addition to the σ-bond, there is also the possibility that a π-bond may be formed providing that suitable d electrons of the metal are present in an orbital which can overlap with a vacant orbital on the donor atom. This bond will change the charge distribution on both the metal and the ligand in such a way as to strengthen the σ-bond.

The strongest covalent bond will be formed when the charge clouds overlap one another as much as possible. In order to satisfy this criterion it has been shown that the original atomic orbitals should be hybridized to form a new set of equivalent bonding orbitals having definite directional properties. Since hybridization of orbitals has already been treated in Chapter 5, we have given in Table 9–6 only the results of the calculations which determine the shape and the relative strength of several hybrid bonds important in connection with complexes. The convenient representation of bonding devised by Pauling is illustrated in the examples given

TABLE 9–6. / **The Shapes and Relative Strengths of the Important Hybrid Orbitals.**

Coordination Number	Orbital Configuration	Spatial Configuration	Relative Bond Strengths
—	s	—	1.000
—	p	—	1.732
2	sp	linear	1.932
3	sp^2	trigonal	1.991
4	sp^3	tetrahedral	2.000
4	dsp^2	square planar	2.694
5	dsp^3, d^3sp	trigonal bipyramid	—
5	d^2sp^2, d^4s	square pyramid	—
6	d^2sp^3	octahedral	2.923

TABLE 9-7. / **Examples of Commonly Encountered Hybridizations Showing Electron Distribution and Calculated and Experimental Magnetic Moments.**

Complex	Electron Distribution			μ_{calc}	μ_{exp}
	3d	4s	4p		
[Co en_3]$^{3+}$	↑↓ ↑↓ ↑↓ ↑↓ ↑↓	↑↓	↑↓ ↑↓ ↑↓ — d^2sp^3	0	~0
[Mn(CN)$_6$]$^{3-}$	↑↓ ↑↓ ↑ ↑↓ ↑↓	↑↓	↑↓ ↑↓ ↑↓ — d^2sp^3	1.73	1.80
[Ni(CN)$_4$]$^{2-}$	↑↓ ↑↓ ↑↓ ↑↓ ↑↓	↑↓	↑↓ ↑↓ — dsp^2	0	0
[Cu(NH$_3$)$_4$]$^{2+}$	↑↓ ↑↓ ↑↓ ↑↓ ↑↓	↑↓	↑↓ ↑↓ ↑ — dsp^2	1.73	1.89
[Ni(Et_3P)$_2$(NO$_3$)$_2$]	↑↓ ↑↓ ↑↓ ↑ ↑	↑↓	↑↓ ↑↓ ↑↓ — sp^3	2.83	3.05
[MnCl$_4$]$^{1-}$	↑ ↑ ↑ ↑ ↑	↑↓	↑↓ ↑↓ ↑↓ — sp^3	5.92	5.95

in Table 9–7 for the three most commonly encountered hybridizations, d^2sp^3, sp^3, and dsp^2.

The $d_{x^2-y^2}$ and d_{z^2} orbitals are directed toward the ligands in an octahedral complex, and they are therefore used in the formation of the d^2sp^3 hybrid bonds. The square planar, dsp^2 hybrid bonds, utilize only the $d_{x^2-y^2}$ orbital. The magnetic moments shown in Table 9–7 were calculated using the spin-only formula, and they are expressed in Bohr magneton units. It is seen that the agreement is quite good between the calculated and the observed magnetic moments. It can also be seen that the known stereochemistries of the complexes are consistent with the spatial arrangements predicted by the hybrid orbitals. The fact that the experimentally determined magnetic moments are slightly higher than predicted can be attributed to the use of the spin-only formula. This assumes that the orbital angular momentum of the unpaired electrons is completely quenched. This, of course, is not necessarily true, and the resultant orbital moments contribute to the total magnetic moment.

Defects in the Early Model

Difficulties are encountered in the original Pauling approach when the number of orbitals needed to accommodate the bonding electrons is too low. This can result from the occupancy of the orbitals by either paired or unpaired electrons from the metal ion. As an example, we can consider the complex ion $[FeF_6]^{3-}$, which has a magnetic moment corresponding to five unpaired electrons and the complex ion $[Ni(NH_3)_6]^{2+}$, which has two unpaired electrons. In neither of these complexes is it possible for $3d^2 4s 4p^3$ hybridization to occur. As shown below, there are but four orbitals of approximately the same energy beyond the occupied d orbitals.

	3d	4s	4p
$[FeF_6]^{3-}$	↑ ↑ ↑ ↑ ↑	□	□ □ □
$[Ni(NH_3)_6]^{2+}$	↑↓ ↑↓ ↑↓ ↑ ↑	□	□ □ □

Pauling originally overcame this problem by assuming that such complexes are primarily ionic. That is, he assumed that the metal orbitals were left free to accommodate only metal ion electrons, and the bonding electrons were contained in separated orbitals located primarily on the ligands. The introduction of the term "ionic" to describe these complexes is unfortunate since many of them, such as the strongly paramagnetic $[Fe(acac)_3]$, behave like typical covalent compounds. An alternative suggestion was put forth in 1937 by Huggins.[14] He proposed that outer d orbitals might be used in bond formation. However, at that time it was generally considered that the $4d$ orbitals could not hybridize satisfactorily with the $4s$ and $4p$ orbitals to give strong covalent octahedral bonds. However, more recent calculations by Craig, *et al.*,[15] have shown that with highly electronegative ligands the use of $4d$ orbitals probably leads to stronger bonds than those formed with $4s 4p^3$ orbitals alone. Thus the complexes originally described by Pauling as ionic are supposed now to be employing *upper level* covalent bonds as opposed to *lower level* covalent bonds for those termed covalent by Pauling. Other terms which have been introduced to distinguish the apparent two types of complexes are: *outer* and *inner* orbital (Taube), *spin-free* and *spin-paired* (Nyholm), and *high-spin* and *low-spin* (Orgel). In the third edition of Pauling's classic book, "The Nature of the Chemical Bond," the terms *hypoligated* and *hyperligated* are introduced.

Multiple Bonding

In the discussion thus far, it has been tacitly assumed that all ligands will have a readily accessible and easily donated pair of σ-bonding electrons, i.e., that ligands are all good Lewis bases. This is far from the true situation.

There are many ligands, such as CO, RNC, PX_3 (X = halogen), PR_3, AsR_3, SR_2, etc., which are very poor electron pair donors, and yet they form many stable metallic complexes. Furthermore, nothing has yet been said about the unusually high negative charge which would be placed upon a central atom by six negative groups if each donates a pair of electrons.

It was partially to explain the latter situation that Pauling suggested that the atoms of the transition groups are not restricted to the formation of single covalent bonds. Rather, he proposed that they are capable of forming multiple bonds with electron-accepting groups by making use of the electrons and orbitals of the shell below the valence shell. To illustrate, let us consider the hexacyanoferrate(II) ion, $[Fe(CN)_6]^{4-}$, in which a charge of -4 appears to be placed on the iron atom. By allowing double bonding between the iron and carbon, this unlikely concentration of charge may be more suitably distributed. The following would be one Lewis structure showing how the charge on the iron might be reduced to a more reasonable value of -1. Other similar resonance structures can be drawn. Further

reduction of the negative charge on the iron would be expected if ionic structures were also permitted. This would allow the iron to become neutral or even positively charged as we might expect it to be.

It is now generally recognized that multiple or π-bonding in metallic complexes is important and may arise in, at least, two ways: (1) donation of d_ϵ electrons which cannot form σ-bonds to empty p_π orbitals located on the ligands, or (2) donation of d_ϵ electrons to empty d_π orbitals located on the ligands. The first type, sometimes designated as $d_\pi - p_\pi$, will occur when the donor atom is of a first-row element like N in NO_2^-, or C in CO or CN^-. The second type, called $d_\pi - d_\pi$, will be formed if the donor atom is an element in the second or later row, e.g., P, S, etc., which possesses empty and available d orbitals. This so-called back donation of electrons from metal to ligand will serve not only to strengthen the bond, but also to relieve the otherwise excessive negative charge on the metal ion. A third type of π-bonding involving $p_\pi - p_\pi$ overlapping is thought to occur in certain boron complexes, but it must be considered to be very uncommon. Finally, a fourth type of π-bonding involving donation of π-bonding electrons from the ligand to vacant metal d orbitals has been postulated to occur in certain transition state complexes,[3] but it has only very indirect experimental support.

The strong coordinate bonds formed by such poor Lewis bases as those mentioned above are readily accounted for by π-bonding. One example should suffice to illustrate this point. We can consider M to represent a transition metal ion which has an available nonbonding pair of d electrons. The bonding of this ion to PX_3, for example, may be pictured as follows:

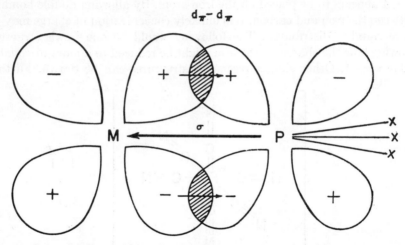

One of the filled d orbitals of the metal is shown as overlapping one of the empty d orbitals of the phosphorus, thereby giving rise to a $d_\pi - d_\pi$ bond. This bond is, perhaps, even stronger than the σ-bond. It is interesting to note that this picture receives support from the fact that as the electronegativity of the X groups bonded to the phosphorus increases, the stability of the metal-ligand bond increases. This would be predicted since a shift of electron density toward the X group, while decreasing the donor capacity of the phosphorus, should make the phosphorous atom more receptive to electron donation from the metal. Of course, the enhancement of the strength of the σ-bond by the closer approach of the atoms must also contribute to the bond strength. However, the relative magnitude of this factor has not yet been determined.

We may now summarize the major defects of the valence bond theory when applied to metallic complexes[3] as: (1) being limited to qualitative explanations, (2) not permitting the interpretation or prediction of spectra, (3) not accounting for or predicting detailed magnetic properties, (4) being unable to account for or to predict even the relative energies of different structures, and (5) not taking into account the splittings of the d energy levels.

Finally, in favor of the valence bond theory, we should point out that it has for many years provided a very convenient model of bonded atoms based upon a set of simple rules. Although it is now a relatively poor model for complex ion formation, we should not forget that it served long and well during the early stages of the development of the theory of bonding in complexes. And, even today, it is still conceptually the simplest model for the experimental chemist to use.

ELECTROSTATIC THEORY — CRYSTAL FIELD THEORY

Simple Electrostatic Model

The application of a simple electrostatic theory to the bonding in metallic complexes was carried out primarily by Van Arkel and DeBoer[16] and by Garrick[17] around 1930. They simply applied the well-known potential energy equations of classical electrostatics to their bonding model. This required a knowledge of the charges and sizes of the central ions, and the charges, dipole moments, polarizabilities, and sizes of the ligands. It is relatively easy to show that if a purely electrostatic model is adopted, then, with identical ligands, regular configurations will be expected for all of the possible coordination numbers. Thus, for the most common coordination numbers of 2, 4, and 6, the expected configurations would be linear, tetrahedral, and octahedral, respectively, since these would reduce the electrostatic repulsion between the ligands to a minimum. Using this simple model, it is possible to calculate bond energies for some complexes which compare quite favorably with the experimentally determined values.[3]

Nevertheless, one does not have to search far to find many phenomena which are inexplicable in terms of the simple electrostatic model. There are also many inconsistencies which arise from its application. For instance, the existence of the numerous square coplanar complexes cannot be justified on the basis of this model since only tetrahedral configurations are predicted for 4-coordinated complexes, and the stability of complexes involving nearly nonpolar ligands such as CO, PF_3, etc., is untenable. In addition, the ions of the second and third transition series form many complexes of greater stability than those of the first-row transition elements; yet, because of the greater size of the heavier ions their complexes would be predicted to be less stable. Finally, along with the other shortcomings, the simple theory cannot account for or predict magnetic, spectral, or kinetic properties.

Crystal Field Theory

The next step in the evolution of the electrostatic approach is the crystal field theory. This theory proposes that metal complexes be treated as if the only interaction between the central atom and the surrounding ligands is an electrostatic one. Unlike the simple electrostatic theory, however, it deals with orbitals and electrons. To a first approximation the orbitals of the central ion are considered as separated from the ligand orbitals. In particular, the theory is concerned with the effect of the various possible electrostatic fields, which arise from the differing geometries and strengths of various ligands, on the five d orbitals of a transition metal. Although applications have been made to compounds where the degeneracy of f orbitals is assumed to be affected by a crystal field, the greatest success and widest application has been achieved with the complexes of the transition metals where the outer electrons move in d orbitals.

Crystal field theory is not new. Ionic bonding in complexes was suggested by Langmuir in 1919 and the quantum mechanical theory was developed by Bethe[18] a decade later. The first application to transition metal complexes was made in 1932 by Schlapp and Penney[19] and by Van Vleck,[20] who used the theory to calculate magnetic susceptibilities. In 1935, Van Vleck[21] summarized and compared the valence bond, crystal field, and molecular orbital theories. But in the succeeding twenty years only a relatively few physicists employed the theory of crystal fields, and this was primarily for the study of the fine details of magnetochemistry and absorption spectra. The recent renewed interest in crystal field theory probably stems from the 1951 work of the chemists, Ilse and Hartmann,[22] who applied it to the weak visible absorption band shown by titanium(III) hexaquo ions. Following that, Orgel[23] probably had more to do with pointing up the significance of the crystal field theory in the study of complexes than any other chemist. In the past decade significant contributions to the theory and its application have been made by Jorgensen, Ballhausen, Bjerrum, Griffith, Nyholm, Owen, Liehr, and many others.

The d orbitals have already been mentioned and one representation of them has been given in Figure 9-6. For the field-free ion or atom in $vacuo$, these orbitals are degenerate, but their energies become differentiated when an electrostatic field, such as that due to the presence of ligands, is imposed upon them. The orbitals lying in the direction of the ligands are raised in energy in comparison with those which lie between the ligands. For example, when six identical ligands approach a metal ion along the x, y and z axes, the charges of the ligands will repel an electron to a greater extent if it is in a d_{z^2} or $d_{x^2-y^2}$ orbital than if it is in a d_{xy}, d_{xz}, or d_{yz} orbital, since the former point towards the ligands. In terms of energy levels, the original degeneracy is split into two parts for octahedral complexes, and

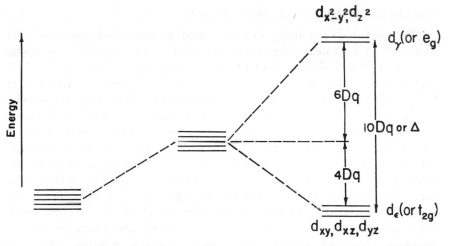

FIGURE 9–7. Energy Level Diagram Illustrating the Splitting of the Five-fold d Orbital Degeneracy in an Octahedral Ligand Field.

the d_γ orbitals assume a higher energy than they would have if they were not directed towards the ligands, whereas the d_ϵ orbitals assume a lower energy. This is illustrated in Figure 9–7.

The fact that all of the d levels are repelled slightly by the ligands is indicated by the displacement of the entire d level to some new, but unknown, value. The level then splits into new sublevels. The higher of these is doubly degenerate and is designated as d_γ or e_g, and the lower is triply degenerate and is designated as d_ϵ or t_{2g}. This splitting is just that which would be obtained by a crystalline field of cubic symmetry (O_h) such as is characteristic of six octahedrally disposed identical ligands. The crystal field splitting is the energy difference between the d_ϵ and d_γ orbitals, and it is frequently measured in terms of a parameter, Dq. Dq is a measure of the crystal field strength; the stronger the field, the larger is Dq. The magnitude of the splitting is arbitrarily set at $10Dq$. This has also been designated variously as Δ, ΔE, and ($E_1 - E_2$).

A theorem of quantum mechanics requires that the average energy of the perturbed d-levels remain unchanged. Thus, according to this theorem, if we add up the crystal field energy of the six d_ϵ electrons with the energy of the four d_γ electrons, we should get zero. Therefore the d_ϵ level must be $4Dq$ below the unknown original energy, and the d_γ level must be $6Dq$ above this original energy. Since we do not know the original energy, the zero of energy for the crystal field effect is taken to be that for a random occupation of the three d_ϵ and the two d_γ orbitals by an electron. The gain in energy achieved by the preferential filling of the lower-lying d levels is called the *crystal field stabilization energy* (CFSE) and we shall have more to say about this later, including the ways in which it is determined.

Distribution of Electrons in the d Orbitals

The picture is not really so simple, and we must look more carefully at the principles which determine the distribution of the d electrons among the d_ϵ and d_γ orbitals. Considering the ground state, we find that there are at least two opposing tendencies which are of significance in determining the population distribution of d electrons under the effect of a crystal field. One is the tendency for the electrons to occupy, as far as possible, the lower-lying orbitals. The second is the tendency for electrons to enter different orbitals with their spins parallel. The latter lowers the coulombic repulsive energy among the electrons and also allows a more favorable exchange energy. When there are only 1, 2 or 3 d electrons, both of these tendencies can be satisfied when the electrons occupy different d_ϵ orbitals with spins parallel. With 4, 5, 6 or 7 d electrons we have to choose between the maximum spin state with a maximum number of unpaired electrons and the minimum spin state which requires pairing of electrons in the d_ϵ level. As we shall see presently this choice will be determined by the strength of the electrostatic field offered by the particular set of ligands.

As an illustration, let us consider octahedral complexes of the first transition series of elements. For scandium(III) there are no d electrons, hence no crystal field stabilization is possible. With titanium(III) we have an ion containing one d electron. This electron enters a d_ϵ orbital giving $4Dq$ of CFSE. The second d electron, present in vanadium(III) and titanium(II), will also enter the d_ϵ level, and its spin will be parallel to that of the first d electron. This results in $8Dq$ total CFSE.[†] The third d electron enters the third degenerate d_ϵ orbital, and in chromium(III) and vanadium(II) complexes we have three unpaired electrons and a CFSE amounting to $12Dq$. Now, when we consider the manganese(III) or chromium(II) ions, we find that the fourth electron may enter a d_γ orbital, reducing the CFSE by $6Dq$, or it may enter a d_ϵ orbital, pairing with an electron already present and thereby increasing the CFSE by an additional $4Dq$. Notice that the difference in energy between the two possible states is just $10Dq$ or Δ. Which of these choices the fourth electron will take will now depend upon how large the energy separation is between the d_ϵ and d_γ orbitals. If the splitting of the d levels is small compared to the Hund stabilization energy, then we can expect the fourth electron to enter a destabilizing d_γ orbital. The CFSE will be lower, but the over-all energy, which includes the energy required for electron pairing, will be more favorable. On the other hand, if the splitting is large, the fourth d electron may

[†] This will only be approximately true since the d orbital energy levels for various crystal fields, in this case octahedral, are only readily obtained for the case of a single d electron. Systems with more than one d electron have energies which are complicated by electron interaction. However, satisfactory results may still be obtained, particularly with octahedral complexes, if the latter complication is ignored.

be forced to pair up with an electron in the d_ϵ level. This would add another $4Dq$ to the total CFSE and would reduce the total spin below that of the field-free ion. However, the total gain in energy for the ion is not really $4Dq$ since electron-pairing energy must be supplied, and indeed this is often very large. But if the electrons do pair up, then it is safe to conclude that the ligands have caused a large splitting. Correspondingly, this would indicate that they are closer and more strongly bound to the central ion, thereby lowering the total energy of the system.

Weak and Strong Ligand Fields

For convenience we now must distinguish two limiting situations known as the *weak field* case (small splitting) and the *strong field* case (large splitting). The strength of the field will be primarily determined by the nature of the ligand and by the charge density of the central ion. Consideration of the split levels for the octahedral case will reveal, as was stated earlier, that for d^4, d^5, d^6 or d^7 ion systems the CFSE and the number of unpaired electrons will depend upon whether the field is strong or weak. The Pauling magnetic criterion of bond type predicts a sharp transition from one spin state to another for these particular d^n systems. Now we see that the transition is a gradual one which may be pictured diagrammatically as in Figure 9–8. When the crystalline field exceeds Δ', the spin-paired or low-spin complex is more stable than the spin-unpaired complex.[24]

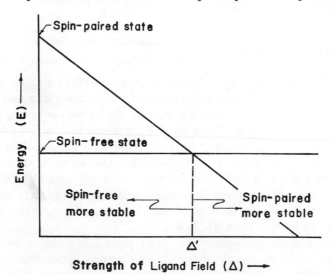

FIGURE 9–8. Diagrammatic Representation of the Gradual Change from the Spin-free to the Spin-paired State with Increasing Ligand Field Strength. (After Gillespie, R. J. and Nyholm, R. S., *Quart. Revs.*, **11**, 339 (1957).)

Griffith and Orgel[25] have approached this problem of the distribution of d electrons in d^4 to d^7 systems from a more quantitative point of view. Pointing out that the gain in orbital energy for a strong field over a weak field is Δ for d^4 and d^7 systems and 2Δ for d^5 and d^6 systems, as can be seen in Table 9–8, they then consider the corresponding increases of repulsive

TABLE 9–8. / **Crystal Field Stabilization Energies and Differences in Energies for Weak and Strong Fields.**

Examples	Weak Field			Strong Field			Gain in Orbital Energy in Strong Field
	$d\epsilon$	$d\gamma$	Dq	$d\epsilon$	$d\gamma$	Dq	Dq
d^0 Ca^{2+}, Sc^{3+}, etc.	0	0	0	0	0	0	0
d^1 Ti^{3+}, V^{4+}	1	0	4	1	0	4	0
d^2 Ti^{2+}, V^{3+}	2	0	8	2	0	8	0
d^3 V^{2+}, Cr^{3+}	3	0	12	3	0	12	0
d^4 Cr^{2+}, Mn^{3+}	3	1	6	4	0	16(1)^a	10$(\Delta)^b$
d^5 Mn^{2+}, Fe^{3+}	3	2	0	5	0	20(2)	20(2Δ)
d^6 Fe^{2+}, Co^{3+}	4	2	4	6	0	24(2)	20(2Δ)
d^7 Co^{2+}, Ni^{3+}	5	2	8	6	1	18(1)	10(Δ)
d^8 Ni^{2+}, Pd^{2+}, Pt^{2+}	6	2	12	6	2	12	0
d^9 Cu^{2+}, Ag^{2+}	6	3	6	6	3	6	0
d^{10} Cu$^+$, Zn^{2+}, etc.	6	4	0	6	4	0	0

^{a} The numbers in parentheses represent the number of electrons that must be paired when the field goes from weak to strong.
^{b} The parentheses enclose the gain in orbital energy in terms of the parameter, Δ ($=10Dq$).

energy, calling these π and 2π, respectively. π represents a mean energy of pairing of d electrons per unit of ligand field stabilization Δ. π may be considered as being made up of two parts, π_c, the coulombic part, which is not very different among the several d^n systems and π_e, the exchange energy. Then for $d^{(4-7)}$ systems $(\Delta - \pi)^{\dagger\dagger}$ must be greater than zero for electron pairing to occur. For example, for the aqueous divalent ions Cr^{2+}, Mn^{2+}, Fe^{2+}, and Co^{2+}, and for aqueous Mn^{3+} and Fe^{3+}, the mean pairing energy, π, far exceeds the orbital splitting energy, Δ;[25] and hence we would predict high-spin magnetism, as is actually observed for these ions. This can be seen from Table 9–9.

In Table 9–8 we have summarized the crystal field stabilization energies for d^n octahedral complexes showing the electron populations of the d_ϵ and d_γ orbitals.

$\dagger\dagger$ Δ must be evaluated from molecular spectra and is strongly dependent upon the nature of the ligand, and π is evaluated from atomic spectra and depends more upon the particular d^n system.

TABLE 9-9. / **Orbital Splittings, Δ, for Aqueous Ions, and Mean Pairing Energies, π, in Cm^{-1}.**

d^n	Ion	Δ	π	Ion	Δ	π
d^4	Cr^{2+}	13,900	23,500	Mn^{3+}	21,000	28,000
d^5	Mn^{2+}	7,800	25,500	Fe^{3+}	13,700	30,000
d^6	Fe^{2+}	10,400	17,600			
d^7	Co^{2+}	9,700	22,500			

As was pointed out, the magnitude of the splitting will depend to a first approximation upon the magnitude of the crystal field presented by the ligands. The properties of the ligand which influence the strength of this field will include the classical factors such as size, charge, dipole moment (permanent plus induced), and polarizability, as well as its π-bonding capabilities. The following rough generalizations concerning Dq may be made at the present time:

(1) Dq is about 45 per cent larger in a $4d^n$ and about 75 per cent larger in a $5d^n$ complex than in the corresponding $3d^n$ complex.[26]

(2) Dq is between 40 per cent and 80 per cent larger in a tervalent than in a divalent $3d^n$ complex. For example, for hydrated divalent ions, $10Dq$ falls in the range 7,500 to 12,500 cm^{-1}, whereas for hydrated tervalent ions the range is 13,500 to 21,000 cm^{-1}.

(3) Dq varies between about 8,000 and 14,000 cm^{-1} (23 and 40 kcal/mole) for most divalent hexa-coordinated $3d^n$ complexes.

(4) The common ligands may be arranged in a sequence such that Dq for their complexes with any given metal ion increases along the sequence. This sequence is essentially the same as the spectrochemical series arrived at experimentally by Tsuchida[27] in 1938.

(5) Van Vleck[28] has obtained the following approximate expressions for $10Dq$ by a quantum mechanical calculation:

$$10Dq \sim \frac{5eq\overline{a^4}}{3r^5} \quad \text{or} \quad 10Dq \sim \frac{5e\mu\overline{a^4}}{r^6}$$

where e is the electron charge, q is the charge and μ the dipole moment of a given ligand, r is the distance from the metal ion center to the ligand atom center, and $\overline{a^4}$ is the average value of the fourth power of the radius of the d electron orbitals.

Ligand Fields Other Than Octahedral

Thus far we have considered only octahedral complexes. When other field geometries are considered we obtain the relative crystal field splittings shown in Figure 9-9. The octahedral splitting is included for rough comparison. Table 9-10 gives the actual values for the 1-electron d-orbital

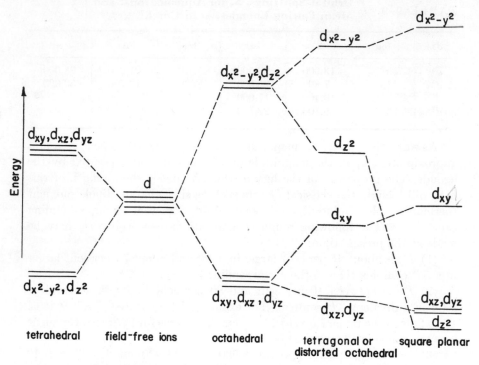

FIGURE 9–9. Relative *d*-Orbital Splittings for Ligand Fields of Several Different Symmetries. (Diagrammatic only.)

TABLE 9–10. / **The d-Orbital Energy Levels in Crystal Fields of Different Symmetries.**

CN	Structure	d_γ		d_ϵ		
		$d_{x^2-y^2}$	d_{z^2}	d_{xy}	d_{xz}	d_{yz}
2	linear[a]	−6.28	10.28	−6.28	1.14	1.14
3	trigonal[b]	5.46	−3.21	5.46	−3.86	−3.86
4	tetrahedral	−2.67	−2.67	1.78	1.78	1.78
4	square planar[b]	12.28	−4.28	2.28	−5.14	−5.14
5	trigonal bipyramid[c]	0.82	7.07	−0.82	−2.72	−2.72
5	square pyramid[c]	9.14	0.86	−0.86	−4.57	−4.57
6	octahedron	6.00	6.00	−4.00	−4.00	−4.00

[a]Bonds lie along the *z* axis.
[b]Bonds lie in the *xy* plane.
[c]Pyramid base in the *xy* plane.

energies for various crystal fields of importance.[3] It is seen that in the tetrahedral fields, the two d_γ orbitals have lower energy than the three d_ϵ orbitals, i.e., the energy levels are inverted from the octahedral case. Ballhausen has shown that the energy difference is roughly 4/9 that of the corresponding octahedral complex. It will be seen that it is this fact which accounts in large measure for the low number of tetrahedral transition metal complexes compared to the number of octahedral ones. As we shall discuss later, this table can be used to predict coordination numbers and stereochemistries for various d^n systems solely on the basis of favorable energy relationships.

Value of the Crystal Field Theory

The crystal field theory, as used to extend the simple electrostatic model, can be employed to interpret or predict for complexes the most favorable coordination numbers, stereochemistry, reaction paths for substitution reactions, detailed magnetic properties, absorption spectra, and thermodynamic properties. We will consider several of these topics in some detail. In particular, we will consider the stereochemistry, magnetic properties, absorption spectra, and thermodynamic properties of complex ions. From this, it will be apparent that the crystal field theory is a more satisfactory as well as a more general approach to the study of complexes than is the valence bond theory. However, due to its emphasis on the orbitals and electrons of the central atom, the crystal field theory must necessarily become less accurate as delocalization of ligand electrons and orbitals becomes more important, that is, as covalent bonding increases. Thus, we find that the crystal field theory cannot properly explain the relative strengths of ligands, and it will give little information concerning excited states in which there is electron or charge transfer occurring. Furthermore, it cannot take into account the possibility of double bonding between the metal ion and the ligand. Yet, this has been shown to be very important in many complexes.[29] Consequently, we can conclude that, although the crystal field theory has proven successful in some instances, it still has some serious limitations.

MOLECULAR ORBITAL THEORY

Of the various approaches to complex ion formation, the molecular orbital approach is the most general. It was first applied to complex ions by Van Vleck.[21] The method employs the same orbitals of the central ion as does the Pauling method, but it also uses the available orbitals of the N coordinating ligands which are directed toward the central atom. Thus, with six ligands there will be a total of fifteen atomic orbitals available for molecular orbital construction. For the octahedral case, there will be three degenerate nonbonding d orbitals, d_{xy}, d_{xz}, and d_{yz}, having their four lobes directed between the ligands, six bonding orbitals derived from the d^2sp^3 grouping and six corresponding antibonding orbitals. By analogy with the Pauling method we may represent a molecular orbital configuration in the manner shown below. Here, the heavy lines separate orbitals of differing

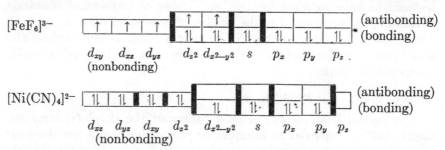

energy and the individual boxes represent the molecular orbitals. However, since the molecular orbital method can deal quantitatively with energy levels, it is usually more instructive, although not nearly so simple, to construct a molecular orbital energy-level diagram. In order to do this we must first make group or composite orbitals for the set of ligands. Then, as the symmetries permit, these are combined with the atomic orbitals of the metal ion to produce the desired bonding and antibonding molecular orbitals. The latter are usually constructed by taking a linear combination of atomic orbitals. When this mathematical operation is completed, we then simply fill up the orbitals successively with the available electrons starting with the lowest energy orbitals. As an example, we can consider the procedure followed in the case of a regular octahedral complex of a $3d$ transition element.[28,30]

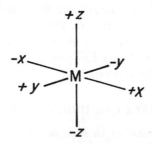

The nine significant metal atomic orbitals will be designated as $\Phi_{3d_{xy}}$, $\Phi_{3d_{xz}}$, ... Φ_{4s}, ... Φ_{4p_z}. The metal orbitals outside the $4p$ shell will be neglected. These nine orbitals will fall into one of four symmetry classes: totally symmetric A_{1g}, triply degenerate T_{1u}, doubly degenerate E_g, and triply degenerate T_{2g}, as shown in Table 9–11. The ligand σ-orbitals will

TABLE 9-11. / **Symmetry Classification of Orbitals for Regular Octahedral Complexes.**

Symmetry Class	Metal Atomic Orbitals	Composite of Ligand σ-Orbitals	Composite of Ligand π-Orbitals
A_{1g}	Φ_{4s}	$\chi_{a_{1g}} = \dfrac{1}{\sqrt{6}}(\sigma_x + \sigma_{-x} + \sigma_y + \sigma_{-y} + \sigma_z + \sigma_{-z})$	
E_g	$\Phi_{3d_{z^2}}$	$\chi_{e_g,z^2} = \dfrac{1}{2\sqrt{3}}(2\sigma_z + 2\sigma_{-z} - \sigma_x - \sigma_{-x} - \sigma_y - \sigma_{-y})$	
	$\Phi_{3d_{x^2-y^2}}$	$\chi_{e_g,x^2-y^2} = \dfrac{1}{\sqrt{2}}(\sigma_x + \sigma_{-x} - \sigma_y - \sigma_{-y})$	
T_{1u}	Φ_{4p_x}	$\chi_{t_{1u},x} = \dfrac{1}{\sqrt{2}}(\sigma_x - \sigma_{-x})$	$\pi_{t_{1u},x} = \dfrac{1}{\sqrt{2}}(\pi_{x,y} + \pi_{x,-y} + \pi_{x,z} + \pi_{x,-z})$
	Φ_{4p_y}	$\chi_{t_{1u},y} = \dfrac{1}{\sqrt{2}}(\sigma_y - \sigma_{-y})$	$\pi_{t_{1u},y} = \dfrac{1}{\sqrt{2}}(\pi_{y,x} + \pi_{y,-x} + \pi_{y,z} + \pi_{y,-z})$
	Φ_{4p_z}	$\chi_{t_{1u},z} = \dfrac{1}{\sqrt{2}}(\sigma_z - \sigma_{-z})$	$\pi_{t_{1u},z} = \dfrac{1}{\sqrt{2}}(\pi_{z,x} + \pi_{z,-x} + \pi_{z,y} + \pi_{z,-y})$
T_{2g}	$\Phi_{3d_{xy}}$		$\pi_{t_{2g},xy} = \dfrac{1}{\sqrt{2}}(\pi_{y,x} - \pi_{y,-x} + \pi_{x,y} - \pi_{x,-y})$
	$\Phi_{3d_{xz}}$		$\pi_{t_{2g},xz} = \dfrac{1}{\sqrt{2}}(\pi_{z,x} - \pi_{z,-x} + \pi_{x,z} - \pi_{x,-z})$
	$\Phi_{3d_{yz}}$		$\pi_{t_{2g},yz} = \dfrac{1}{\sqrt{2}}(\pi_{z,y} - \pi_{z,-y} + \pi_{y,z} - \pi_{y,-z})$

then be combined to form composite molecular orbitals designated as $\chi_{a_{1g}}$, χ_{e_g,z^2}, χ_{e_g,z^2-y^2}, etc. These are also shown in Table 9–11. These ligand orbitals fall into the three different symmetry classes, A_{1g}, E_g, and T_{1u}. There are no ligand σ-orbitals formed from orbitals having the T_{2g} symmetry. However, composite ligand π-molecular orbitals can be formed having T_{1u} and T_{2g} symmetries, and these are also listed in Table 9–11. Next, the pairs of orbitals, the metal atomic and the ligand molecular of the exact same symmetry, are combined to form the bonding and the antibonding molecular orbitals for the complex. The results of the application of this LCAO procedure are shown in Table 9–12. It is seen that the

TABLE 9–12. / **Molecular Orbitals for Regular Octahedral Complexes Neglecting π-Bonding.**

Symmetry Class	Bonding Orbitals	Nonbonding Orbitals	Antibonding Orbitals
A_{1g}	$N_{a_{1g}}(\Phi_{4s} + \lambda\,\chi_{a_{1g}})$	—	$N'_{a_{1g}}(\chi_{a_{1g}} - \lambda'\Phi_{4s})$
T_{1u}	$N_{t_{1u}}(\Phi_{4p_x} + \mu\,\chi_{t_{1u},x})$ $N_{t_{1u}}(\Phi_{4p_y} + \mu\,\chi_{t_{1u},y})$ $N_{t_{1u}}(\Phi_{4p_z} + \mu\,\chi_{t_{1u},z})$	— — —	$N'_{t_{1u}}(\chi_{t_{1u},x} - \mu'\Phi_{4p_x})$ $N'_{t_{1u}}(\chi_{t_{1u},y} - \mu'\Phi_{4p_y})$ $N'_{t_{1u}}(\chi_{t_{1u},z} - \mu'\Phi_{4p_z})$
E_g	$N_{e_g}(\Phi_{3d_{x^2-y^2}} + \nu\,\chi_{e_g,x^2-y^2})$ $N_{e_g}(\Phi_{3d_{z^2}} + \nu\,\chi_{e_g,z^2})$	— —	$N'_{e_g}(\chi_{e_g,x^2-y^2} - \nu'\Phi_{3d_{x^2-y^2}})$ $N'_{e_g}(\chi_{e_g,z^2} - \nu'\Phi_{3d_{z^2}})$
T_{2g}	— — —	$\Phi_{3d_{xy}}$ $\Phi_{3d_{xz}}$ $\Phi_{3d_{yz}}$	— — —

T_{2g} metal orbitals are termed nonbonding since they are not matched in symmetry by any composite ligand orbital formed from σ-orbitals. This means that the approach of the ligands toward the metal ion should not perturb electrons in these orbitals. However, it will be necessary to examine this point further when we discuss π-bonding.

The composite wave function of the A_{1g} symmetry class is seen to be a two-component wave function. That is, it is constructed from the Φ_{4s} orbital of the metal ion and the $\chi_{a_{1g}}$ orbital of the ligand. Now, according to the molecular orbital theory these will be combined to produce two new orbitals of energies E_S and E_A. These correspond to the symmetric and antisymmetric solutions of the quadratic equation

$$E^2 - (E_1 + E_2)E + E_1E_2 - \beta^2 = 0 \qquad (5\text{–}22)$$

where E_1 and E_2 are the energies of the two components and β is the exchange integral. The extent of the lowering in energy of the new bonding orbital will be dependent on the difference $(E_1 - E_2)$ and on the value of β; the smaller the difference $(E_1 - E_2)$ and the larger the value of β, the lower will be the energy. These quantities must be estimated in various more or less empirical ways. The E_1 and E_2 values usually come from ionization potential data whereas the β values are even more arbitrary, usually being taken to reproduce some measured quantity. It is for this reason that the exact order of the various molecular orbital levels in any given complex is uncertain. However, it is certainly true that the bonding orbitals lie below the nonbonding orbitals, which in turn lie below the antibonding orbitals. One possible order of levels is shown in Figure 9–10 for a hypothetical regular octahedral complex.

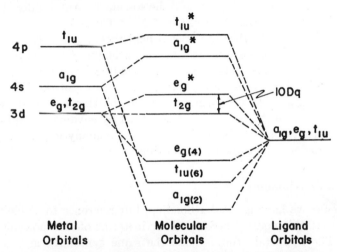

FIGURE 9–10. Energy Level Diagram for a Hypothetical Regular Octahedral Complex Illustrating the Formation of Molecular Orbitals Derived from Metal Atomic Orbitals and Combined Ligand Group Orbitals. (Diagrammatic only.)

It should be pointed out that if a molecular orbital is derived from two orbitals of equal energy, then the numerical coefficients of these two are equal but of opposite sign in the bonding and antibonding functions. However, where the combining local orbitals are of differing energies, then the numerical coefficient of the local orbital of lower energy is larger in the bonding function than that of the other local orbital. The reverse is true in the antibonding function. What this means physically is that if, for example, the ligand composite orbitals are of lower energy than the metal orbitals with which they are combined, the electrons in the bonding molecular orbitals will be concentrated more in the region of space close to the ligands, and electrons in antibonding orbitals will be concentrated more in the neighborhood of the metal ion. The electrons in nonbonding orbitals are, of course, located on the metal ion.

From Figure 9–10, it is seen that the twelve ligand electrons can be accommodated by the bonding orbitals and the n metal d electrons must be placed in the non-σ-bonding t_{2g} orbitals and in the antibonding $e_g{}^*$ orbitals. The antibonding orbitals are of interest because it is these into which electrons may be excited from the t_{2g} orbitals by absorption of energy. The greater the extent of overlap of the $3d$ orbitals of the metal ion and the ligand orbitals, the higher will be the energy of the antibonding e_g orbital, $e_g{}^*$. The overlap will be greater the smaller the effective nuclear charge on the bonding ligand atom and/or the greater the electronegativity of the central ion. These two properties will help explain, respectively, the spectrochemical series of ligands and the so-called natural order of stability of complexes (e.g., Mn < Fe < Co < Ni < Cu > Zn).

It should be noted that the crystal field theory is concerned only with the t_{2g} and the e_g orbitals and the splittings which may further occur within these levels for various fields. We note also that both the crystal field theory and the molecular orbital theory predict a splitting of the $3d$ orbitals on complex formation. In the former case, the splitting is caused by electrostatic fields and in the latter case it is caused by covalent bond formation. Therefore, they can both be used to explain the many important phenomena that are dependent upon this splitting.

Inclusion of π-Bonding

Thus far we have ignored π-bonding, but reference to Table 9–11 will suggest that this may be accounted for in terms of the molecular orbital theory. The t_{2g} metal orbitals have the same symmetry as some of the ligand molecular orbitals derived from ligand π-orbitals. Hence t_{2g} orbitals, which we earlier termed nonbonding, may actually take part in π-bond formation. The procedure followed in setting up molecular orbitals from π-bonding local orbitals is much the same as that employed when setting up molecular orbitals from σ-bonding orbitals. We obtain a splitting of the t_{2g} orbitals into bonding and antibonding levels as shown in Figure 9–11. The depression in energy pictured for the t_{2g} π-bonding orbitals increases the energy difference between the t_{2g} and the unaffected antibonding level. This has the effect of increasing the magnitude of $10Dq$, and we can therefore say that the ligand which can form a π-bond is a stronger ligand than it would be if it could not π-bond. According to the molecular orbital theory, the increased energy difference between t_{2g} and $e_g{}^*$ caused by π-bonding is seen to be responsible for causing electron-pairing or low-spin complexes. In the crystal field theory, this was attributed to an increased electrostatic field of the ligand. In other words, as we have previously stated, according to the molecular orbital theory the splitting is caused by increased covalent bonding and not by increased electrostatic fields.

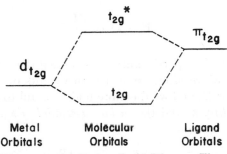

FIGURE 9–11. Energy Level Diagram Illustrating the Formation of Molecular Orbitals from π-bonding Orbitals of t_{2g} Symmetry Located Originally on the Metal Ion and on the Ligands.

Of these three theories, there is no doubt that the molecular orbital theory is potentially the most powerful. It can be modified to include any degree of covalent or electrostatic bond character, and it can accommodate π-bonding. Its use will probably increase with an increased interest in more precise models of complex ion systems and also with the increased mathematical proclivity of the chemist.

MAGNETIC PROPERTIES OF COMPLEXES

Considerable emphasis has been placed on the determination of magnetic properties of transition metal complexes.[6,31,32] Such studies contribute valuable information with respect to stereochemistry and bond types in complexes, as well as information concerning the oxidation state of the central metal ion. However, before we consider just how this is possible, it will be of value to examine the types of magnetic behavior exhibited by complexes.

Types of Magnetic Behavior

In general there are several types of magnetic behavior which can arise, but not all of these are of importance in complex ion systems. *Ferromagnetism, anti-ferromagnetism,* and *ferrimagnetism* are relatively rare phenomena in complexes and of importance only in special cases. For this reason, they will not be considered here. Of much greater importance for our purposes are *normal paramagnetism* and *diamagnetism,* and it is these that we shall consider in some detail.

When a sample of some compound is placed in an inhomogeneous magnetic field, it experiences a force, $\mathbf{F}$, which is proportional to the field strength, $\mathbf{H}$, to the field gradient, $\partial \mathbf{H}/\partial y$, and to the volume of the sample, V. Mathematically we may express this as follows:

$$\mathbf{F} = \kappa V \mathbf{H}\, \frac{\partial \mathbf{H}}{\partial y} \qquad (9\text{-}1)$$

where the constant of proportionality, κ, is termed the *volume susceptibility* of the compound. More often we deal with weights of solids rather than with volumes of solids, and we therefore find it useful to define the *specific* or *gram susceptibility*, χ, and the *molar susceptibility* χ_M, by the following relations:

$$\chi = \frac{\kappa}{\rho} \qquad \chi_\text{M} = \frac{\kappa \text{M}}{\rho} \qquad (9\text{-}2)$$

where ρ is the density and M is the molecular weight of the compound. χ_A and $\chi_{\text{A}+}$ are analogously defined as the atomic and the ionic susceptibilities, respectively.

Diamagnetism

Diamagnetism is a property possessed by all atoms regardless of what other type of magnetic behavior they may exhibit. It arises from the interaction of the applied magnetic field with the field induced in the closed shells of electrons. This field must necessarily oppose the applied field. The effect of this interaction is to cause the diamagnetic sample to move away from the applied field in order to diminish the interaction. Hence the diamagnetic susceptibility is a negative quantity, and from both a classical and a quantum mechanical treatment the atomic susceptibility is found to be,

$$\chi_\text{A} = -\frac{Ne^2}{6mc^2} \sum_n \overline{s_n^2} = -2.832 \times 10^{10} \sum_n \overline{s_n^2} \qquad (9\text{-}3)$$

for any polyelectron atom. Here, N is Avogadro's number, e is the unit of electric charge, m is the mass of the electron, and c is the velocity of light. $\sum_n \overline{s_n^2}$ is the sum of the squares of the projections of the orbits for all of the electrons on a plane. From Eq. (9-3) it is apparent that the diamagnetism will be very sensitive to changes in the value of $\overline{s^2}$. Thus, both an increase in the size of an atom or ion as well as an increase in the number of electrons will increase the magnitude of the diamagnetic susceptibility. Temperature should have little or no effect on this type of magnetic behavior since it arises from closed electronic orbits. Also, it is independent of the strength of the applied field.

The magnitude of the diamagnetic effect is normally ten to a hundred times less than that of the paramagnetic effect which arises from unpaired electrons. For this reason, its importance in inorganic systems is primarily as a correction in precise work. Diamagnetism is observed, therefore, only when all electrons in a system are paired, and it is operative only while the external field is applied. All substances which do not have the necessary electronic and structural features to give rise to para-, ferro-, antiferro-, or ferrimagnetism will necessarily show diamagnetism.

Paramagnetism

Atomic or ionic systems which contain one or more unpaired electrons will have a permanent magnetic moment which arises from the residual spin and orbital angular momenta of the unpaired electrons. Those substances with permanent magnetic moments display normal paramagnetism. Thus, when a paramagnetic substance is placed in an external magnetic field the individual atomic or molecular permanent magnets will align themselves in the same direction as the field and thus be attracted to it. This gives a positive magnetic susceptibility which must be dependent upon temperature, since thermal agitation will oppose orientation of the magnetic dipoles. Hence the effectiveness of the magnetic field will diminish with increasing temperature. Mathematically this dependence is expressed by either the Curie or the more precise Curie-Weiss law:

$$\chi \propto \frac{1}{T} \quad \text{or} \quad \chi \propto \frac{1}{T + \Delta} \tag{9-4}$$

where Δ, the Curie temperature, is a property of each individual substance and must be determined from temperature-dependence studies of the particular paramagnetic material.

Quantum mechanical treatment of the interaction between an applied magnetic field and the elementary permanent moments yields the following expression for the total molar magnetic susceptibility, χ_{TM}:

$$\chi_{TM} = \frac{N^2 \mu^2}{3RT} \tag{9-5}$$

where the symbols N, R, and T have their usual meaning and μ is the permanent magnetic moment. In practice, the gram susceptibility is usually measured, and this is then converted to the molar susceptibility. This susceptibility is really the sum of the diamagnetic and the paramagnetic susceptibilities in addition to an almost inevitable small contribution from *Van Vleck paramagnetism*. The exact magnitude of this latter quantity is generally not known, but it accounts for roughly a few per cent of the Curie law susceptibility at room temperature. Now, rearranging Eq. (9-5) and evaluating the constants, we obtain the effective magnetic moment μ_{eff}:

$$\mu_{eff} = 2.84 \sqrt{\chi_{TM} T} \text{ BM} \qquad (9-6)$$

BM is the unit of magnetic moment, the *Bohr magneton*, and it is equal to $eh/4\pi mc = 9.7 \times 10^{-21}$ erg/gauss.

Types of Paramagnetic Behavior

Since our first concern with magnetism in transition metal complexes is for the determination of the number of unpaired electrons, it is necessary to derive an expression which relates the experimentally determined magnetic moments to the number of unpaired electrons. As previously mentioned, paramagnetism originates in the spin and orbital angular moments of the unpaired electrons. According to the usual symbolism, S is the total spin angular momentum quantum number ($S = \sum_i m_{s_i}$ where m_s may be $+1/2$ or $-1/2$), and L is the total orbital angular momentum quantum number ($L = \sum_i l_i$, where l_i are the individual electron angular momentum quantum numbers), which must be added according to the quantum rules for addition of vectors. We might note at this point that $S = n/2$, where n is the number of unpaired electrons. Now, normal paramagnetism of a complex ion is dependent upon at least three factors: (1) the number of unpaired electrons; (2) the spectroscopic ground state,[†††] and upper states if the separation is of the order of kT; and (3) the symmetry and strength of the electric field arising from the ligands present in the coordination sphere. In order to see how the paramagnetism of transition metal complexes depends upon these factors we shall find it convenient to subdivide paramagnetic behavior into four general types.[32] These are:

(1) *Large Multiplet Separation.* This arises if the unpaired electrons are well-shielded from external ligand field forces, and if the ground state of the atom is separated from the next higher excited state by an energy difference, $h\nu$, which is large compared to kT. Under these circumstances spin-orbit coupling is significant, and for a given state of L and S, J will take on all values from $(L + S)$ to $(L - S)$, so there will be $(2L + 1)$ or $(2S + 1)$ values of J, whichever is the smaller. The one which gives the ground state is either $(L + S)$ or $(L - S)$ depending upon whether the

---

[†††] The ground state is understood to be those energy levels which are appreciably populated at normal temperatures and which therefore lie within approximately kT of the lowest possible energy levels.

electronic shell is more or less than half full. The magnetic moment is given by the expression

$$\mu_{eff} = g \sqrt{J(J + 1)} \quad \text{BM} \tag{9-7}$$

where g is the so-called Lande or splitting factor and is given by

$$g = \left[1 + \frac{J(J + 1) + S(S + 1) - L(L + 1)}{2J(J + 1)} \right] \tag{9-8}$$

In a magnetic field each J level is split into $(2J + 1)$ components, each separated by an energy, $g\beta H$, where β represents the Bohr magneton.

For this type of magnetic behavior, μ is independent of the stereochemical environment and the amount of magnetic dilution.‡ We find this type of behavior primarily with rare earth ions where the incompleted level lies well shielded from the surface of the ion.

(2) *Small Multiplet Separation.* This arises if the energy separation between successive J values is very small compared to kT. Spin-orbit coupling is now negligible and may be ignored. Under these circumstances, L and S each interact independently with an external magnetic field giving

$$\mu_{eff} = \sqrt{4S(S + 1) + L(L + 1)} \quad \text{BM} \tag{9-9}$$

At least this is the limit towards which μ approaches as $h\nu_{J_i \rightarrow J_j}$ approaches zero. This type of magnetic behavior is important as the limiting case in the first transitional series when orbital contributions to the magnetic moment are not quenched. Cases of intermediate multiplet separation are actually rare and of relatively little importance.

(3) *Spin-only.* For many of the first transition series ions, particularly those in the first half of the series, experimental results have indicated that the orbital contribution to the magnetic moment may be completely ignored. This leads to the simple expression

$$\mu_{eff} = \sqrt{4S(S + 1)} \quad \text{BM} \tag{9-10}$$

which is called the *spin-only formula*. Recalling that $S = n/2$, we may write

$$\mu_{eff} = \sqrt{n(n + 2)} \quad \text{BM} \tag{9-11}$$

which relates the magnetic moment directly to the number of unpaired electrons. A knowledge of the number of unpaired electrons is obviously of value in the determination of the oxidation state of a metal ion in a complex. It can also be used to distinguish bond types in terms of the

‡ A magnetically dilute substance is one in which the paramagnetic atoms or ions are effectively separated from each other by large numbers of diamagnetic atoms, molecules or ions.

Pauling picture of hybridized orbitals. And, in addition, we will see that deviations from the spin-only formula may be of value in determining the stereochemistry of a complex.

How well the spin-only moment agrees with actual experimental moments for several first-row transition element ions in both weak and strong fields may be seen from Table 9–13. It should be pointed out that the spread of experimental values listed in the table for certain ions represents the range observed for many complexes of the given metal ion, complexes which may have differing stereochemistries. This is particularly true for Fe(III), Co(II), and Ni(II), which along with Mn(II) and Cu(II) have perhaps received the most attention to date.

TABLE 9–13. / **Some Magnetic Moments of First-row Transition Element Ions.**[6]

Ion	No. of d Electrons	SPIN-FREE COMPLEXES		SPIN-PAIRED COMPLEXES	
		Spin-only Moment (BM)	Experimental Moment (BM)	Spin-only Moment (BM)	Experimental Moment (BM)
Ti^{3+} V^{4+}	1	1.73	1.73 1.68–1.78	— —	— —
V^{3+}	2	2.83	2.75–2.85	—	—
V^{2+} Cr^{3+} Mn^{4+}	3	3.88	3.80–3.90 3.70–3.90 3.8–4.0	— — —	— — —
Cr^{2+} Mn^{3+}	4	4.90	4.75–4.90 4.90–5.00	2.83	3.20–3.30 3.18
Mn^{2+} Fe^{3+}	5	5.92	5.65–6.10 5.70–6.0	1.73	1.80–2.10 2.0–2.5
Fe^{2+}	6	4.90	5.10–5.70	—	—
Co^{2+} Ni^{3+}	7	3.88	4.30–5.20 —	1.73	1.7–2.0 1.8–2.0
Ni^{2+}	8	2.83	2.80–3.50	—	—
Cu^{2+}	9	1.73	1.70–2.20	—	—

(4) *Heavy Atoms.* For second and, particularly, third transition series elements, there occurs a further reduction in observed magnetic moment below the spin-only value and this reduction cannot be attributed to the

ligand field strength. Rather, the strong central field of the heavy nucleus effects an alignment of L and S vectors in opposite directions, and this results in destruction of much of the paramagnetism which might be expected from the unpaired electrons.[‡‡]

Magnetic Criterion of Bond Type

Pauling stressed the importance of magnetic susceptibility measurements in the study of the transition metal complexes. For central ions with 4, 5, 6, 7, or 8 d electrons, there was proposed a magnetic criterion of bond type. By this criterion, a metal ion in a complex with the same number of unpaired electrons as the simple free gaseous metal ion was considered to be ionic (or later, of the outer-orbital or hypoligated type). On the other hand, a complex with a reduced paramagnetism was classified as covalent (or later, of the inner-orbital or hyperligated type). For example, in 1931 Pauling predicted the following magnetic moments, in units of Bohr magnetons, for manganese(II) complexes:

Ionic Bonds	sp^3 Bonds	dsp^2 Bonds	d^2sp^3 Bonds
5.92	5.92	3.88	1.73

These are the values calculated from the spin-only formula for 5, 3, and 1 unpaired electrons, respectively. They can be compared with the experimental values below.[33]

$[Mn(H_2O)_4]SO_4$	5.96
$[Mn\ py_2Br_2]$	5.96
$[Mn\ py_6]Br_2$	6.00
$K_4[Mn(NCS)_6] \cdot 3H_2O$	6.06
$K_4[Mn(CN)_6] \cdot 3H_2O$	2.13

For the first two complexes, the magnetic moments do not distinguish between ionic bonds and sp^3 hybrid bonds. The third and fourth complexes are assumed to possess ionic bonds or, in the later terminology, outer orbital sp^3d^2 hybrid bonds, while the fifth complex must be judged covalent with d^2sp^3 hybrid bond orbitals. The high experimental value in this latter instance has been attributed to manganese impurities.

Similar abrupt changes in magnetic moments are predicted between planar and tetrahedral stereochemistries of the d^8 systems of Ni(II), Pd(II) and Pt(II) complexes. The use of sp^3 hybrid bonds will result in

[‡‡] A comprehensive table of magnetic moments of paramagnetic ions of the second and third row transition elements may be found in Lewis, J. and Wilkins, R., "Modern Coordination Chemistry," Interscience Publishers, Inc., New York, N.Y., 1960, pp. 444–451.

two unpaired electrons, while the use of planar dsp^2 hybrid bonds requires electron pairing with resultant diamagnetism. All tetra-coordinated complexes of Pd(II) and Pt(II) are diamagnetic and therefore are presumed to be planar and covalent. This is indeed supported by a considerable body of chemical and X-ray evidence. However, with Ni(II) it has long been known that two broad classes of complexes exist. One of the more satisfying features of the magnetic criterion was the elegant way in which it explained their existence. The blue or green paramagnetic complexes were necessarily either tetrahedral with sp^3 bonds or octahedral with ionic bonds, whereas the yellow or red diamagnetic complexes must be employing dsp^2 square planar bonds. The electron pairings for these structures are:

	d	s	p
Ni²⁺, gaseous ion	⇅ ⇅ ⇅ ↑ ↑	☐	☐ ☐ ☐
[Ni(NH₃)₄]Cl₂, green, sp^3	⇅ ⇅ ⇅ ↑ ↑	⇅	⇅ ⇅ ⇅
K₂[Ni(CN)₄], yellow, dsp^2	⇅ ⇅ ⇅ ⇅ ⇅	⇅	⇅ ⇅

If we rule out nickel to nickel bonds, it would appear that the determination of the magnetic susceptibility of a nickel(II) complex should be sufficient to place the complex into one of these two classes. However, we find that it is exactly upon this point that one of the inadequacies of the valence bond approach was realized. This occurred when a paramagnetic nickel(II) complex was shown by X-ray examination to be planar or tetragonal instead of the predicted tetrahedral or octahedral.

Nevertheless, the rationalization and prediction of the stereochemistry and magnetic properties of virtually all the known complexes of twenty years ago must be considered as a significant achievement of the Pauling approach.

Spin and Orbital Contributions

The contribution of the spin angular momentum of the electron to the total magnetic moment can be attributed to the intrinsic spin of the particle. This contribution to the permanent magnetic moment is not affected by the environment in which the electron finds itself. For this reason, the only possible quenching of the spin moment in chemical bond formation is the complete quenching that results from electron pairing. This, of course, is what occurs when an ion with more d electrons than low-lying degenerate orbitals finds itself in a strong ligand field. The contribution of the orbital angular momentum to the total magnetic moment is not quite so straightforward. However, with regard to our discussion, it is sufficient to know that an electron will have a moment around a given axis if it is possible to transform the orbital which it occupies into an equivalent degenerate orbital by a rotation about that axis. If we consider an electron to occupy the $d_{x^2-y^2}$ orbital, it can be seen from Figure 9–6, that a 45-degree rotation about the z axis will transform it into the d_{xy} orbital. In the same manner, it can be seen that a 90-degree rotation around the z axis will transform the d_{xz} orbitals into the d_{yz} orbital. In the first case, the electron will have an angular momentum of ± 2 in units of $h/2\pi$, and in the latter case it will have an angular momentum of ± 1 in the same units.

Since a ligand field of any possible symmetry splits the degeneracy of the d orbitals, it is easily seen how the orbital contribution may be quenched. In the presence of a ligand field, the $d_{x^2-y^2}$ and d_{xy} orbitals are no longer equivalent in energy, and their orbital contribution is destroyed completely. Only the d_ϵ orbitals may be degenerate in a symmetrical field, but they will contribute no orbital angular momentum when filled or half-filled. Thus, for octahedral complexes we can say that all orbital contributions will be quenched for the spin-free configurations $d_\epsilon{}^3$, $d_\epsilon{}^3 d_\gamma{}^1$, $d_\epsilon{}^3 d_\gamma{}^2$, $d_\epsilon{}^6 d_\gamma{}^2$ and $d_\epsilon{}^6 d_\gamma{}^3$ and for the spin-paired configurations, $d_\epsilon{}^6$ and $d_\epsilon{}^6 d_\gamma{}^1$. For all other configurations, that is, 1, 2, 4, or 5 d_ϵ electrons, there will be some orbital contribution, and to a first approximation this will account for the difference between the experimental magnetic moments and those predicted by the spin-only formula. Other field symmetries may be treated analogously.

In spite of this argument, it can be seen from Table 9–13 that after allowing for complete or partial orbital quenching, some of the experimental values still do not agree with the predicted moments. This can be attributed to spin-orbit coupling which can mix-in some of the higher levels having the same S value as the ground state.[34] In order to account for such coupling effects, we may write the following equation for the effective magnetic moment:

$$\mu = \mu_0 \left(1 - \alpha \, \frac{\lambda}{\Delta} \right) \qquad (9\text{–}12)$$

Here, μ_0 is the spin-only moment; α is a constant which depends upon the spectroscopic ground state and the number of d electrons; Δ ($= 10Dq$) is the separation between the ground energy level and the level being mixed-in, and λ is the spin-orbit coupling constant. λ is a positive quantity for the first-row transition element ions with less than a half-filled d shell, and it is negative for those with more than a half-filled shell. Since both α and Δ are positive quantities, it is seen that the observed moment will be greater or lesser than the spin-only moment as λ is negative or positive. It is thus that we explain the generally lower than spin-only moments observed for Cr(III), $d_\epsilon{}^3$; spin-free Cr(II), $d_\epsilon{}^3 d_\gamma{}^1$; V(III), $d_\epsilon{}^2$; and V(IV), $d_\epsilon{}^1$. Also, we can explain the generally higher than spin-only moments observed for spin-free Fe(II), $d_\epsilon{}^4 d_\gamma{}^2$; Co(II), $d_\epsilon{}^5 d_\gamma{}^2$; Ni(II), $d_\epsilon{}^6 d_\gamma{}^2$; and Cu(II), $d_\epsilon{}^6 d_\gamma{}^3$. It is interesting that the deviations from the spin-only values are greatest with Co(II) and Fe(II), both of which have some unquenched orbital contribution. The magnitude of this contribution will, of course, depend upon the symmetry of the ligand field.

Application to Cobalt(II) Complexes

One of the most fruitful applications of magnetic measurements has been realized in the study of Co(II) complexes. In terms of this d^7 ion system, it is possible to illustrate many of the ideas presented thus far. In Table 9-14, a summary is given of the magnetic data on Co(II) complexes along with the expected or proven stereochemistry. In an attempt to give a qualitative explanation of the observed magnetic moments, we can say that the observed moments for the spin-free octahedral (or tetragonal)

TABLE 9-14. / **Summary of Magnetic Data on Co(II) Complexes.**

Stereochemistry	SPIN-FREE			SPIN-PAIRED		
	Confign.	Calcd.	Obsd.	Confign.	Calcd.	Obsd.
1. Octahedral or tetragonal	$d_\epsilon^5 d_\gamma^2$	3.88	4.8–5.3	$d_\epsilon^6 d_\gamma^1$	1.73	1.7–2.0
2. Tetrahedral	$d_\gamma^4 d_\epsilon^3$	3.88	4.3–4.7	—	—	—
3. Square planar	$d_\epsilon^5 d_\gamma^2$ (very likely tetragonal)	3.88	4.8–5.2	$d_\epsilon^6 d_\gamma^1$ $d_\epsilon^5 d_{z^2}^2$	1.73	2.1–2.9

complexes which are in excess of the spin-only value by 1.1 to 1.4 BM undoubtedly arise from the unquenched orbital contribution of both the ground state, $d_\epsilon^5 d_\gamma^2$, and the first excited state, $d_\epsilon^4 d_\gamma^3$. The latter is certainly mixed-in to some extent, dependent upon the ligand field. The observed moments for the spin-paired octahedral complexes are much closer to the calculated spin-only value since the ground state configuration $d_\epsilon^6 d_\gamma^1$ allows no orbital contribution. Values in excess of the spin-only value must therefore arise from the orbital contribution of the first excited level. Note that if the complex is tetragonally distorted, the d_{z^2} orbital is much higher than in the case of the square planar complex, and this will account for the higher observed moments in the latter case. This assumes, of course, that the first excited level of octahedrally coordinated Co(II) has the configuration $d_\epsilon^5 d_{z^2}^2$.

The observed high moments for tetrahedral complexes must also be caused by mixing-in of higher levels, e.g., $d_\gamma^3 d_\epsilon^4$ or even $d_\gamma^4 d_\epsilon^2 4p$. This is necessary, since the symmetrical ground state, $d_\gamma^4 d_\epsilon^3$, allows no orbital contribution. However, it is important to note that because the more heavily populated ground state does not contribute to the orbital moment, the observed values are lower than those for the octahedral or tetragonal situations where the ground state does contribute to the orbital moment. The argument, that some of the spin-free Co(II) complexes with moments of 4.8 to 5.2 BM are square planar, is not conclusive, and in all probability they are tetragonal. The cases of spin-paired Co(II) complexes with moments in the range of 2.1 to 2.9 BM are more certainly square planar and, as pointed out above, the possibility of mixing-in of the first excited level $d_\epsilon{}^5d_{z^2}{}^2$, with its orbital contribution, would account for the greater than spin-only moments.

STEREOCHEMISTRY

One of the outstanding features of the Valence Bond approach to the stereochemistry of complex ions is its ability to predict many structures. If the set of hybridized orbitals can be determined by some means, such as magnetic measurements, the stereochemistry usually follows. However the theory does not explain why certain stereochemistries are favored over others. Nor is it always capable of predicting when a particular arrangement will be expected. In fact, as we have already noted in the previous section, it may at times mislead us entirely as to the correct stereochemistry. The crystal field theory will be seen to be more reliable in this respect and will give us a greater insight into the important factors which control the detailed stereochemistry of transition metal complexes.[25,35-38]

Regular Symmetries

We have already discussed, in the chapter on stereochemistry, the controlling factors governing the shapes of inorganic molecules derived from the nontransitional elements. In particular, these are the size and charge of the central ion, the presence of nonbonding lone-pair electrons, the possibility of expansion of the bonding shell beyond the octet limit of the first short period, the ability to π-bond, the steric requirements of the groups bonded to the central species, and perhaps most important of all, the operation of the Pauli exclusion principle. When we are dealing with a spherically symmetrical central atom, as is the case with complexes of all the representative metals without lone pair electrons, we expect and we find regular shapes. Thus coordination numbers 2, 3, 4, 5, 6, 7, and 8 give molecules which are linear, triangular, regular tetrahedral, trigonal bipyramidal, octahedral, pentagonal bipyramidal, and square (or Archimedes) antiprismatic, respectively. Thus, we may expect that whenever we have a spherically symmetrical nonbonding electron shell with the transition elements, the stereochemistry will be regular and determined only by the coordination number. We may, therefore, write out the configurations which will be expected to lead to perfectly symmetrical complexes. For the most common coordination numbers, 6 and 4, we obtain the following:

	Spin-free (Weak Field)	Spin-paired (Strong Field)
Perfect octahedron	d^0; $d_\epsilon{}^3$; $d_\epsilon{}^3 d_\gamma{}^2$; $d_\epsilon{}^6 d_\gamma{}^2$; d^{10}	d^0; $d_\epsilon{}^3$; $d_\epsilon{}^6$ d^{10}
Perfect tetrahedron	d^0; $d_\gamma{}^2$; $d_\gamma{}^2 d_\epsilon{}^3$; $d_\gamma{}^4 d_\epsilon{}^3$; d^{10}	d^0; $d_\gamma{}^4$; d^{10}

All other configurations must lead either to distorted geometries or, in certain cases, to the square planar arrangement. However, even the latter may be pictured as arising from a strongly tetragonally distorted octahedron in which the groups on the z axis have moved away from the central ion to a point where they are not considered to be bonded to it and do not contribute to the effective crystal field. Thus, all stereo arrangements that are not regular as outlined above may be considered to be distortions, ranging from small to very large, of the regular arrangements. Our interest, then, is to determine when and how these distortions occur, and it is obvious that we need consider only those configurations that are not listed above.

Distortions from Regular Symmetries

Whenever the d_ϵ orbitals, which point between the ligands, contain 1, 2, 4, or 5 electrons we shall expect only slight distortion of the octahedral configuration. Thus, depending upon the ligand field strength we will expect to get slightly distorted octahedra for the following configurations:

Spin-free	Spin-paired
$d_\epsilon{}^1$; $d_\epsilon{}^2$; $d_\epsilon{}^4 d_\gamma{}^2$; $d_\epsilon{}^5 d_\gamma{}^2$	$d_\epsilon{}^1$; $d_\epsilon{}^2$; $d_\epsilon{}^4$; $d_\epsilon{}^5$

Whenever the d_γ orbitals, which point towards the ligands are unsymmetrically occupied in a weak field or occupied at all in a strong field, we will expect strong distortions leading to tetragonal or square complexes. These configurations are:

Spin-free	Spin-paired
$d_\epsilon{}^3 d_\gamma{}^1$; $d_\epsilon{}^6 d_\gamma{}^3$	$d_\epsilon{}^6 d_\gamma{}^1$; $d_\epsilon{}^6 d_\gamma{}^2$; $d_\epsilon{}^6 d_\gamma{}^3$

If we were to use Table 9–15 in trying to decide when a square planar (or tetragonally distorted) complex would be more likely to form than an octahedral one, we would arrive at the same conclusion on the basis of differences in crystal field stabilization energies as we did above on the basis of electron distributions. Thus, we note that the ΔDq values for differences between the square planar and the octahedral structures for the weak field d^4 and d^9 systems and for the strong field d^7, d^8, and d^9 systems are all large. This, of course, favors the square planar structure. However, it is not quite appropriate to consider only ΔDq values for the

TABLE 9–15. / **Differences in CFSE in Weak and Strong Fields for the Structure Differences, Square-Planar and Octahedral, Octahedral and Tetrahedral.**

d^n	WEAK FIELD		STRONG FIELD	
	ΔDq (square planar-octahedral)	ΔDq (octahedral-tetrahedral)	ΔDq (square planar-octahedral)	ΔDq (octahedral-tetrahedral)
d^0	0	0	0	0
d^1	1.14	1.33	1.14	1.33
d^2	2.28	2.66	2.28	2.66
d^3	2.56	8.44	2.56	3.99
d^4	6.28	4.22	3.70	5.32^b
d^5	0	0	4.48	11.10
d^6	1.14	1.33	5.12	16.88
d^7	2.28	2.66	8.84	12.66
d^8	2.56	8.44	12.56^a	8.44
d^9	6.28	4.22	6.28	4.22
d^{10}	0	0	0	0

[a]One electron must be paired in the square planar case but not in the octahedral case.
[b]Two electrons must be paired in the tetrahedral case, but only one must be paired in the octahedral case.

two arrangements. The parameter Dq is, itself, dependent upon geometry, being larger for the square planar case. In addition, the fact that the mutual repulsion of four groups is less than that of six groups also favors the square planar structure. On the other hand, the total bond energy of six ligands is much greater than that of four ligands. This factor strongly favors the octahedral arrangement, and it is for this reason that the ΔDq value must heavily favor the square planar structure before it can be realized. Values from Table 9–15 may also be used to indicate why the tetrahedral configuration is rarely found among the complexes of the transition elements. Except for d^0, d^{10}, and weak field d^5 systems, the ΔDq values strongly favor the octahedral structure. As an example, it is found that with the weak field ligand Cl^-, we obtain tetrahedral $[FeCl_4]^-$ and $[MnCl_4]^{2-}$, but with the strong field ligand CN^- we obtain octahedral $[Fe(CN)_6]^{3-}$ and $[Mn(CN)_6]^{4-}$.

All of these stereochemical deductions from the crystal field theory are in good accord with the known facts concerning the stereochemistry of transition metal complexes. Where exceptions to the predictions of crystal field theory arise, and there are an increasing number being discovered, there is generally a ready explanation to be found in some property or phenomenon which has been previously overlooked. However, here we wish only to emphasize how general and substantial is the treatment of stereochemistry of complexes by the crystal-field theory.

There is another area of stereochemistry which we have not touched upon, but which is nevertheless of current interest. That area concerns the stereochemical changes which complexes undergo during *substitution,* *isomerization,* or *racemization* reactions. We shall not attempt a discussion of this large field.‡‡‡ We only mention here that the crystal field theory has been used so far with moderate success in this area, particularly in the interpretation of kinetic data and the formulation and understanding of inorganic reaction mechanisms.

STABILITY OF COMPLEXES

The subject of the stability of metallic complexes is indeed a large and varied one.[4,6,40-43] The many variables associated with the central atom, M, and the ligand, L, in addition to the variables which arise from different solvent conditions and temperature serve to greatly complicate the study of this subject. The only reasonable approach to the study of stability is to maintain constant as many variables as possible and then to examine a small area of the whole subject. This we can do conveniently by first recognizing that we may be interested in stability from either a thermodynamic or a kinetic point of view. When we are concerned with the former, we deal with metal-ligand bond energies, stability constants, and the thermodynamic variables which are derivable from them, or with oxidation-reduction potentials which measure valence state stabilization. When we are interested in the kinetic stability, we deal with the rates and mechanisms of chemical reactions, as well as with the thermodynamics involved in the formation of the activated complex. In the kinetic sense it will be more proper to speak of complexes as being *inert* or *labile*[44] rather than stable or unstable. Too often these terms are confused and used incorrectly. Stable complexes may be inert or labile and unstable complexes, while usually labile, may be inert. For example, we find that although $[Fe(H_2O)_6]^{3+}$ and $[Cr(H_2O)_6]^{3+}$ have roughly the same energy per bond

‡‡‡ This field has been the object of extensive investigation for the past decade and has been very adequately covered in recent books[3,6,39] one of which[3] is devoted almost entirely to this subject.

(116 and 122 kcal/mole, respectively), the former is labile and therefore exchanges its ligands rapidly while the latter is inert and therefore exchanges its ligands only slowly. Numerous similar examples may be cited.

Thermodynamics of Coordinate Bond Formation

Ideally, if we wish to know the absolute coordinate bond energy we must have thermodynamic data on reactions in the gas phase, such as

$$M_{(g)} + L_{(g)} \rightarrow ML_{(g)} - \Delta H_1 \qquad (9\text{--}13)$$

Recognizing that reactions occur in a stepwise fashion, we may further write

$$ML_{(g)} + L_{(g)} \rightarrow ML_{2(g)} - \Delta H_2$$

or, in general

$$ML_{(n-1)\ (g)} + L_{(g)} \rightarrow ML_{n(g)} - \Delta H_n \qquad (9\text{--}14)$$

where n is the coordination number of the metal, M, and $\Delta H_1 \neq \Delta H_2 \neq \ldots \Delta H_n$. Actually, very little direct data of this kind is available, and in many cases it can not be obtained. However, as is so often done in thermodynamic studies, we may make a good approximation to the desired information by an alternative but measurable path. Thus, we can study formation constants in solution, where for example, the reactions in aqueous media may be represented as follows:

$$[M(H_2O)_n]_{(aq)} + L_{(aq)} \rightarrow [M(H_2O)_{n-1}L]_{(aq)} + H_2O_{(aq)}$$

$$[M(H_2O)_{n-1}L]_{(aq)} + L_{(aq)} \rightarrow [M(H_2O)_{n-2}L_2]_{(aq)} + H_2O_{(aq)}$$

or over-all:

$$[M(H_2O)_n]_{(aq)} + nL_{(aq)} \rightarrow [ML_n]_{(aq)} + nH_2O_{(aq)}$$

In addition to the heat change involved in the gas phase reaction, any one of these reactions also includes the heats of hydration of both complexes, the ligand, and water.

In measuring the heats of these reactions, we actually determine the difference in bond energies between those of the coordinated water molecules and those of the coordinated ligands. In order to evaluate metal-ligand bond energies, it is necessary that we, therefore, know the heats of hydration of the gaseous metal ions as well as the heats of aquation of the various species involved in the reaction. These terms are generally available or can be estimated in most instances. Thus, it should be possible to get a reasonably good approximation of the desired metal-ligand bond energies.

For each of the above equations, we can write an equilibrium expression according to the law of mass action. Omitting the solvent water, whose activity does not change if we assume low concentrations, we can obtain the following expressions:

$$M + L \rightarrow ML \quad ; \quad k_1 = \frac{[ML]}{[M]\ [L]}$$

$$ML + L \rightarrow ML_2 \quad ; \quad k_2 = \frac{[ML_2]}{[ML]\ [L]} \qquad (9\text{-}16)$$

$$\vdots \qquad\qquad\qquad \vdots$$

$$ML_{n-1} + L \rightarrow ML_n \quad ; \quad k_n = \frac{[ML_n]}{[ML_{n-1}]\ [L]}$$

where the constants k_1, k_2, ... k_n are called the *stepwise* stability or formation constants and the bracketed quantities represent the activities of the enclosed species. The over-all formation constant, K, is the product of the successive formation constants, and it is the value which is used to determine the thermodynamic functions.

The standard free energy change, ΔF^0, is related to the equilibrium constant, K, by the relation

$$\Delta F^0 = -2.303\ RT \log K \qquad (9\text{-}17)$$

Recalling that

$$\Delta F^0 = \Delta H^0 - T\Delta S^0 \qquad (9\text{-}18)$$

we see that by measuring K at several temperatures we may obtain ΔH^0 by a graphical solution to the equation

$$2.303\ R \log K = (\Delta S^0 - \frac{\Delta H^0}{T}) \qquad (9\text{-}19)$$

Other refinements are necessary when ΔH^0 varies appreciably with temperature, but we shall ignore this complication here. ΔS^0 is then obtained from Eq. (9-18).§

From Eq. (9-19) it is obvious that complex formation is favored by negative enthalpy changes and positive entropy changes. In many instances both changes are found to favor complex formation, but there are also many examples where only one of these quantities is favorable. The relative importance of these effects is found to be dependent on variations in the

§ A very thorough treatment of the thermodynamics of complex ion formation in solution is given by Rossotti in Chapter 1 of Lewis, J. and Wilkins, R., "Modern Coordination Chemistry," Interscience Publishers, Inc., 1960, and the reader is referred to that source for additional information concerning the experimental methods and the detailed significance of the thermodynamic variables.

ligand as well as the central metal ion. From the stepwise formation constants we may obtain stepwise enthalpy changes. In aqueous solution, these generally have values in the range of $+5$ to -5 kcal/mole for complexation involving ionic ligands, and 0 to -5 kcal/mole for complexation involving neutral unidentate ligands. For multidentate ligands the values may run as high as -22 kcal/mole. Various properties of both the ligand and the metal ion have a marked influence on the over-all heat of formation of a complex, and we shall consider these properties shortly.

Entropy changes involving unidentate ligands are complicated by several factors in addition to those which affect heat changes. One might think that the ordering process associated with the formation in solution of one ionic species at the expense of two or more others would lead to an entropy decrease. Actually, this causes an over-all entropy increase due to the whole or partial neutralization of charge and the freeing of several bound solvent molecules from the solvation spheres of each of the reactants. By the same reasoning the entropy changes occurring when complexation involves neutral ligands will not be as favorable. Additional factors are involved when multidentate ligands coordinate. Loss of vibrational and rotational as well as translational entropy will generally be larger, but this will be compensated for by the displacement per ligand of more solvent molecules from the solvation spheres. Over-all entropy changes generally range from small negative values of the order of -2 eu to large positive values of the order of 20 to 60 eu for multidentate ligands. Generally, the higher the charge and the greater the number of donor atoms of the chelating ligand, the larger will be the entropy increase.

Factors Which Determine Stability

In considering the effect of the metal ion on the stability of a complex, it is convenient to separate the metal ions into those categories which we outlined earlier. The reason for this is that the number of major factors which affect the stability of complexes formed by metals falling into categories I to III is less than the number for metals of category IV. In the first three categories the metal ions (or atoms) are generally spherically symmetrical, and the stability of the complexes formed by them will be primarily dependent upon their effective ionic radius and effective nuclear charge. If we define the *ionic potential*, ϕ, as the ratio of cationic charge to the cation crystal radius, we can then state that, in general, with small and/or highly charged ionic ligands and with multidentate ligands the complex stability will increase as the ionic potential increases. The following observed stability sequences bear out this prediction: Li > Na > K > Rb > Cs; Mg > Ca > Sr > Ba > Ra; Al > Sc > Y > La; Lu > ... Gd > ... La, within families where charge remains constant, and Th >

Y > Ca > Na; La > Sr > K, within series where charge changes but size is relatively constant.

Apparent anomalies arise when we compare the similarly sized and charged members of two families in the same Periodic Group, e.g., K and Cu(I), Ca and Cd, or Sc and Ga(III). The B family elements invariably form the more stable complexes and the reason must be traced to the fundamental electronic difference; the ions of the A families have inert gas $(n - 1)$ s^2p^6 configurations while the ions of the B families have pseudo-inert gas $(n - 1)$ $s^2p^6d^{10}$ or pseudo-inert gas plus two $(n - 1)$ $s^2p^6d^{10}ns^2$ configurations. It is well known that the latter two configurations are much poorer shields for the excess positive charge located on the nucleus of a positive monatomic ion. Hence the effective nuclear charge, for instance, is actually larger in Cu(I) than it is in K.

One measure of this greater effective nuclear charge is found in the ionization potential. Thus, while Na^+ and Cu^+ are almost identical in size (0.95 *vs.* 0.93 Å) the ionization potential for Na is 118.5 kcal/mole while that for Cu is 178 kcal/mole. The difference may be considered as representing the much greater electron affinity of the Cu(I) ion over the Na ion. This is translated into greater attraction for the electrons offered by the ligand atoms. Also, greater penetration and polarization of the more diffuse 18-electron cloud undoubtedly is responsible for the greater degree of covalent character found with B family compounds. But, thus far we have considered the metals whose ions are in a minority when it comes to the formation of complexes. By far the most complexes are found for the metals in category IV.

Transition Metal Complexes and π-Bonding

It is not really appropriate to compare the metal ions discussed above with the transition metal ions wherein the incompleted d orbitals play such an important role in complexation. Indeed, it is difficult enough to compare these metal ions among themselves. The stability of the complexes formed from this varied group depends not only upon ionic potential, but upon such variables as crystal-field stabilization energy, electron-pairing energy, stereochemistry, availability of empty d orbitals for acceptance π-bonding, and availability of d-electron pairs for back-donation π-bonding. We might summarize all these factors by saying that the stability depends significantly upon the particular number of d electrons in the transition metal ion or atom.

It is clear that those ligands which owe so much of their ligational strength to π-bonding, such as CN^-, CO, PR_3, AsR_3, SR_2, etc., should not form stable complexes with metal ions having filled tightly bound electron levels which are incapable of supplying π-bonding electron pairs. This is borne out by the experimental facts. The contribution of the CFSE to the over-all enthalpy change has been seen to depend upon the number of d electrons and upon the geometry and strength of the ligand field, i.e., the amount of splitting of the d orbitals and their electron population.

Correlation of Thermodynamic Properties by the Crystal Field Theory

One of the most satisfying applications of crystal field theory has been its ability to correlate certain thermodynamic properties. For example, let us consider the heats of hydration of the divalent and tervalent transition metal cations shown in Table 9–16. It can be seen from the table that

TABLE 9–16. / **Ionic Radii (in Å) and Negative Heats of Hydration (in kcal/mole) for Some Divalent and Tervalent Transition Metal Ions.**[a]

d^0	d^2	d^3	d^4	d^5	d^6	d^7	d^8	d^9	d^{10}	
Ca	Ti	V	Cr	Mn	Fe	Co	Ni	Cu	Zn	
0.99	(0.85)	(0.82)	(0.80)	0.91	0.83	0.82	0.78	(0.72)	0.83	
382	446	453	460	445	468	497	507	507	492	
					Ru	Rh	Pd	Ag	Cd	
					(0.81)	(0.80)	(0.85)	(0.93)	1.03	
					448	486	505	411	437	
					Os	Ir	Pt	—	Hg	
					(0.88)	(0.92)	(1.24)		1.12	
					444	477	523		441	
d^0	d^1	d^2	d^3	d^4	d^5	d^6	—	—	—	d^{10}
Sc	Ti	V	Cr	Mn	Fe	Co				Ga
0.83	(0.64)	(0.69)	0.65	(0.66)	0.67	0.65				0.62
947	1027	1053	1105	1098	1072	1126				1124

[a]Values in parentheses are estimated.

the values increase from Ca to Cr, decrease at Mn, increase again to Cu and decrease at Zn. If all ions were spherically symmetrical and there were no preferential filling of certain d orbitals, we would expect a smooth, rising curve for the hydration energies as a function of atomic number. This curve would be defined by the values for the spherically symmetrical ions, $d^0(Ca^{2+})$, $d^5(Mn^{2+})$ and $d^{10}(Zn^{2+})$, due to their gradual contraction in size. This ideal curve and the actual experimental values are plotted in Figure 9–12 for both divalent and tervalent ions. The additional stabilization over that predicted by a simple electrostatic picture may be shown to be due to the CFSE, which may be summarized once again for spin-free octahedral complexes:

Number of d Electrons	CFSE
0, 5, 10	0 Dq
1, 6	4 Dq
2, 7	8 Dq
3, 8	12 Dq
4, 9	6 Dq

When the CFSE — calculated from the above table using the experimentally determined Dq values — is subtracted from the experimental ΔH values, the two-humped curve approaches the smooth-rising curve. This characteristic two-humped uncorrected curve is found for a great variety of octahedral, spin-free compounds of these metals, including both solids and complexes in solution. For complexes with symmetries other

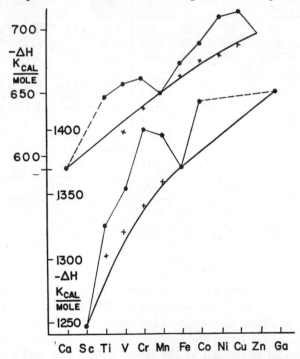

FIGURE 9–12. Heats of Hydration of Divalent (upper curves) and Tervalent (lower curves) Transition Metal Cations. The upper curve in each set joins experimental points, the lower curve connects the spherically symmetrical d^0, d^5, and d^{10} ions. The values designated by x result from subtracting the CFSE from each $-\Delta H$ value. (After Holmes, O. G. and McClure, D. S., *J. Chem. Phys.*, **26**, 1686 (1957).)

than octahedral, the same type of variation of ΔH with atomic number is found, but with different details. Again the minima or maxima occur at d^0, d^5 and d^{10}.

There is one other important point which we have so far neglected and that is that from the above CFSE, it would appear that the peaks of the two humps should occur at d^3 and d^8, not at d^4 and d^9 as is observed. The explanation undoubtedly lies in the fact that a regular octahedral structure for d^4 and d^9 configurations such as are found for Cr(II) and Cu(II), is not possible, but rather these ions usually adopt a tetragonally distorted octahedral configuration. The spin-free ground-state configurations $d_\epsilon^3 d_\gamma^1$ and $d_\epsilon^6 d_\gamma^3$ indicate that the antibonding d_γ orbital is degenerate. Thus, the electron may be in the $d_{x^2-y^2}$ or the d_{z^2} orbital. However, a theorem due to Jahn and Teller requires *that if the ground state of a system has several equivalent degenerate energy levels, a distortion of the system must occur to remove the degeneracy and make one energy level lower.* If there are two degenerate energy levels, as in this case, one will be raised in energy by the same amount that the other is lowered. We now know that, at least for Cu(II) complexes, this distortion amounts to four planar groups in the xy plane moving in closer to the copper ion and two *trans* groups along the z axis, moving farther away. Thus, the d_{z^2} and $d_{x^2-y^2}$ orbitals are no longer degenerate, the former lying lower and being preferentially filled. The extra stability found for d^4 and d^9 systems is what we might term *Jahn-Teller stabilization energy*. Actually, it is just Dq which increases in value due to the four ligands being closer-in. For the hydrated Cu(II) ion this extra stabilization has been estimated to be of the order of 8 kcal/mole. The Jahn-Teller distortions for other spin-free configurations are predicted to be very slight and have not been experimentally observed.

We may now summarize the predictions of the effect of the number of d electrons upon the stability of complexes in terms of the stability constant, K, or the negative enthalpy, ΔH_n, for the equation

$$M(H_2O)_n + nL \rightarrow ML_n + nH_2O$$

K will increase and $-\Delta H$ will increase according to the sequence $d^0 < d^1 < d^2 < d^3 \gtrless d^4 > d^5 < d^6 < d^7 < d^8 \gtrless d^9 > d^{10}$ for the formation of di- and tervalent metal complexes. The sequence $d^3 > d^4$ and $d^8 > d^9$ will be expected when the Jahn-Teller stabilization is low and the coordination number is 5 or 6. The sequences $d^3 < d^4$ and $d^8 < d^9$ will be expected when the Jahn-Teller stabilization is large and the coordination number is 4 or less.

Properties of the Ligand

We have already discussed briefly the general effect of the donor atom on the stability of complexes. Going further, we recognize that for monodentate ligands, the complex ion stability will generally increase as the

Lewis base character of the ligand increases providing the metal ion is not capable of forming π-bonds. Otherwise, for most transition metals, both the Lewis base and the π-bonding capabilities play important roles in determining stability, with the latter often the more significant. For monodentate negative ions the size and the charge are thus important, and for monodentate neutral molecules the size, dipole moment and polarizability are significant. Steric factors may become important with monodentate ligands and if they do, the protonic base affinities of the ligands will not reflect their coordinating abilities as Lewis bases toward metal ions.

The picture becomes much more complicated in the case of multidentate ligands. Here we must consider such additional factors as ring size and strain, number of rings, and substituents present in or conjugated to the ring system. In general, if the donor atom remains the same and its properties nearly so, the formation of chelate rings enhances the stability of complexes (the *chelate effect*). This is illustrated in Table 9–17, where the

TABLE 9–17. / **Stability Constants for Some Ammonia and Polyamine Complexes.**

Metal Complex	No. of Chelate Rings	LOG K						
		Mn^{2+}	Fe^{2+}	Co^{2+}	Ni^{2+}	Cu^{2+}	Zn^{2+}	Cd^{2+}
$M(NH_3)_4$	0	—	—	5.31	7.79	12.59	9.06	6.92
$M(en)_2$	2	4.9	7.7	10.9	14.5	20.2	11.2	10.3
$M(trien)$	3	4.9	7.8	11.0	14.1	20.5	12.1	10.0
$M(tren)$	3	5.8	8.8	12.8	14.0	18.8	14.6	12.3
$M(dien)_2$	4	—	—	14.1	18.9	21.3	14.4	13.8
$M(penten)$	5	9.4	11.2	15.8	19.3	22.4	16.2	16.8

en = ethylenediamine, $NH_2CH_2CH_2NH_2$
trien = triethylenetetramine, $NH_2CH_2CH_2NHCH_2CH_2NHCH_2CH_2NH_2$
tren = triaminotriethylamine, $(NH_2CH_2CH_2)_3N$
dien = diethylenetriamine, $NH_2CH_2CH_2NHCH_2CH_2NH_2$
penten = tetrakis(aminoethyl)ethylenediamine,
  $(NH_2CH_2CH_2)_2NCH_2CH_2N(CH_2CH_2NH_2)_2$

stability constants for several ammonia and amine complexes are listed. As is seen, the greater the number of chelate rings in the complex, the greater will be its stability. A huge amount of similar stability constant data has confirmed the generality of the chelate effect. Examination of the data will further reveal that four-membered rings, including the metal ion, are almost nonexistent. Five-membered rings are by far the most common and stable except when conjugation is possible in the ring system, and then six-membered rings appear to be the most stable. Larger rings are decreasingly stable and therefore very uncommon. This may be attributed primarily to strain set up in the heterocyclic rings. Recently stability constant data has been summarized for about 60 metal ions with 464 organic[45] and 56 inorganic[46] ligands. The recent book by Chaberek and Martell[4] gives an even more comprehensive discussion of the field.

ABSORPTION SPECTRA OF TRANSITION METAL COMPLEXES

Most of the complexes of the transition metals are highly colored compounds, which means they are capable of absorbing energy in the visible region of the spectrum. However, if we study the absorption spectra of these compounds in the solid state or dissolved in various solvents, we find that they also absorb energy in the ultraviolet region. The band or bands found in the visible region or in the fringes of the ultraviolet and infrared regions, having relatively low molar extinction coefficients (weak intensity) of the order 0.1 to 100, are believed to involve the transitions of central ion d electrons among the several split-energy levels established by the strength and symmetry of the particular ligand field. These have therefore been called d-d or *ligand field transitions*, and their weak intensities are due to the fact that, at least for the free ion, these electronic jumps are forbidden by symmetry selection rules. In the ultraviolet region, the band, or what is sometimes observed, the *continually rising absorption*, is of much higher intensity. The molar extinction coefficients here generally fall in the range of 1000 to 10,000 and are believed to be due to the movement of an electron from one component of the complex to another. As a rule, this means electron transfer from the ligand which, since it is usually a base and/or a reducing agent, presumably has more excess charge than the central metal. The spectra are referred to as *charge transfer spectra* and occur commonly in many chemical systems outside the scope of coordination compounds. We shall not concern ourselves with these absorptions, but we will consider in a little more detail the d-d spectra.[6,3,47,48]

Application of the Crystal Field Theory

Ilse and Hartmann[22] first called to the attention of chemists the value of the crystal field theory in the study of the absorption spectra of complexes when they applied the theory to the single weak visible absorption band of the d^1 system $[Ti(H_2O)_6]^{3+}$. The band maximum occurs at 4900 Å or 20,400 cm^{-1}. If the splitting of the d orbitals into two new levels, a triply degenerate d_ϵ and a doubly degenerate d_γ, occurs as predicted by crystal field theory, then this band can be assumed to arise from the excitation of the lone d electron from the d_ϵ to the d_γ level. Setting this energy difference at $10Dq$ then gives $Dq = 20,400$ cm$^{-1}/10 = 2040$ cm^{-1}, for water as the ligand. Looking at this picture from a spectroscopist's point of view, we would say that the ^2D term of the free Ti^{3+} has split into the two levels $^2T_{2g}$ and ^2E_g under the influence of the octahedral field. Each of these levels will split further in a tetragonal field, which, for example, might arise from a Jahn-Teller distortion, particularly of the excited ^2E_g level. A similar, but inverted, picture will hold for the analogous d^9 (^2D term) system, Cu^{2+}. For example the broad maximum for $[Cu(H_2O)_6]^{2+}$ occurs at 12,600 cm^{-1}, for $[Cu(NH_3)_6]^{2+}$ at 15,100 cm^{-1}, and for $[Cu(en)_3]^{2+}$ at 16,400 cm^{-1}, indicating the effect of increasing ligand field strength in the order $H_2O < NH_3 < en$.

When we deal with ion systems having more than one but less than nine d electrons, the number of terms which arise in the free ion from interelectronic repulsions serves to complicate the picture. For example some of the free ion terms which arise are: for d^2 or d^8, ^3F, ^1D, ^3P, ^1S, and ^1G; for d^3 or d^7, ^4F, ^2G, ^4P, ^2P, $^2H \cdots$; for d^4 and d^6, ^5D, ^3H, ^3G, ^3D, $^3P \cdots$; and for d^5, ^6S, ^4G, ^4P, ^4D, $^4F \cdots$. In addition, it is necessary to consider how each of these terms is split further by the various ligand fields. For this discussion, we shall consider only cubic perturbing fields.

We may construct a diagram, called an *Orgel diagram*, which shows how the atomic terms are split by the crystal field as it increases in intensity. A calculation of the splittings requires a quantum mechanical perturbation calculation using approximated unperturbed wave functions and approximated values for perturbing fields. For this reason, the calculations are necessarily only approximate. However, they do yield much valuable semi-quantitative information, including the number of levels to be expected,

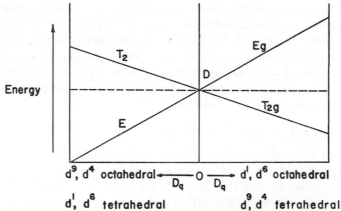

FIGURE 9–13. Orgel Diagram Illustrating the Splitting of a Field-free Ion D Term by a Cubic Perturbing Field of Increasing Strength. The right-hand side applies to an octahedral perturbation, the left-hand side to a tetrahedral perturbation. The dashed line represents the zero of energy and corresponds to the field-free ion ground term energy with the addition of the spherically symmetrical term in the perturbation energy. (After Dunn, T. M., in Chap. 4 of Lewis, J. and Wilkins, R., "Modern Coordination Chemistry," Interscience Publishers, Inc., New York, N. Y., 1960.)

even if the exact location of the levels on an energy scale cannot be obtained. The diagram is simplest for the splitting of a D term. This is shown in Figure 9–13, for the ground state term in d^1, d^9, d^4, and d^6 systems. The splitting for F and P terms, which are the lowest maximum spin states in d^2, d^8, d^3 and d^7 systems is shown in Figure 9–14, and Figure 9–15 shows the splittings for the d^5 system. Only the lower terms having the same spin multiplicity are shown; e.g., in Figure 9–14 we have left out the ^1D term since transitions between levels arising from it and from ^3F and ^3P are spin-forbidden.

Now we see that the single visible band found in titanium(III) complexes is due to the *Laporte*[§§] *forbidden transition* $^2T_{2g} \rightarrow {}^2E_g$. The Orgel diagram for octahedral vanadium(III) as seen in Figure 9–14 predicts three spin-allowed transitions. These are:

$$\nu_1 \qquad {}^3T_{1g}(F) \rightarrow {}^3T_{2g}(F)$$
$$\nu_2 \qquad {}^3T_{1g}(F) \rightarrow {}^3T_{1g}(P)$$
$$\nu_3 \qquad {}^3T_{1g}(F) \rightarrow {}^3A_{2g}$$

Furthermore, it predicts that ν_1 will lie lowest in energy. Experimentally it is found that $[V(H_2O)_6]^{3+}$ has bands at 17,700 cm^{-1} and 25,000 cm^{-1} assigned, respectively, to transitions ν_1 and ν_2. Dq may be determined from the Orgel diagram, assuming the correctness of the assignment for the transition ν_1; and from this it is calculated (also from the Orgel diagram) that ν_3 should be of the order of 37,000 cm^{-1}. This third band has not yet been verified, perhaps because of its weakness or due to the overlapping of intense charge transfer bands. How well the theory works can be seen from how well it theoretically predicts other transitions, once the assignment of one band in a spectrum has been made. Some values are given in Table 9–18 where comparison has been possible between theory and experiment, and it is seen that quite acceptable agreement can be obtained. For a very thorough and excellent treatment of this subject, see Chapter 4, by T. M. Dunn, of Lewis and Wilkins' "Modern Coordination Chemistry."[6]

Finally, we should mention that, since it is possible to calculate Dq values from the absorption spectra of symmetrical complexes with various ligands, we can then arrange the ligands in a sequence which will be a measure of their field strength. Such a series is known as a *spectrochemical series*, and it turns out to have just the order of ligands arrived at by Fajans in 1922 and more extensively by Tsuchida in 1938. This is understandable when we realize that the Fajans-Tsuchida series was found by

§§ Laporte forbidden transitions are of two types: (a) those transitions in which the higher and lower levels both are derived from the same free ion term and are therefore degenerate in the limit of zero field, and (b) those transitions in which the higher and lower levels are derived from different free ion terms but whose terms arise from the same electron configuration. The latter transitions will not have zero energy in the limit of zero field.

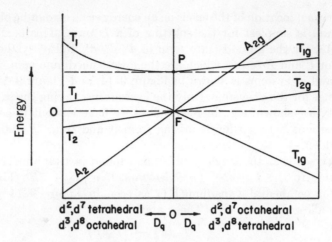

FIGURE 9–14. Orgel Diagram Illustrating the Splitting of the Field-free Ion F and P Terms Arising from the Configurations d^2, d^3, d^7, and d^8, by a Cubic Perturbing Field. The notation is the same as for Fig. 9–13. (After Dunn, T. M., in Chap. 4 of Lewis, J. and Wilkins, R., "Modern Coordination Chemistry," Interscience Publishers, Inc., New York, N. Y., 1960.)

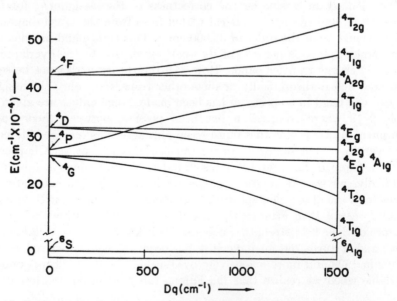

FIGURE 9–15. Orgel Diagram Arising from the Effect of a Cubic Perturbing Field upon the Field-free Ion Energy Levels of Manganese(II), a d^5 Ion. (After Dunn, T. M., in Chap. 4 of Lewis, J. and Wilkins, R., "Modern Coordination Chemistry," Interscience Publishers, Inc., New York, N. Y., 1960.)

observing the spectral shifts which occur when one ligand is replaced by another. An extensive series arrived at by much additional work places the common ligands in the order:

$$I^- < Br^- < -SCN^- \sim Cl^- < NO_3^- < F^- < urea \sim OH^- \sim ONO^-$$
$$\sim HCOO^- < C_2O_4^{2-} < H_2O < -NCS^- < glycine^- \sim EDTA^{4-} < py$$
$$\sim NH_3 < en \sim dien \sim trien < dipy < o\text{-phen} < -NO_2^- < < CN^-.$$

TABLE 9–18. / **Comparison of Calculated and Experimental Absorption Band Maxima (in cm^{-1}).**

	Calculated	Experimental
$[Cr(ox)_3]^{3-}$	$\nu_1 = (17,390)$ $\nu_2 = 23,990$ $\nu_3 = 15,000$ $\nu_4 = 25,000$	17,390 23,810 14,350 (*)
$[Co(en)_3]^{3+}$	$\nu_1 = (21,400)$ $\nu_2 = 29,400$ $\nu_3 = 14,400$ $\nu_4 = 18,400$	21,400 29,600 14,000 (*)
$[Ni(NH_3)_6]^{2+}$	$\nu_1 = (10,700)$ $\nu_2 = 19,260$ $\nu_3 = 28,600$	10,700 17,500 28,100
$[Co(H_2O)_6]^{2+}$	$\nu_1 = 7,200$ $\nu_2 = 16,200$ $\nu_3 = 20,300$	8,000 16,000 20,200
$[Co(NH_3)_6]^{2+}$	$\nu_1 = 8,400$ $\nu_2 = 18,900$ $\nu_3 = 21,700$	9,000 18,500 21,100
$[Co(en)_3]^{2+}$	$\nu_1 = 8,800$ $\nu_2 = 19,800$ $\nu_3 = 22,000$	9,800 18,700 21,700
$[Ni(H_2O)_6]^{2+}$	$\nu_1 = 7,600$ $\nu_2 = 13,700$ $\nu_3 = 26,000$ $\nu_2/\nu_1 = 1.80$	8,000 14,000 14,000 $\nu_2/\nu_1 = 1.75$
$[Ni(en)_3]^{2+}$	$\nu_1 = 10,500$ $\nu_2 = 18,900$ $\nu_3 = 29,580$ $\nu_2/\nu_1 = 1.80$	11,200 18,350 29,000 $\nu_2/\nu_1 = 1.64$

*Perhaps covered by large spin-allowed band.

BIBLIOGRAPHY

1. Graddon, D., "An Introduction to Coordination Chemistry," Pergamon Press, New York, N.Y., 1961.
2. Bailar, J., Jr., Ed., "The Chemistry of the Coordination Compounds," Reinhold Publishing Corp., New York, N.Y., 1956.
3. Basolo, F. and Pearson, R., "Mechanisms of Inorganic Reactions," John Wiley & Sons, Inc., New York, N.Y., 1958.
4. Chaberek, S. and Martel, A., "Organic Sequestering Agents," John Wiley & Sons, Inc., New York, N.Y., 1958.
5. Smith, R., "The Sequestration of Metals," Chapman & Hall Ltd., London, 1959.
6. Lewis, J. and Wilkins, R., "Modern Coordination Chemistry," Interscience Publishers, Inc., New York, N.Y., 1960.
7. Emeleus, H. and Anderson, R., "Modern Aspects of Inorganic Chemistry," 3rd ed., D. Van Nostrand Co., New York, N.Y., 1960.
8. Orgel, L., "An Introduction to Transition-Metal Chemistry: Ligand Field Theory," John Wiley & Sons, Inc., New York, N.Y., 1961.
9. Ahrland, S., Chatt, J., and Davies, N., *Quart. Revs.*, **12**, 265 (1958).
10. Sidgwick, N., *J. Chem. Soc.*, **123**, 275 (1923); *Trans Faraday Soc.*, **19**, 469 (1923); *Chem. & Ind.*, **42**, 901, 1203 (1923).
11. Sidgwick, N., "The Electronic Theory of Valence," Clarendon Press, Oxford, 1927.
12. Lowry, T., *Chem. & Ind.*, **42**, 316 (1923).
13. Pauling, L., "The Nature of the Chemical Bond," 3rd ed., Cornell University Press, Ithaca, New York, 1960.
14. Huggins, M., *J. Chem. Phys.*, **5**, 527 (1937).
15. Craig, D., Maccoll, A., Nyholm, R., Orgel, L., and Sutton, L., *J. Chem. Soc.*, **1954**, 332.
16. Van Arkel, A. and DeBoer, J., *Rec. Trav. Chim.*, **47**, 593 (1928).
17. Garrick, F., *Phil. Mag.*, **9**, 131 (1930); **10**, 71, 76 (1930); **11**, 741 (1931); **14**, 914 (1932).
18. Bethe, H., *Ann. Physik*, **3**, No. 5, 133 (1929).
19. Penney, W. and Schlapp, R., *Phys. Rev.*, **41**, 194 (1932); **42**, 666 (1932).
20. Van Vleck, J., *Phys. Rev.*, **41**, 208 (1932).
21. Van Vleck, J., *J. Chem. Phys.*, **3**, 803, 807 (1935).
22. Ilse, F. and Hartmann, H., *Z. Physik. Chem.*, **197**, 239 (1951).
23. Orgel, L., *J. Chem. Soc.*, **1952**, 4756; *J. Chem. Phys.*, **23**, 1819 (1955); *Tenth Solvay Conference*, Brussels, May 1956.
24. Gillespie, R. and Nyholm, R., *Quart. Revs.*, **11**, 339 (1957).
25. Griffith, J. and Orgel, L., *Quart. Revs.*, **11**, 381 (1957).
26. Jorgensen, C., *Acta Chem. Scand.*, **10**, 500 (1956).
27. Tsuchida, R., *Bull. Chem. Soc. Japan*, **13**, 338, 436, 471 (1938).
28. Van Vleck, J., *J. Chem. Phys.*, **7**, 72 (1939).
29. Owen, J., *J. Inorg. Nuclear Chem.*, **8**, 430 (1958).
30. Sutton, L., *J. Chem. Ed.*, **37**, 498 (1960).
31. Nyholm, R., *Quart. Revs.*, **7**, 377 (1953).
32. Nyholm, R., *Record Chem. Progr.*, **19**, 45 (1958).
33. Asmussen, R. and Soling, H., *Acta. Chem. Scand.*, **11**, 1331 (1957).
34. Figgis, B., *Nature*, **182**, 1568 (1958).
35. Nyholm, R., *Quart. Revs.*, **3**, 321 (1949); *Progr. in Stereochem.*, **1**, 322 (1954).

36. Dunitz, J. and Orgel, L., "Advances in Inorganic Chemistry and Radio-chemistry," Vol. II, H. Emeleus and A. Sharpe, Eds., Academic Press, Inc., New York, N.Y., 1960.
37. Gillespie, R. and Nyholm, R., *Progr. in Stereochem.*, **2**, 196 (1958).
38. Cartmell, E. and Fowles, G., "Valency and Molecular Structure," Butterworths Scientific Publs., London, 1956.
39. Taube, H., "Advances in Inorganic Chemistry and Radiochemistry," Vol. I, H. Emeleus and A. Sharpe, Eds., Academic Press, Inc., New York, N.Y., 1959.
40. Bjerrum, J., *Chem. Revs.*, **46**, 381 (1950).
41. Berkin, A., *Quart. Revs.*, **5**, 1 (1951).
42. Jonassen, H., *Record Chem. Progr.*, **13**, 135 (1952).
43. Williams, R., *Ann. Rep. Chem. Soc.*, **56**, 87 (1959).
44. Taube, H., *Chem. Revs.*, **50**, 69 (1952).
45. "Stability Constants, Part I, Organic Ligands," The Chemical Society, London, 1957.
46. "Stability Constants, Part II, Inorganic Ligands," The Chemical Society, London, 1958.
47. Jorgensen, C., "Energy Levels of Complexes and Gaseous Ions," Gjellerups, Copenhagen, 1957; "Absorption Spectra of Complexes of Heavy Metals," *Technical Report to the U.S. Army* (1958).
48. Jorgensen, C., *Report to the Xth Solvay Council*, Brussels, May, 1956.

10 / *Nonaqueous Solvents*

In the days of the alchemist, the search for the universal solvent was almost as ardent as that for the philosopher's stone. Needless to say, the search proved fruitless in both instances. Strangely enough, however, after several hundred years we find that water, which is the oldest and most convenient of all solvents, is still the nearest thing we have to a universal solvent. And with regard to convenience and versatility, it is not likely that it will ever be replaced. In fact, before 1900, it was quite generally felt that water was unique in its ability to dissolve ionic substances. We now recognize the fallacy of such a view and in retrospect may wonder why it persisted so long. However, since the turn of the century, we have made great strides in the use and understanding of nonaqueous solvents. Primarily, the present day advances can be attributed to a realization that the differences between water and other media are usually only differences in degree. Yet, in spite of all our efforts, we have only scratched the surface, and the study of nonaqueous solvents offers one of the remaining frontiers of chemistry.

There are numerous factors that give water its favored position, and its availability is not the least of these. A more or less allied factor is found in its ease of purification. Additionally, such factors as the dipole moment, amphoteric character, and the high dielectric constant all contribute to this unique position of water as a solvent. In spite of its many desirable properties, there are, nevertheless, instances where a nonaqueous medium can serve certain needs that an aqueous one cannot. These vary from studies of the Debye-Huckel theory to use as a medium for organic reactions. In fact, we have even come to use such an unlikely solvent as anhydrous HF on an industrial scale. In this light, it seems quite surprising to find that so little is known of the many possible nonaqueous solvents.

In choosing a solvent, various practical factors must be considered. For instance, if a particular solvent is to be worthy of development, it should be reasonably available, have physical properties which permit its relatively convenient study, and it should show a sufficiently unique character to justify its use. When extremes of temperature or pressure are necessary to obtain a liquid phase, or when various hazards are encountered, one cannot help but wonder if the chemical properties of the solvent are such as to warrant further study.

In spite of serious handicaps, the study of some solvents has proved to be extremely profitable. With regard to health hazards, anhydrous HF and anhydrous HCN are obviously quite dangerous. Yet a considerable amount of work has been done with both solvents, and in some instances it has led to large scale industrial applications. One of the more common problems with many solvents is that of obtaining a liquid phase. Liquid ammonia has been the most extensively studied of all nonaqueous solvents, and its normal boiling point is $-33.35°C$. Anhydrous SO_2 is somewhat more favorable in this respect, inasmuch as its normal boiling point is $-10.2°C$. But in either case, it is necessary to work at lower temperatures or under higher pressures than normal. At the other extreme, we find that very high temperatures are necessary to obtain the liquid phases for fused salt solvents such as fused KNO_3 and fused NaCl. A very large number of the common nonaqueous solvents such as methanol, ethanol, acetic acid, and sulfuric acid, of course, have liquid ranges that coincide with our normal room temperatures.

SOLVENT CLASSIFICATION

A variety of approaches have been used in the classification of non-aqueous solvents. However, none of these can be considered to be generally acceptable. From an historical standpoint, much of the interest in non-aqueous solvents has been centered around acid-base concepts, and for this reason classifications of these solvents are frequently based on acid-base properties. Such a classification is rather restrictive, but no more so than the other conventional classifications. It is generally found that the manner of classification one chooses will depend on the particular solvent properties of interest.

One of the simplest and also most obvious solvent classifications is in terms of *polarity*. The extreme differences in the properties of polar and nonpolar solvents certainly justifies such a division. There will be many instances where such a classification can prove valuable, but it would appear that it is too broad to be of general utility.

A classification that is closely allied to the Bronsted-Lowry concept of an acid is that which distinguishes *protonic* and *nonprotonic solvents*.

Frequently, it is useful to refer to a solvent that will yield a solvated proton on autoionization, such as water, hydrofluoric acid, ammonia, and low molecular-weight alcohols. However, a more valuable breakdown along these same lines is in terms of the *protophylic* character of the solvent. Here we can define four general types of solvents: (1) *acidic solvents* such as sulfuric acid, hydrofluoric acid, and acetic acid, which have a strong tendency to donate a proton; (2) *basic solvents* such as ammonia, pyridine, and hydrazine, which have a strong affinity for a proton; (3) *amphoteric solvents* such as water and low molecular-weight alcohols, that can act as either acids or bases; and finally (4) *aprotic solvents*, which are those that are inert to proton transfer. Solvents such as benzene and carbon tetrachloride are typical of this last class. There is only one significant weakness of this classification, and it is that we are again emphasizing the acid-base relationships of the solvent. A second, less serious shortcoming of the classification is inherent in the protonic concept of an acid and a base. According to the protonic concept, acidity and basicity are relative to the reference acid or base. Thus, all of the solvents except the aprotic solvents can act as either acidic or basic solvents depending on the particular solute. Nevertheless, the distinction of the four classes is ordinarily valid, and such a classification is quite valuable.

Another very useful classification of solvents is in terms of the so-called *parent solvent* concept. A particular solvent can be considered to be a parent solvent from which a system of compounds can be derived, and the behavior of analogous compounds should be related in their respective parent solvents. Examples of a few such analogous groups are shown in Table 10–1. As an illustration, we observe that the OH⁻ group in the parent solvent,

TABLE 10–1. / **Formally Analogous Groups in Different Solvents.**

Solvent	Analogous Group	
H_2O	H_3O^+	OH^-
NH_3	NH_4^+	NH_2^-
NH_2OH	NH_3OH^+	$NHOH^-$
$(CH_3CO)_2O$	CH_3CO^+	$CH_3CO_2^-$
H_2S	H_3S^+	SH^-

H_2O, is analogous to the NH_2^- group in the parent solvent, NH_3. We would thus expect these two groups to behave similarly in their respective parent solvents, and this is found to be the case. In terms of the parent solvent concept, it has been possible to successfully correlate a vast number of chemical reactions in different solvents.

TYPE REACTIONS

Although our knowledge of nonaqueous systems is such that we cannot always be confident of our understanding of many reactions, we find that some classification of reactions is possible. Needless to say, the same reaction types are defined in nonaqueous media as are defined in aqueous media. However, the specific reactions are certainly quite different from one solvent to another, and it is for this reason that nonaqueous solvents are of such interest.

Metathetical Reactions

The interest in this type of reaction is usually associated with precipitation both from a preparative and an analytical standpoint. Just as in an aqueous medium, the course of a metathetical reaction in a given nonaqueous solvent can be predicted from the solubilities of the products in that solvent. These are normally of sufficient difference in various solvents as to lead to quite divergent reaction paths. For this reason it is often found that separations and analyses can better be effected in nonaqueous media than in water.

Acid-Base Reactions

Probably the most thoroughly studied phase of nonaqueous chemistry is that of acid-base reactions. Actually, acid-base reactions have been rather significant in initiating and furthering studies in the field of nonaqueous chemistry, primarily through the solvent-system concept of acid-base behavior. According to the solvent-system definition, an acid can be considered to be any substance that, by direct dissociation or reaction with the solvent, gives the cation characteristic of the solvent; and a base to be any substance that, by direct dissociation or reaction with the solvent, gives the anion characteristic of the solvent. In the case of protonic solvents, the cation is nothing more than a solvated proton, and under these conditions, the protonic concept of an acid is essentially equivalent to the solvent system concept of an acid, as long as we remain in a given solvent. As an example, we would expect some typical neutralization reactions in ammonia to be

$$NH_4Cl + NaNH_2 \rightarrow NaCl + 2NH_3$$
$$NH_4Cl + PbNH \rightarrow PbCl_2 + 3NH_3$$
$$NH_4Cl + NaOH \rightarrow NaCl + NH_3 + H_2O$$

We should not lose sight of the fact that NH_4Cl is equivalent to a solvated HCl molecule, and we can consider the reaction of NH_4Cl with NaOH to be analogous to the reaction of H_3OCl with NaOH.

In nonprotonic solvents we may find it convenient to again use the solvent system concept for acid-base behavior. For an acid-base reaction in anhydrous SO_2, we find that a typical reaction is

$$SOCl_2 + Na_2SO_3 \rightarrow 2NaCl + 2SO_2$$

In addition, we should recognize that a variety of other types of acid-base reactions can be considered in these solvents if we accept either the Lewis or the protonic definition. In such cases, we can consider the solvent to be nothing more than a medium in which the reaction takes place. This, of course, is a necessity in an aprotic solvent such as benzene or carbon tetrachloride. These solvents show no autoionization, and the solvent system concept has no significance here. Yet, it is still possible to carry out acid-base type reactions in such media.[1]

Oxidation-Reduction Reactions

It would be expected that the same types of oxidation-reduction reactions occur in nonaqueous media as occur in an aqueous system, and this is generally true. However, at the same time, it is found that the oxidizing and reducing abilities do not necessarily hold from one solvent to another. Although the magnitudes of the oxidation potentials will vary with the solvent, it is not likely that the actual order of potentials will change too significantly, but even this is certainly possible. For instance, lithium has the highest standard potential in an aqueous medium. This is primarily due to the relatively high hydration energy of the lithium ion. In a less polar solvent, it is not likely that the lithium would still hold this position. Unfortunately, much of the available data along these lines is of questionable validity, and it is difficult to make even general correlations.

Although redox reactions follow a rather normal pattern in most instances, a quite anomalous behavior is noted for solutions of the alkali and alkaline earth metals in liquid ammonia and some of the lower aliphatic amines. Both groups of elements dissolve readily in liquid ammonia, and on evaporation, the alkali metals are obtained in their original form, whereas the alkaline earth metals form crystalline ammoniates of the form $M(NH_3)_6$. In dilute solutions, all of these metals give a characteristic blue color. For iven concentrations, the absorption spectra in this region are identical for all of these metals, thereby indicating that the blue color is due to a common species. In addition, it is found that the conductance of these solutions is extraordinarily high. At all concentrations, the equivalent conductance is found to be greater than that of any known salt in any solvent, and at high concentrations, the conductance approaches very closely that of metal conductors.

Very little is known of the detailed structure of these solutions, but the basic interpretation of their general behavior can be attributed to Kraus.[2]

It is assumed that the metal atoms are dissociated into metal ions and free electrons, and these products are then solvated as

$$M = M^+ + e^-$$
$$M^+ + x\text{NH}_3 = M(\text{NH}_3)_x{}^+$$
$$e^- + y\text{NH}_3 = e(\text{NH}_3)_y{}^-$$

With regard to redox reactions, a solution containing free electrons would be expected to show unusually great reducing ability, and ammonia solutions of the alkali and alkaline earth metals show just such behavior. Much of the interest in the solvent properties of ammonia has been centered around the theoretical as well as the experimental nature of these solutions.[3]

Solvolytic Reactions

In order to differentiate between solvation reactions and solvolytic reactions, we can define a *solvolytic* reaction as one in which the dissolved solute reacts with the solvent in a manner such as to change the normal anion and cation concentrations of the solvent. In an aqueous medium, an example of a solvolytic reaction would be

$$\text{POCl}_3 + \text{HOH} \rightarrow \text{PO(OH)}_3 + \text{HCl}$$

In the resultant solution, we have HCl and H_3PO_4. Both of these compounds are strong acids, and the *pH* of the solution will obviously show a sharp decrease. As an example of a solvolytic reaction in a nonprotonic solvent, we can consider the reaction

$$\text{SnCl}_4 + 2\,\text{SeOCl}_2 \rightarrow 2\,\text{SeOCl}^+ + \text{SnCl}_6{}^=$$

The cation characteristic of the solvent is SeOCl^+ and its concentration is seen to be increased as a result of the reaction.

One great advantage in considering solvolytic-type reactions results from the similarity of reactions in terms of the parent solvent concept. If for instance, we consider reactions of protonic solvents with a compound such as *R*COCl, we would expect to obtain products that are formally related in terms of their own parent solvents. In the case of the solvent water, we would obtain the reaction

$$R\text{COCl} + \text{HOH} \rightarrow R\text{COOH} + \text{HCl}$$

If now we would use other protonic solvents such as alcohols, ammonia, or a primary amine, we should observe analogous type reactions. For instance, we would expect

$$\left.\begin{array}{l}\text{HOH}\\ \text{HO}R\\ \text{HNH}_2\\ \text{HNH}R\end{array}\right\} + R\text{COCl} \rightarrow \left.\begin{array}{l}R\text{COOH}\\ R\text{COO}R\\ R\text{CONH}_2\\ R\text{CONH}R\end{array}\right\} + \text{HCl}$$

Each of these resultant compounds would be expected to behave in an analogous manner in its own parent solvent. Thus, it would be expected that RCOOH would behave in water in a manner similar to $RCONH_2$ in ammonia. It is for this reason that solvolytic reactions are of rather significant value as a means of reaction classification.

THE DIELECTRIC CONSTANT

In attempting to rationalize experimental data, it is frequently found that several apparently different models of a system can be used with equal success. However, these are usually found to be manifestations of some more fundamental concept. This is particularly true of solution chemistry in nonaqueous solvents. We can attribute our observations to ion-pair formation, deviations in activity coefficients, ionic interactions of various types, and so on, but these can all be related through the dielectric constant of the solution. Consequently, it would be expected that many solvent characteristics should be understandable in terms of the dielectric constant of the solvent; and this is found to be the case.

The most familiar usage of the dielectric constant is found in the expression for the force of attraction or repulsion between two charged bodies,

$$F = \frac{QQ'}{\epsilon r^2} \tag{10-1}$$

Here, Q and Q' are two charges separated by a distance, r, in a homogeneous dielectric. In this particular case, we can think of the dielectric constant, ϵ, as a constant of proportionality dependent on the particular solvent medium. For a vacuum, we define ϵ to be unity, and for all other media, it is found to have a value greater than unity. Alternatively, we can obtain a mechanistic picture by considering the dielectric constant in terms of the charging of the plates of a parallel condenser. If we imagine a condenser having two parallel plates with surface areas that are large compared to the distance between them, and we allow them to become charged electrically to the extent of $+\sigma A$ and $-\sigma A$, we will find that there is an essentially homogeneous electric field established inside the condenser. This field will be directed perpendicular to the surface of the plates and, if the medium between the plates is a vacuum, the field will have a magnitude given by

$$E_0 = 4\pi\sigma \tag{10-2}$$

Now, if we place a homogeneous dielectric material of dielectric constant ϵ between the condenser plates, we will find that the field strength will be decreased to

$$E = \frac{4\pi\sigma}{\epsilon} \tag{10-3}$$

The decrease in field strength in the presence of the dielectric is the result of the displacement of electric charges in the body of the dielectric. These displacements are of two general types. If the molecules have a permanent dipole, they will arrange themselves in a preferential position in the field. This is referred to as *orientation polarizaion*. If no permanent dipole exists in the molecules, a form of polarization known as *distortion polarization* will still result from the displacement of the charges in the molecules. In either case, we can recognize that the energy of the condenser is stored as a result of the alignment of the solvent dipoles in such a manner as to neutralize the effects of the charges on the condenser plates.

The importance of the dielectric constant in ionic solutions becomes apparent when we note its relationship with respect to the interactions of adjacent ions. It can be seen from Eq. (10–1), that the force of attraction between two ions is critically dependent on the dielectric constant of the medium. As the dielectric constant decreases in magnitude, the force of attraction between adjacent ions increases. Consequently, in solvents with low dielectric constants the ionic interactions extend over much greater distances than in solvents with high dielectric constants. Since nonideality can usually be attributed to ion-ion interactions, it follows that systems with high dielectric constants should show greater conformity to ideal behavior than those of the same ionic concentration having low dielectric constants.

By now, the qualitative relationship between the dipole moment of a solvent molecule and the dielectric constant of the solvent should be obvious. If a solvent molecule has a large dipole moment, the solvent will have a correspondingly large dielectric constant. By virtue of their large dipole moment, such solvent molecules are readily capable of absorbing the energy of an electric field. On the other hand, if the solvent molecules are symmetrical or, at best, have only a small dipole moment, they will not be so successful in neutralizing an electric field, and the dielectric constant will be small. These trends can be appreciated from the list of dielectric constants given in Table 10–2.

TABLE 10–2. / **Dielectric Constants of Some Typical Solvents.**

Solvent	Dielectric Constant	Temperature (°C)
Hydrogen cyanide	118.3	18
Sulfuric acid	110	20
Formamide	109	25
Water	78.5	25
Methanol	31.5	25
Ethanol	24.2	25
Ammonia	22	−34
Acetone	20.4	25
Benzene	2.275	25
Dioxane	2.213	25

THE ACTIVITY COEFFICIENT

From a strictly thermodynamic point of view, it is not necessary to relate the activity coefficient of a solute to any particular mechanistic picture of solute behavior. On the other hand, we cannot help but wonder why such deviations from ideality do occur. Thus, in the light of our present-day understanding of solution chemistry, it has been possible to show that the activity coefficient of an electrolyte is intimately dependent on a variety of factors, most of which can be discussed in terms of electrostatic interactions. These are factors involving, primarily, ion-ion interactions such as ionic association and ion-ion repulsions. Virtually, all such factors are dependent on the dielectric constant of the solvent, and we should, therefore, expect a direct correlation between the solvent dielectric constant and the activity coefficients of the solute.

A common means of determining the activity coefficients of an ionic solute is by use of a galvanic cell. The relationship between the molar activity coefficient and the measured potential of the cell is given for a uni-univalent electrolyte by the Nernst equation in the form

$$E = E^0 - \frac{RT}{F} \ln C^2 f_{\pm}^2 \qquad (10\text{–}4)$$

Thus, it can be seen that, if the standard potential of the cell E^0 is known, it is possible to evaluate the activity coefficients of the electrolyte, $f_{\pm}$, for a given molar concentration C. The most convenient cell to use for this purpose is one without liquid junction, and the most commonly used cell of this type is the cell

$$\text{Pt,H}_{2(1 \text{ atm})} | \text{HCl}_{(m)} \text{ (nonaqueous)} | \text{AgCl, Ag}$$

Although there is always some question of the validity of such data because, in particular, of trace impurities of water, there appears to be a definite correlation between the activity coefficients of the solute and the solvent dielectric constant.

One rather significant use of anhydrous solvents as well as mixed solvents is found in the testing of the Debye-Huckel theory. According to the Debye-Huckel theory, the molar activity coefficients of the solute will be given by the general expression

$$-\log f_{\pm} = \frac{A \sqrt{C}}{1 + \beta a_0 \sqrt{C}} \qquad (10\text{–}5)$$

where C is the molar concentration of the solute, a_0 is the apparent ionic radius of the solute ions, and A and β are constants dependent on the temperature and the solvent. In more detailed form, the expression for the molar activity coefficients is given by

$$-\log f_{\pm} = 1.8123 \times 10^6 \, \frac{\sqrt{C}}{(\epsilon T)^{\frac{3}{2}}} \cdot \frac{1}{1 + 50.288 \times 10^8 \, (\epsilon T)^{-\frac{1}{2}} \, a_0 \, \sqrt{C}} \qquad (10\text{–}6)$$

where ϵ is the dielectric constant of the solvent and T is the absolute temperature. It can readily be seen from Eq. (10–6), that the dielectric constant does enter into the theoretical calculations of the activity coefficients. The extent of this dependence can be appreciated from Figure 10–1, where the log of the molal activity coefficient is plotted against the square root of the molal concentration of hydrochloric acid in different mixtures of dioxane and water. The dielectric constant, of course, decreases with an increase in the dioxane concentration. The straight lines represent the Debye-Huckel limiting slope. Thus, in general, we can state that for a given ionic concentration, the deviation of the solute activity coefficient from unity increases with a decrease in solvent dielectric constant. This point may be better illustrated by comparing the activity coefficients of an electrolyte directly with the square root of the concentration of that electrolyte. Thus, in Figure 10–2, we see a plot of experimental activity coefficients versus the square root of the molal concentration of hydrochloric acid in three solvents having quite different values for their dielectric constants. It is apparent that the activity coefficients are affected in a consistent manner by the change in solvent dielectric constant.

If we assume that the nonideality of a solute is reflected in its activity coefficient, then we conclude that for a given ionic concentration, a decrease

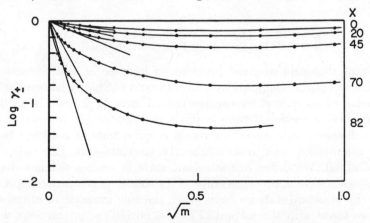

FIGURE 10–1. Comparison of the Molal Activity Coefficients of HCl to the Limiting Slope of the Debye-Huckel Theory in Various Mixtures of Dioxane and Water. The weight per cent of dioxane is given under **X**. (After Harned, H., Morrison, J., Walker, F., Donelson, J., and Calmon, C., *J. Am. Chem. Soc.*, **61**, 49 (1939).)

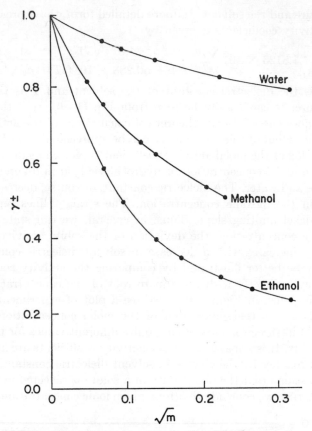

FIGURE 10–2. Dependence of the Molal Activity Coefficients of HCl on the Solvent Dielectric Constant.

in solvent dielectric constant leads to an increase in solute nonideality. This is evident since an ideal electrolyte would ordinarily have an activity coefficient of unity, and we can see from Figure 10–2 that the deviation of the activity coefficient from unity is greatest for the solvent with the lowest dielectric constant. This result is quite understandable when we recall the method used to determine the standard state electrode potential of a cell. We define our standard state in such a manner that the activity coefficient approaches unity as the solute concentration approaches zero. This standard state is one in which the only interactions of the solute ions are those with the solvent. That is, no ion-ion interactions will be present at infinite dilution. Consequently, at finite concentrations, ion-ion interactions become significant and lead to deviations in the activity coefficients from unity. Of course, the lower the solvent dielectric constant, the more pronounced will be these ionic interactions.

SOLUBILITY

As a general rule, we expect ionic and polar solutes to dissolve in polar solvents and nonpolar solutes to dissolve in nonpolar solvents. From a qualitative point of view, this behavior can be attributed to the types of forces that exist between a solute and a solvent molecule as compared to those that exist between two solvent molecules. If, for instance, the possibility of dissolving carbon tetrachloride in water is considered, we note that the only interaction between a carbon tetrachloride molecule and a water molecule involves van der Waals forces. Yet, the interaction of a water molecule with another water molecule involves the considerably greater energy of a hydrogen bond. Thus, from the standpoint of energetics, we would not expect carbon tetrachloride to be water-soluble. On the other hand, if we consider the solubility of carbon tetrachloride in a solvent such as benzene, it can be seen that both solute and solvent can offer only van der Waals type forces. Consequently, it would seem reasonable to expect that the benzene molecule would have little preference between a carbon tetrachloride molecule and another benzene molecule. Finally, if we raise the temperature of an immiscible system, it might be expected that thermal energies, which are of the order of kT, would be of sufficient magnitude to overcome hydrogen bonding effects and lead to an increase in solubility.

Attempts have been made to calculate the solubility of an ionic species in various solvents, but they have met with only limited success. In carrying out such a calculation, we must first recognize that in a solvation process involving ionic species, the dielectric constant of the solvent plays a major role. This can be appreciated by considering the dissolution of a crystal such as shown in Figure 10–3. If we remove an ion to an infinite distance from the crystal surface in a vacuum, we would obtain a potential energy curve of the general form seen in Figure 10–4(a). If we now place the crystal in the presence of a dielectric, we would obtain a curve of the type seen in Figure 10–4(b), for the potential energy change as the ion is taken to infinity. The energy necessary to bring about the separation of the ion

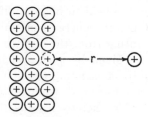

FIGURE 10–3. Removal of an Ion from a Crystal Lattice.

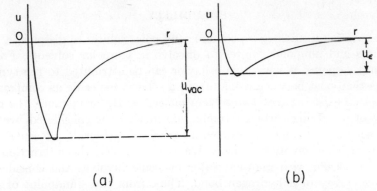

(a)   (b)

FIGURE 10-4. Potential Energy Diagrams for the Removal of an Ion from a Crystal Lattice in a Vacuum (a), and in the Presence of a Dielectric (b).

from the crystal will be considerably less when a dielectric exists between the ion and the crystal. In essence, this means that the ion can see the crystal through a greater distance in a vacuum than it can in the presence of a dielectric. The dielectric, of course, will be the solvent in which the dissolution takes place, and it should be apparent that the higher the dielectric constant of the solvent, the less will be the work required to separate the ions. Thus, it would be considerably easier to separate two ions in water where the dielectric constant is 78.5 at 25° C, than it would be in ethanol where the dielectric constant is 24.2 at this temperature. This, then, results in a general decrease in solubility of a salt with a decrease in the dielectric constant of the solvent.

Application of the Born Equation

A detailed calculation of the solubility of a salt can be attempted strictly on the basis of electrostatic interactions. The starting point of the calculation is the Born equation[4] for the electrical work involved in charging a sphere of radius a, in the presence of a uniform dielectric. Basically, the equation can be developed by considering a uniform field of intensity E in a vacuum. The energy associated with the field will be $E^2/8\pi$ per unit volume. If we now allow the field to be nonuniform, its total energy can be obtained by multiplying the energy per unit volume by the volume increment, dv, and integrating from the surface of the sphere to infinity. The field intensity will be given by q/r^2, and by the usual method, the integration can be made by considering the volume of a spherical shell of thickness dr at a distance r to $r + dr$ from the center of the sphere. This increment is given by $4\pi r^2 dr$, thereby leading to

$$W = \int \frac{E^2}{8\pi}\, dv = \int_a^\infty \frac{q^2 4\pi r^2}{8\pi\; r^4}\, dr = \frac{q^2}{2a} \qquad (10\text{-}7)$$

In the presence of a dielectric, the equation can be shown to be

$$W = \frac{q^2}{\epsilon 2a} \tag{10-8}$$

If we make the assumption that an ion can be treated as a sphere with a fixed radius and that the dielectric constant of the solvent is uniform, then our calculations for the work involved in the charging of the sphere can be equated to the free energy of the ion with respect to the uncharged species in the same solvent.

In applying the Born equation to solubility problems, we will express the work of charging an ion in the more general form

$$W = \frac{1}{\epsilon} \frac{z_i^2 e^2}{2r_i} \tag{10-9}$$

where z_i is the number of unit charges on the ion and e is the electron charge. If the same form of the equation holds for both ion types, the total work for N ions of each type will be

$$W_+ + W_- = \frac{N\nu_+ z_+^2 e^2}{2r_+ \epsilon} + \frac{N\nu_- z_-^2 e^2}{2r_- \epsilon}$$

$$= \frac{Ne^2}{2r\epsilon} (\nu_+ z_+^2 + \nu_- z_-^2) \tag{10-10}$$

in which r is the average ionic radius of the two ion types. In determining solubility relationships, we will be interested in the solubility of a salt in one solvent with respect to another solvent. Now, the work necessary to charge the ions of a given electrolyte in solvent 1 with respect to the work necessary in another solvent, 2, can be expressed as

$$W_t = (W_+ + W_-)_1 - (W_+ + W_-)_2$$

$$= \frac{Ne^2}{2r_1\, \epsilon_1} (\nu_+ z_+^2 + \nu_- z_-^2) - \frac{Ne^2}{2r_2\, \epsilon_2} (\nu_+ z_+^2 + \nu_- z_-^2)$$

$$= \frac{Ne^2}{2r} (\nu_+ z_+^2 + \nu_- z_-^2) \left(\frac{1}{\epsilon_1} - \frac{1}{\epsilon_2} \right) \tag{10-11}$$

where r is the average ionic radius of the electrolyte in solvents 1 and 2.

The final step in the development of the Born equation as it applies to solubility relationships involves equating the energy of transferring the ions from solvent 1 to solvent 2, to the ideal relation between the free energy and the solute concentration,

$$\Delta F = \Delta F^0 + RT \ln C \tag{10-12}$$

If we use the same standard state in both solvents, we can further say that

$$\Delta F_1 - \Delta F_2 = RT \ln C_1 - RT \ln C_2 \tag{10-13}$$

Now, by equating the work of transferring the electrolyte, W_t, to Eq. 10–13 and recognizing that there will be formed ν_+ positive ions and ν_- negative ions from the ionization of the electrolyte, we can obtain

$$\frac{Ne^2}{2r} (\nu_+ z_+{}^2 + \nu_- z_-{}^2) \left(\frac{1}{\epsilon_1} - \frac{1}{\epsilon_2} \right) = RT \ln \frac{(\nu_+ C_1)^{\nu_+} (\nu_- C_1)^{\nu_-}}{(\nu_+ C_2)^{\nu_+} (\nu_- C_2)^{\nu_-}} \qquad (10\text{–}14)$$

We can further note that due to the symmetry of z with respect to ν,

$$(\nu_+ z_+{}^2 + \nu_- z_-{}^2) = z_+ z_- (\nu_+ + \nu_-)$$

This fact can be coupled with the rearrangement of the right side of Eq. (10–14) to $RT (\nu_+ + \nu_-) \ln C_1/C_2$ to give, on division by $RT (\nu_+ + \nu_-)$,

$$\ln C_1 = \ln C_2 + \frac{Ne^2}{2RTr} z_+ z_- \left(\frac{1}{\epsilon_1} - \frac{1}{\epsilon_2} \right) \qquad (10\text{–}15)$$

Here we have a relationship between the concentration of an electrolyte and the dielectric constant of the solvent, with the ionic radius as a parameter. If it were possible to assign reasonable values to the ionic radii, then we would be able to calculate the solubility of an electrolyte in a solvent of known dielectric constant.

Actually, the Born equation is greatly over-idealized. For one thing, we have completely ignored all interactions other than ion-solvent interactions, and for this reason it could not be hoped to be adequate except at extremely low concentrations. This factor would be particularly important in solvents of low dielectric constant. With regard to this point, we can improve the Born equation by correcting for ion-ion interactions with the Debye-Huckel theory. If we substitute activity for concentration in Eq. (10–15) we obtain

$$\ln a_1 = \ln a_2 + \frac{Ne^2}{2RTr} z_+ z_- \left(\frac{1}{\epsilon_1} - \frac{1}{\epsilon_2} \right) \qquad (10\text{–}16)$$

But, $a = C/f$, so we can state that

$$\ln C_1 - \ln f_1 = \ln C_2 - \ln f_2 + \frac{Ne^2}{2RTr} z_+ z_- \left(\frac{1}{\epsilon_1} - \frac{1}{\epsilon_2} \right) \qquad (10\text{–}17)$$

Since the molar activity coefficient, f, can be expressed at low concentrations by the Debye-Huckel theory, a theoretically more sound equation relating the solubilities should be obtained.

Empirical Equation for Salt Solubility

In spite of the detail embodied in our final equation, the agreement with experiment is not favorable. A careful study of the effect of dielectric constant on the solubility of slightly soluble electrolytes has been made in dioxane-water mixtures by Davis and Ricci[5] in which the dielectric con-

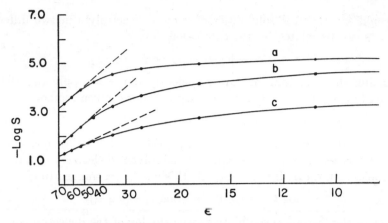

FIGURE 10–5. Molar Solubilities of **(a)** Silver Acetate, **(b)** Silver Sulfate, and **(c)** Barium Iodate-Hydrate in Water-Dioxane Mixtures. (After Davis, T. and Ricci, J., *J. Am. Chem. Soc.*, **61**, 3274 (1939).)

stant of the solvent was varied from that of pure dioxane to that of pure water. The extent of the agreement between the calculated and the observed solubilities of several salts is shown in Figure 10–5. As is evident, the agreement is valid only in solvent mixtures where the dielectric constant is of the order of 60 or greater.

Although the theoretical approach to electrolyte solubility based on the Born equation is not overly successful, an empirical approach proposed by Ricci and Davis[6] has proved to be somewhat better. They noted the interesting fact that the activity coefficient of a slightly soluble electrolyte in its saturated solution is essentially constant regardless of solvent. This can be seen from Table 10–3 to be the case for silver acetate in several different solvents. Thus, based on the general validity of this observation,

TABLE 10–3. / **Mean Ionic Activity Coefficient of Silver Acetate at Saturation.**

Solvent	ϵ	$f_\pm$
Water	78.55	0.800
Acetone, %		
10	73.0	0.804
20	67.0	0.805
30	61.0	0.798
Dioxane, %		
10	69.7	0.786
20	60.8	0.771

we could say that the solubilities of such an electrolyte in two different solvents can be related by the expression

$$- \log f_1 = - \log f_2 \qquad (10\text{–}18)$$

Assuming that our solutions are sufficiently dilute to apply the Debye-Huckel limiting law, we can further say that for a given temperature,

$$A \; \epsilon_1^{-\frac{3}{2}} \, C_1^{\frac{1}{2}} = A \; \epsilon_2^{-\frac{3}{2}} \, C_2^{\frac{1}{2}} \qquad (10\text{–}19)$$

Here, we are merely equating the Debye-Huckel limiting relations for solvent 1 and solvent 2, but separating the solvent dielectric constant from the constant term A. By canceling A, this can be rearranged to give

$$\log C_1 = \log C_2 + 3(\log \epsilon_1 - \log \epsilon_2) \qquad (10\text{–}20)$$

A plot of the log of the solubility versus the log of the dielectric constant of the solvent is shown in Figure 10–6 for $Ba(IO_3)_2 \cdot H_2O$ in dioxane-water

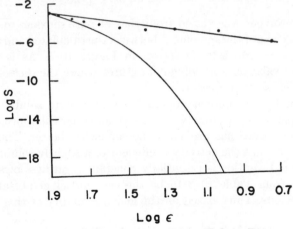

FIGURE 10–6. Solubility of $Ba(IO_3)_2 \cdot H_2O$ in Dioxane-Water Mixtures. The straight line represents the solubilities predicted on the basis of constant activity coefficients, and the curve represents solubilities predicted on the basis of the Born equation. The experimental data is given by the dots. (After Ricci, J. and Davis, T., *J. Am. Chem. Soc.*, **62**, 407 (1940).)

mixtures, and the observed data is compared to the calculated curves from both the Born equation and the empirical approach based on a constant activity coefficient. In this instance, the agreement with the empirical approach is quite good.

IONIC ASSOCIATION

If a solution contains a sufficiently large number of ions, it is only reasonable to expect their electrostatic interactions to be appreciable. We, of course, are quite familiar with such interactions and ordinarily account for them in terms of an activity coefficient. Additionally, we recognize that these effects are dependent on the dielectric constant of the system. As the dielectric constant decreases it is expected that the ionic interactions will increase. In fact, if the ions come sufficiently close together, we might expect a point to be reached where their electrostatic attraction is greater than the thermal energies tending to disorder them. If this should be the case, a new entity could be formed in which the two ions are combined to form a neutral species known as an *ion-pair*. This would not be the same as an undissociated molecule inasmuch as the operative forces would be purely electrostatic in character. This difference may be indicated schematically as

$$A^+ + B^- = [A^+B^-]^0 = AB$$

where $[A^+B^-]^0$ represents the ion-pair. Unless the ion concentration were very great, we would not expect ion-pair formation to be particularly significant in a solvent such as water. But in solvents having low dielectric constants, this would not be the case. In fact, we would expect ion-pair formation to be the rule rather than the exception in many nonaqueous solvents.

The Bjerrum Theory

A rather successful theoretical treatment of ionic association was developed by Bjerrum in 1926.[7,8] This model is the simplest possible for such a system. The ions are considered to be rigid unpolarizable spheres, and all interactions are considered to be of the coulombic type. As an additional approximation, the dielectric constant of the solvent is used even though it is unreasonable to consider it to have the same magnitude in the near proximity of an ion as it does in the bulk of the solution. According to the Bjerrum theory, all ions of opposite charge within a particular distance of one another are associated as ion-pairs. This particular distance, q, is given by

$$q = \frac{z_i z_j e^2}{2\epsilon \, kT} \tag{10-21}$$

where k is the Boltzmann constant and the other symbols have their usual significance.

The expression for q can readily be derived by considering the number of ions of type i in the neighborhood of an ion j. More specifically, we can consider the number of i-ions in a spherical shell of thickness dr at a distance, r, from a chosen j-ion. According to the Boltzmann distribution law, this number will be

$$dn_i = n_i \, e^{+U/kT} \, 4\pi r^2 dr \tag{10-22}$$

Here n_i is the number of ions of type i per cc of solution, U is the work necessary to separate an i-ion at a distance of r to infinity from the particular j-ion, and $4\pi r^2 dr$ is the volume of a spherical shell of thickness dr at a distance r to $r + dr$ from the center of the j-ion. As a good approximation, we can replace U by the coulombic potential of two charges in the presence of a dielectric

$$U = -\frac{z_i z_j e^2}{\epsilon r} \qquad (10\text{--}23)$$

and making this substitution into the distribution equation, we obtain

$$dn_i = n_i \left[\exp\left(-\frac{z_i z_j e^2}{\epsilon \, rkT} \right) \right] 4\pi r^2 dr \qquad (10\text{--}24)$$

If we allow the differentials to become deltas, we can now make an approximate calculation of the probability of finding an i-ion in a particular shell at any distance, r, from the chosen j-ion. This will require that we assign a thickness to the spherical shells, and for the sake of calculation we might consider this to be of the order of 0.01 Å.

By carrying out such a calculation for oppositely charged ions, the curve shown in Figure 10–7 can be obtained, where the time average number of i-ions per shell is plotted against the distance, r, of the shell from the center of the chosen j-ion. From this it can be seen that there is a distance of minimum probability of finding an i-ion in a spherical shell surrounding the central j-ion. The position of this minimum is the distance, q, and it can be evaluated by differentiating the expression

$$r^2 \exp\left(-\frac{z_i z_j e^2}{\epsilon \, kTr} \right)$$

and equating it to zero. It also can be noted that with a decrease in r less than q, the probability of an i-ion being in the neighborhood of a j-ion increases rapidly. On the other hand, it is seen that there is a less rapid

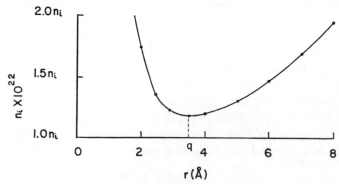

FIGURE 10–7. Distribution of Oppositely Charged Ions Around a Central Ion. (Based on Bjerrum, N., *K. Danske Vidensk, Selsk. Mat.-fys. Medd.*, 7, No. 9 (1926).)

increase in the probability as r increases past q. Bjerrum arbitrarily assumed that two ions were associated if their separation were less than q.

It should be emphasized that the Bjerrum theory applies to systems where only electrostatic interactions need be considered. If covalent bonding is present, such as is found in the case of weak electrolytes, the potential term in the Boltzmann equation cannot be represented by the simple coulombic potential $e^2/\epsilon r$.

Conductance Studies on Ionic Association

A rather convincing experimental verification of ionic association is found in a series of conductance studies made by Kraus and Fuoss.[9] Their measurements were made on solutions of the salt tetraisoamylammonium nitrate in dioxane-water systems. By varying the relative amounts of dioxane and water, they were able to carry out the studies over a dielectric

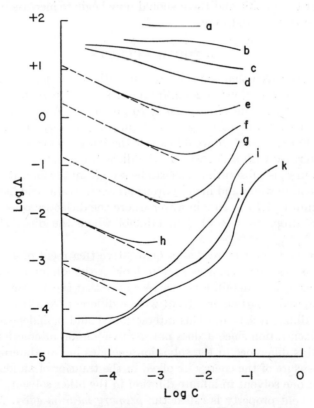

FIGURE 10–8. Conductance Curves of Tetraisoamylammonium Nitrate in Various Mixtures of Dioxane and Water. (After Kraus, C. A. and Fuoss, R. M., *J. Am. Chem. Soc.*, **55**, 2 (1933).)

range of 2.2 for pure dioxane to 78.5 for pure water. The results were very significant in that they showed quite anomalous behavior in solvent mixtures having low dielectric constants. As can be seen in Figure 10–8, a normal conductance curve is obtained only for the pure water solvent. As the dielectric constant is successively decreased it is noted that the minima in the conductance curves become quite pronounced. Also, it can be seen that as the concentrations are increased, the conductance curves again begin to rise.

In this classic series of papers, Kraus and Fuoss[9] interpret their conductance curves in terms of ionic association. Basically, they assume that the decrease in the conductance curves arises from the formation of ion-pairs. Inasmuch as the resultant pair is effectively neutral, the ions will not contribute to the conductance of the solution. However, as the concentrations of the solutions become greater, there is a tendency to form triple ions rather than pairs, and these should now begin to increase the conductance of the system, and so on.

MEDIUM EFFECTS

It has been seen that ion-solvent interactions and ion-ion interactions will show wide variations in going from one solvent to another. And, from a qualitative standpoint, it is possible to predict the direction that certain solute properties will take by considering the change in the dielectric constant. For example, we would expect the ionization constant of a weak acid to decrease with a decrease in the dielectric constant of the solvent. This, of course, is substantiated as can be seen from the ionization constant of acetic acid in water and in anhydrous ethanol. Acetic acid has an ionization constant of 1.75×10^{-5} in water where the dielectric constant is 78.5, whereas it drops to 2×10^{-11} in ethanol where the dielectric constant is 24.2.

If we wish to give more than a qualitative treatment of electrolytes in nonaqueous systems, it is necessary to look at the ion-ion and ion-solvent interactions in some detail. First, we recognize that the interaction between a given ion and a particular solvent will be different from that of the same ion and a different solvent. This interaction should be independent of the solute concentration since it does not involve ion-ion interactions. We can consider this difference in the solvation energies in two different solvents to be a measure of the energy involved in the transfer of an ion at infinite dilution in one solvent to infinite dilution in the other solvent. This difference of solvent property is called the *primary medium effect*. A *secondary medium effect* can be seen to arise from a difference in ion-ion interactions in two different solvents. This can be attributed primarily to a difference in solvent dielectric constant. The secondary medium effect will, of course, be concentration-dependent. We can thus break down into three steps the transfer of solute of a finite concentration in one solvent to a finite concentration in another solvent. These steps involve (1) the transfer of the solute from a finite concentration in the first solvent to infinite dilution in the same solvent, (2) the transfer of the solute to an infinitely dilute solution in the second solvent, and (3) the transfer of the solute to a finite concentration in the second solvent. This represents the *total medium effect* which is the summation of the primary and secondary medium effects.

Thermodynamic Representation of the Primary Medium Effect

In order to give a general thermodynamic treatment of medium effects, we can consider the transfer of a strong acid such as HCl of molal concentration m, from an aqueous medium to a mixed solvent such as ethanol-water. Such studies can be made by means of a galvanic cell without liquid junction of the type

$$\text{Pt, H}_{2(1 \text{ atm})} | \text{HCl}_{(m)} \text{ ethanol } (X), \text{ water } (Y) | \text{AgCl, Ag}$$

where the mole fraction of ethanol may vary anywhere from 0 to 1. If, for the moment, we consider the cell when the mole fraction of ethanol is 0, we will have the common aqueous cell

$$\text{Pt, H}_{2(1 \text{ atm})} | \text{HCl}_{(m)} | \text{AgCl, Ag}$$

and its potential can be expressed as

$$\text{E} = \text{E}_m^0 - \frac{2RT}{\text{F}} \ln \gamma_{\pm} m \tag{10--25}$$

We are here expressing the concentration of HCl in terms of molality, and the activity coefficient $\gamma_{\pm}$ is measured on same scale.

To illustrate a symbolism,[8] the potential given in Eq. (10--25) can be represented as

$$^w\text{E} = {}^w\text{E}_m^0 - \frac{2RT}{\text{F}} \ln {}^w_w\gamma_{\pm} m \tag{10--26}$$

The superscript w indicates that the measurements were made in water as a solvent, and the subscript w on the activity coefficient indicates that the activity coefficients are compared to unity at infinite dilution in water. We can now say that the standard state potential will be given by

$$^w\text{E}_m^0 = \lim_{m \to 0} \left({}^w\text{E} + \frac{2RT}{\text{F}} \ln m \right) \tag{10--27}$$

The $\ln {}^w_w\gamma_{\pm}$ term drops out because the activity coefficient approaches unity as $m \to 0$.

If the ethanol-water mixed solvent is now considered, it is found that there exists a choice in defining the standard state. Firstly, we can consider the mixed solvent in the same manner as we did with the pure solvent. That is, the cell potential can be expressed as

$$^s\mathrm{E} = {}^s\mathrm{E}_m^0 - \frac{2RT}{\mathrm{F}} \ln {}_s^s\gamma_\pm m \tag{10-28}$$

The symbolism here indicates that the measurements were made in a solvent, s, and the activity coefficients are relative to unity at infinite dilution in this particular solvent. Thus, the solvent is being treated just as if it were a pure solvent rather than a mixed solvent, and the expression for the standard-state potential will be of the same form as that for a purely aqueous solvent, namely

$$^s\mathrm{E}_m^0 = \lim_{m \to 0} \left({}^s\mathrm{E} + \frac{2RT}{\mathrm{F}} \ln m \right) \tag{10-29}$$

In an alternative manner, we can consider the solvent to still be an aqueous solvent to which a portion of ethanol has been added. We might then be prone to keep our standard reference state in pure water and thereby represent the potential as

$$^s\mathrm{E} = {}^w\mathrm{E}_m^0 - \frac{2RT}{\mathrm{F}} \ln {}_w^s\gamma_\pm m \tag{10-30}$$

Now, since the activity coefficient is measured relative to unity at infinite dilution in a purely aqueous medium, ${}_w^s\gamma_\pm$ does not approach unity as m approaches zero in the mixed solvent. Consequently, the expression for the standard state potential becomes

$$^w\mathrm{E}_m^0 = \lim_{m \to 0} \left({}^s\mathrm{E} + \frac{2RT}{\mathrm{F}} \ln m + \frac{2RT}{\mathrm{F}} \ln {}_w^s\gamma_\pm \right) \tag{10-31}$$

If we now take the difference in the standard state potentials in water and the mixed solvent, we obtain

$$^w\mathrm{E}_m^0 - {}^s\mathrm{E}_m^0 = \lim_{m \to 0} \left(\frac{2RT}{\mathrm{F}} \ln {}_w^s\gamma_\pm \right) \tag{10-32}$$

Since we are actually considering the same cell with the only difference being the arbitrarily defined standard state, the experimentally determined potential, $^s\mathrm{E}$, and the $\ln m$ term will drop out. This leaves the activity coefficient of HCl at infinite dilution as measured in a mixed solvent relative to unity at infinite dilution in water. Inasmuch as ion-ion interactions are absent at infinite dilution in either solvent, we are thus measuring the effect of transferring a pair of ions from one solvent to another when only ion-solvent interactions are present. This, then, is the thermodynamic representation of the primary medium effect.

The Secondary Medium Effect

The secondary medium effect can be determined by considering a total medium effect and then subtracting off the primary medium effect. The total medium effect is concerned with the transfer of the electrolyte from a finite concentration in one solvent to the same concentration in another solvent. This will involve both the ion-solvent interactions and the ion-ion interactions. The thermodynamic expression for the total medium effect can be obtained by coupling together the aqueous and the mixed solvent cells that we have already considered to give the cell

Ag, AgCl | HCl$_{(m)}$ water | Pt, H$_{2(1\,atm)}$ | HCl$_{(m)}$ ethanol(X), water(Y) | AgCl, Ag

The cell reaction will involve the transfer of the HCl from one solvent to the other, but if the HCl molality is the same in both solvents, the potential will not be due to an effective concentration cell. The potential of this cell will be

$$^{s}\mathrm{E} - {}^{w}\mathrm{E} = {}^{s}\mathrm{E}_m^0 - {}^{w}\mathrm{E}_m^0 - \frac{2RT}{\mathrm{F}}\left(\ln\,{}^{s}_{s}\gamma_\pm - \ln\,{}^{w}_{w}\gamma_\pm\right) \qquad (10\text{--}33)$$

This is nothing more than the difference in the potentials of the mixed solvent cell and the aqueous cell in which the concentration of the electrolyte is the same in both solvents. Since there are no concentration changes, the energies involved are those resulting from different degrees of non-ideality in the two systems along with differences in ion-solvent interactions.

It is possible to put Eq. (10–33) into a more useful form by using a different standard state. Expressing the potential of the mixed-solvent cell by Eq. (10–30) it is found that the difference in potential can be represented as

$$^{s}\mathrm{E} - {}^{w}\mathrm{E} = -\frac{2RT}{\mathrm{F}}\left(\ln\,{}^{s}_{w}\gamma_\pm - \ln\,{}^{w}_{w}\gamma_\pm\right) \qquad (10\text{--}34)$$

If we now substitute this result along with Eq. (10–32) into Eq. (10–33), we obtain

$$-\frac{2RT}{\mathrm{F}}\left(\ln\,{}^{s}_{w}\gamma_\pm - \ln\,{}^{w}_{w}\gamma_\pm\right) = -\lim_{m \to 0}\frac{2RT}{\mathrm{F}}\ln\,{}^{s}_{w}\gamma_\pm$$

$$-\frac{2RT}{\mathrm{F}}\left(\ln\,{}^{s}_{s}\gamma_\pm - \ln\,{}^{w}_{w}\gamma_\pm\right) \qquad (10\text{--}35)$$

On rearranging, this becomes

$$\ln\frac{{}^{s}_{w}\gamma_\pm}{{}^{w}_{w}\gamma_\pm} = \lim_{m \to 0}\ln\,{}^{s}_{w}\gamma_\pm + \ln\frac{{}^{s}_{s}\gamma_\pm}{{}^{w}_{w}\gamma_\pm} \qquad (10\text{--}36)$$

The term on the left represents the total medium effect and it is a measure of both the ion-ion and the ion-solvent interactions in the respective solvents. More specifically, it is a measure of the energy involved in the transfer of the electrolyte from a finite concentration in one solvent to the same concentration in the other solvent. The first term on the right hand side of the equation obviously represents the primary medium effect. The second term, however, is a measure of the relative nonideality of the solute in the different solvents at some finite concentration. That is, $_s^s\gamma_\pm$ is the activity coefficient of the solute measured at some finite concentration in the solvent, s, as compared to unity at infinite dilution in that solvent. Thus, if we can assume that ion-ion interactions are zero at infinite dilution in the solvent, s, then $_s^s\gamma_\pm$ would be unity and the nonideality expressed by $_s^s\gamma_\pm$ would correspondingly be zero at infinite dilution in s. Consequently, $_s^s\gamma_\pm$ at some finite concentration would then be a measure of the nonideality of the system due to the ion-ion interactions in the solvent s at a given concentration. Now, the term $_w^w\gamma_\pm$ is of the same type as $_s^s\gamma_\pm$ except that it refers to water as a solvent. Therefore, the secondary medium effect is a measure of the difference in ion-ion interactions in the two solvents.

We can express the medium effects in our solutions in terms of thermodynamic concepts by empirically evaluating the activity coefficients. However, it is of considerably greater interest to attempt a calculation of medium effects and their effect on solution properties in terms of a mechanistic picture. This mechanistic picture is provided by our interpretation of the medium effects, and primarily through the Born equation and the Debye-Huckel theory, we shall see that a means of calculating them is available.

ELECTRODE POTENTIALS

If a solvent system is to be fully investigated it is a necessity to determine a series of standard state electrode potentials. From a practical standpoint, this is of particular interest in the determination of various thermodynamic quantities such as solubility products, ionization constants, and activity coefficients. From a more fundamental standpoint, electrode potentials in nonaqueous solvents have been of considerable significance in evaluating the Debye-Huckel theory and other models of solution processes.

Using a semi-thermodynamic approach, it is possible to propose a series of steps involved in the electrode reaction and attempt to calculate the energies involved in each step. We can begin by recognizing that since

$$\Delta F = - n\mathrm{F}\mathrm{E} = \Delta H - T\Delta S \qquad (10\text{--}37)$$

an electrode potential cannot be considered strictly from an energetic viewpoint. However, it is not unreasonable to expect the entropy terms to be relatively insignificant for the majority of similar solutes. Making the assumption that the entropy terms will be negligible, it would appear that the emf for the anode should be the sum of the energies involved in three steps: (1) the sublimation of the metal, (2) the ionization of the gaseous metal ion, and (3) the solvation of the metal ion. The same sort of processes would be involved at the cathode. In terms of a cycle, these steps can be represented as

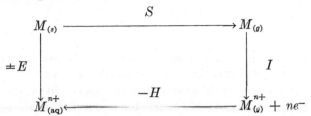

The total energy of the process will be

$$\pm E = S + I - H$$

It is interesting to note that the only one of these terms that is dependent on the solvent is the solvation energy, H. Thus, if it were possible to evaluate this factor, we should be able to make a straightforward determination of an electrode potential. This, however, is not a simple matter. The calculation of an electrode potential has been made in water using free energies, and the results were rather encouraging.[10] However, the necessary data are not available in nonaqueous systems, and as a result, we can only draw qualitative conclusions.

Standard Electrode Potentials from the Born Equation

A more or less allied approach to the calculation of the standard electrode potential can be made in terms of the primary medium effect. Since the standard potential of a cell is defined in terms of ion-solvent interactions only, it is necessary to consider only the primary medium effect. Although there may be some question of its validity, a calculation of this effect can be made by means of the Born equation. Accordingly, the energy necessary to transfer an ion of radius r from a solvent of dielectric constant ϵ_1 to another solvent of dielectric constant ϵ_2 is given by the expression

$$W_t = \frac{e^2}{2r}\left(\frac{1}{\epsilon_1} - \frac{1}{\epsilon_2}\right) \tag{10-38}$$

If we now consider the same equation for a mole of a uni-univalent electrolyte with the cation and anion radii of a_1 and a_2 respectively, we obtain

$$W_t = \frac{Ne^2}{2}\left(\frac{1}{\epsilon_1} - \frac{1}{\epsilon_2}\right)\left(\frac{1}{a_1} + \frac{1}{a_2}\right) \tag{10-39}$$

If this expression for the primary medium effect is now substituted into Eq. (10–32),

$$^{w}\mathrm{E}_m^0 - {^s}\mathrm{E}_m^0 = \lim_{m \to 0} \frac{2RT}{\mathrm{F}} \ln {_w^s}\gamma_\pm \tag{10–32}$$

it is seen that

$$^{w}\mathrm{E}_m^0 - {^s}\mathrm{E}_m^0 = \frac{Ne^2}{2\mathrm{F}} \left(\frac{1}{\epsilon_1} - \frac{1}{\epsilon_2} \right) \left(\frac{1}{a_1} + \frac{1}{a_2} \right) \tag{10–40}$$

From this expression, it is readily apparent that if the ionic radii do not vary from solvent to solvent, the E^0 value should be a linear function of the dielectric constant. This, however, does not appear to be the case. It is possible to propose a variety of reasons for this lack of conformity, but the most logical reason can be found in the Born equation itself. We can recall that the dielectric constants of the Born equation are those of the bulk solvent, and it is unrealistic to think that the dielectric constant in the neighborhood of an ion is the same as that of the solvent. Additionally, we can question the constancy of the ionic radii in various solvents. There is some evidence that such radii do change from solvent to solvent. If the ionic radius term of the Debye-Huckel theory is used here, we would certainly expect it to be somewhat dependent on the dielectric constant of the solvent. It is also possible that ion-pair formation is of some consequence in solvents of very low dielectric constant, and this could lead to erroneous values for the electrode potentials.

It might be mentioned that one very significant factor in the determination of electrode potentials in various solvents is that of solvent purity. Primarily, the problem is that of the removal of water. Virtually all solvents will show some hygroscopic character, and it is a problem of

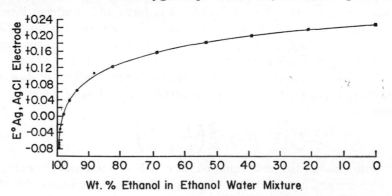

FIGURE 10–9. Estimated E^0 Values for the Ag, AgCl Electrode in Ethanol-Water Mixtures. (After LeBas, C. L. and Day, M. C., *J. Phys. Chem.*, **64**, 465 (1960).)

major proportions to remove and exclude moisture. It has been shown that infinitesimally small portions of water can cause extreme variations in the standard potentials. This can be seen in Figure 10–9, where the square root of the concentration of water is plotted against the E^0 value for the cell

$$\text{Pt, H}_{2(1 \text{ atm})} | \text{HCl}_{(m)} \text{ ethanol } (X), \text{ water } (Y) | \text{AgCl, Ag}$$

The effect is much greater for HCl than it would be for solutes such as the alkali halides, but in all cases it is rather significant.

IONIZATION CONSTANTS OF WEAK ACIDS

Qualitatively, we know that the ionic association effects that accompany a decrease in solvent dielectric constant lead to a corresponding decrease in the ionization constant of a weak acid. Quantitatively, we find that by applying the Born equation along with thermodynamic relations, it is possible to make first order approximations of ionization constants of weak acids. Using the relation between the standard state potentials in terms of the Born equation

$$^w E_m^0 - {}^s E_m^0 = \frac{Ne^2}{2F} \left(\frac{1}{\epsilon_1} - \frac{1}{\epsilon_2} \right) \left(\frac{1}{a_1} + \frac{1}{a_2} \right) \qquad (10\text{--}40)$$

and recalling that

$$\Delta F^0 = -n F E^0 = -RT \ln K \qquad (10\text{--}41)$$

we see that on substitution and rearrangement we obtain

$$\ln {}^w K - \ln {}^s K = \frac{Ne^2}{2RT} \left(\frac{1}{\epsilon_1} - \frac{1}{\epsilon_2} \right) \left(\frac{1}{a_1} + \frac{1}{a_2} \right) \qquad (10\text{--}42)$$

Here we have an expression that should allow us to calculate the ionization constant of a weak acid in any solvent or mixed solvent if we know its value in one solvent, such as water. However, as usual with the Born equation, we should not expect to obtain particularly good results. It is apparent that the equation assumes that the only variable is the dielectric constant of the solvent. This would ignore such factors as have previously been mentioned, as well as specific solvent reactions. Nevertheless, useful approximations can be made.

In some instances, the calculated ionization constants are quite good and in other instances they are not so good. We find the latter to be the case for acetic acid in ethanol. If the value of 1.75×10^{-5} is used for the ionization constant of acetic acid in water, we obtain a value of 1.8×10^{-9} for the ionization constant in ethanol. This value is not in very good agreement with the experimental value of 2×10^{-11}. On the other hand, it can be seen in Figure 10–10, that the calculated values for some weak acids

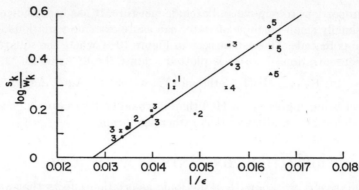

FIGURE 10-10. Dependence of Weak Acid Ionization Constants on Solvent Dielectric Constant. The solvents are (1) methanol-water, (2) ethanol-water, (3) isopropanol-water, (4) glycerol-water, and (5) dioxane-water. The acids are: ▲ formic acid, x acetic acid, ● propionic acid, ■ butyric acid, and ◐ water. (After Robinson, R. A. and Stokes, R. H., "Electrolyte Solutions," Butterworth Scientific Publs., London, 1955.)

are in quite good agreement with the experimental values. We are plotting here the term $\log {}^sK/{}^wK$ against $1/\epsilon$, and for simplicity, ${}^wK$, the acid ionization constant in water, is set equal to unity for each acid. The straight line represents the calculated curve using the Born equation with $a_1 = 3.73$ Å and $a_2 = 1.2$ Å, for the hydrogen ion and the carboxylic anions respectively. It can be seen that some grouping does occur around the calculated curve. However, it is also obvious that the results are not very consistent. The data in Figure 10-10 are for mixed solvent systems in which the major constituent is water. It is interesting to note that the agreement between theory and experiment improves as the percent of water is increased. In all such measurements, it is generally found that fair agreement is obtained between theory and experiment when the percentage of water is sufficiently large to give a dielectric constant greater than about 60.

pH MEASUREMENTS IN NONAQUEOUS MEDIA

It is not particularly unusual to find that we have never truly appreciated the significance of a concept that we have used for years. The concept of pH falls into this category. It might at first appear that the familiar relation

$$\text{pH} = -\log C_{\text{H}^+} \tag{10-43}$$

is quite satisfactory. This was the definition given by Sorenson for the pH in 1909. Unfortunately, there are some more than trivial weaknesses in this simple expression. Basically, the difficulty lies in the fact that we determine the pH by means of emf measurements, and such measurements reflect changes in activity rather than concentration. With this in mind, we might now be prone to think that the way out of our difficulty is simply to define the pH as

$$pH = -\log a_{H^+} \qquad (10\text{--}44)$$

This looks very well, and we will, in fact, finally use this definition of the pH. However, it is not the simple thermodynamic relationship that we might at first think. The problem that arises here is that we are not able, by any known means, to measure a single ion activity. That is, a_{H^+} is not an experimentally observable quantity. In terms of emf measurements, this is evident if we consider the now familiar cell

$$Pt, H_{2(1 \text{ atm})} \,|\, HCl_{(m)} \,|\, AgCl, Ag$$

We should recall that the emf of this cell is given by

$$E = E^0 - \frac{RT}{F} \ln a_{H^+}\, a_{Cl^-} \qquad (10\text{--}45)$$

which can be put into the more realistic form

$$E = E^0 - \frac{RT}{F} \ln a_{\pm}^2 \qquad (10\text{--}46)$$

This emphasizes the fact that emf measurements give us a mean ionic activity rather than the single ion activities. This is true for the simple reason that it is not possible to have an oxidation without a reduction, and a cell emf is the result of both processes taking place simultaneously.

Now that the shortcomings of the simple expressions for the pH are recognized, it is necessary to consider just how a meaning can be given to the concept. Ordinarily, pH is determined by means of a galvanic cell of the type

$$Pt,\ H_2 \,|\, \text{Solution } X \,|\, \text{Sat. KCl} \,|\, \text{Calomel reference electrode}$$

The potential of this cell is given by the relation

$$E = E^0 - \frac{2.3026\ RT}{F} \log a_{H^+}\, a_{Cl^-} + E_j \qquad (10\text{--}47)$$

where E_j is the algebraic sum of all the junction potentials and a_{Cl^-} is the activity of the chloride ion in contact with the calomel electrode. If we now take advantage of the fact that the activity of the chloride ion in the neighborhood of the calomel electrode is a constant and further recognize that E^0 for the hydrogen electrode is zero, it is possible to rearrange Eq. (10–47) to

$$E = \left(E^0 - \frac{2.3026\ RT}{F} \log a_{Cl^-} \right) - \frac{2.3026\ RT}{F} \log a_{H^+} + E_j \qquad (10\text{--}48)$$

and set the term in the parentheses equal to the constant $E^{0\prime}$. This, then can be rearranged to give

$$\frac{(E - E^{0\prime} - E_j)\, F}{2.3026\, RT} = -\log a_{H^+} = pH \qquad (10\text{--}49)$$

In retrospect, we can see that it is not possible to determine the pH from this cell for the simple reason that we do not know a_{cl-} and therefore, $E^{0\prime}$, and we do not know E_j.

Various attempts have been made to circumvent these difficulties by defining pH in terms of quantities that do have thermodynamic significance. An example of such a definition is

$$pH = -\log \gamma_\pm\, m_{H^+} \qquad (10\text{--}50)$$

where $\gamma_\pm$ is the mean molal activity coefficient. Since both $\gamma_\pm$ and the molality of the hydrogen ion are determinable quantities, the pH of the system will now have thermodynamic meaning. However, the relation is not valid if there is more than one uni-univalent electrolyte or any electrolyte that is not uni-univalent present. Both of these situations are more likely to be found than not. In actuality, the definitions of pH that have thermodynamic meaning cannot be used from a practical standpoint, and we therefore find it expedient to resort to *nonthermodynamic* concepts in order to devise a useful pH scale.

Since a purely thermodynamic meaning cannot be given to the pH scale, we are faced with the problem of finding some other basis for it. We are greatly aided in this choice when we recognize that the major purpose of a pH scale is to permit a determination of the relative acidity or alkalinity of a system. Thus, we are primarily interested in a definition that will permit us to make consistent measurements of acidities even if they do not reflect the actual hydrogen ion activity. On the other hand, in order to use the concept to the fullest, we will attempt to make the pH scale conform as closely as possible to the thermodynamic definition.

If we again consider Eq. (10–49), it might appear that most of these requirements could be met. If we were to devise some means for determining the pH of a standard solution and measure the emf of the cell, the only unknown in the equation is the constant $(E^{0\prime} + E_j)$. Even if we admit that this term might change with pH in some manner, we could make up a series of standard solutions for different pH ranges and recalibrate often. Finally, we might say that even if we did lose track of our thermodynamic relations along the way, we at least have a consistent measure of something related to the acidity of the system. Basically, this is the approach that is used today for the determination of a pH scale. In the presence of a pH standard solution, Eq. (10–49) becomes

$$pH_s = \frac{[E_s - (E^{0\prime} + E_j)]\, F}{2.3026\, RT} \tag{10-51}$$

If it is now assumed that the quantity $(E^{0\prime} + E_j)$ is the same in the presence of the unknown as it is in the presence of the standard solution, we can subtract Eq. (10–51) from Eq. (10–49) and obtain the expression

$$pH = pH_s + \frac{(E - E_s)\, F}{2.3026\, RT} \tag{10-52}$$

Thus, it is seen that if the term $(E^{0\prime} + E_j)$ truly remains constant in the region of our interests, we can feel quite confident that the activities as determined from the pH measurement are as thermodynamically meaningful as is the assigned pH of the standard solution. Unfortunately, the term $(E^{0\prime} + E_j)$ does not in general remain constant, and in addition, it is always possible to raise some question with regard to the determination of the pH of the reference solutions. This means that the pH scale is ultimately only a scale of relative acidities, and except for a few instances, it is void of any fundamental thermodynamic meaning.

In attempting to define a pH scale in a nonaqueous medium, we would certainly expect to encounter the same difficulties that were encountered in an aqueous medium. In fact, there is nothing in the definition itself that would restrict the pH concept to an aqueous system, and the same general approach could be used in a nonaqueous medium. Thus, we can still define pH in terms of Eq. (10–52) and, in principle, the resultant nonaqueous pH scale should be as meaningful as the aqueous pH scale. However, from a practical standpoint, this is not true, primarily because we know so very little about nonaqueous solvents.

There are various ways in which the nonaqueous pH scale can be given some meaning. Assuming that we are considering a protonic solvent in order that the acid character can be related to the solvated proton, it would be possible to set up a cell in terms of this solvent only. The same procedure of attempting to make standard solutions of known pH that was used in the determination of an aqueous pH scale would then be followed.

It is true that this scale could not be related to the aqueous pH scale, but this is not necessarily bad. The most serious difficulty arises from the fact that we will not be as successful in relating the pH to the thermodynamic activity of the hydrogen ion as we were in water. This will particularly be true in solvents of low dielectric constant where ionic association is important. Nevertheless, we still recognize that the aqueous pH scale is not thermodynamically valid, and there should, therefore, be no reason why we should expect a nonaqueous pH scale to be superior.

In an alternative determination of a nonaqueous pH scale, we could keep the same basic cell that was used in an aqueous medium, including the calomel reference electrode with its aqueous KCl solution. If, for a given solvent, we use aqueous standard solutions, a series of numbers can be obtained that will give a measure of something that we can vaguely associate with acidity. If the system is a mixed solvent containing water or a water-like solvent, we may even know enough about the system to relate these values to the general order of magnitude of the hydrogen ion concentration in terms of a calibration curve. However, because of the fact that the magnitude of the liquid junction potential changes from solvent to solvent, it should be rather obvious that we cannot relate pH in one solvent to pH in another solvent by this approach. For instance, if the pH meter gives a reading of 5.0 for a particular solution in an ethanol-water solvent and also a reading of 5.0 for a methanol-water solvent where the same aqueous standard solution was used in both cases, it is not legitimate to conclude that the activity of the hydrogen ion is the same in the two solutions. In fact, there should be no similarity at all between the two. Primarily, this will be due to the quite different liquid junction potentials between the ethanol-water solvent boundary with the saturated aqueous KCl of the calomel electrode and the methanol-water solvent boundary with the aqueous KCl of the calomel electrode.

Although, virtually nothing has yet been accomplished towards establishing pH scales that are valid in nonaqueous media, it would appear that such scales are possible, at least, for water-like solvents. Just as in aqueous media, it will be necessary for the term $(E^{0\prime} + E_j)$ to remain constant when the standard solution is replaced by the unknown solution. This is most likely to be the case when the solvent composition is kept constant and the concentration of solute is small. If it can be assumed that the $(E^{0\prime} + E_j)$ term does remain substantially constant, the problem then becomes one of developing standard solutions. At the present time, too little is known of nonaqueous solvents to prepare standard solutions that have any semblance of thermodynamic validity. However, this is a difficulty that will eventually be overcome.

CHELATION IN NONAQUEOUS MEDIA

Although complex ions have received little attention in nonaqueous solvents, considerable work has been conducted on neutral complexes in such solvents. This is particularly true of chelates. Because of the insolubility of a large number of chelates in a purely aqueous medium, it is necessary to use a nonaqueous or mixed solvent for their solution study. The most commonly used solvent for these studies has been dioxane-water. Chelation studies have been exceedingly rare in completely anhydrous solvents.

Of the variety of methods for the study of the stabilities of chelates, probably the most accurate is that developed by Bjerrum[11] and modified for the study of chelates in mixed solvents by Calvin and Wilson.[12] This method takes advantage of the fact that the formation of many chelates results in the displacement of a H^+, and this can be followed by potentiometric means. This is readily apparent if we consider the chelation of a metal ion with a β-diketone. The chelation takes place through the enol form of the molecule, and the first molecule can be considered to enter as follows:

$$R-\underset{\underset{OH}{|}}{C}=CH-\underset{\underset{O}{\|}}{C}-R' + M^{2+} = R-\underset{\underset{O}{|}}{C}=CH-\underset{\underset{O}{\|}}{C}-R' + H^{|}$$
$$\underset{M^{2+}}{\diagdown \quad \diagup}$$

More generally, if HKe is the chelating agent and M^{2+} the metal ion, the equilibrium for the addition of the first molecule of the chelating agent can be expressed as

$$HKe = H^+ + Ke^-$$

$$M^{2+} + Ke^- = MKe^+$$

The first stability constant, k_1, is then given by

$$k_1 = \frac{[MKe^+]}{[M^{2+}][Ke^-]} \tag{10-53}$$

and the second stability constant, for the equilibrium

$$MKe^+ + Ke^- = MKe_2$$

is given by

$$k_2 = \frac{[MKe_2]}{[MKe^+][Ke^-]} \tag{10-54}$$

The determination of stability constants of chelates is a problem of rather great importance. Fortunately, the relative stability of chelates is of more concern than their thermodynamic equilibrium constants. This is fortunate for the simple reason that we are not as yet sufficiently familiar with nonaqueous systems of this complexity to determine thermodynamic constants. Consequently, we take the next best approach and compare chelate stability constants under a fixed set of conditions.

From a practical standpoint, we find that we are faced with serious limitations when we attempt to apply potentiometric methods to these problems in nonaqueous systems. It is almost a necessity that such a reaction be followed with a glass electrode, and in a nonaqueous-water mixed solvent a glass electrode can be used just as in a purely aqueous medium. However, a glass electrode will not function in the complete absence of water, and it would therefore, seem that this approach could not, in general, be used in a system where water must be completely excluded. It is for this reason that virtually no work has been done on these compounds in purely anhydrous solvents. But, since most interest lies in the determination of relative stabilities, dioxane-water systems are usually adequate.

In spite of the handicaps of working in such solvents, a few potentiometric studies of chelate stabilities have been made in purely anhydrous media. In fact, a rather valid attempt to determine true chelate thermodynamic equilibrium constants has been made in both dioxane-water mixtures and in anhydrous ethanol.[13,14] In this latter instance, acetylacetonates of nickel were studied with a cell containing a Ag,AgCl electrode versus a hydrogen electrode. Of course, we should recognize that the stability constant of a chelate determined in one solvent cannot be compared to the stability constant of the chelate in another solvent. At the relatively high concentrations involved, there are too many perturbing factors to permit even a general comparison.

BIBLIOGRAPHY

1. LaMer, V. and Downes, H., *Chem. Revs.*, **13**, 47 (1933).
2. Kraus, C., *J. Am. Chem. Soc.*, **30**, 1323 (1908); **43**, 749 (1921).
3. Watt, G., *Chem. Revs.*, **46**, 289 (1950).
4. Born, M., *Z. Physik.*, **1**, 45 (1920); Harned, H. and Owen, B., "The Physical Chemistry of Electrolytic Solutions," 3rd ed., Reinhold Publishing Corp., New York, N.Y., 1958.
5. Davis, T. and Ricci, J., *J. Am. Chem. Soc.*, **61**, 3274 (1939).
6. Ricci, J. and Davis, T., *J. Am. Chem. Soc.*, **62**, 407 (1940).
7. Bjerrum, N., *K. Danske Vidensk, Selsk. Mat.-fys. Medd.*, **7**, No. 9 (1926).
8. Robinson, R. and Stokes, R., "Electrolyte Solutions," Butterworth Scientific Publs., London, 1955.
9. Fuoss, R. and Kraus, C., *J. Am. Chem. Soc.*, **55**, 21, 476, 1019, 2387 (1933).
10. Latimer, W., Pitzer, K., and Slansky, C., *J. Chem. Phys.*, **7**, 108 (1939).
11. Bjerrum, J., "Metal Ammine Formation in Aqueous Solution," P. Haase & Son, Copenhagen, 1941.
12. Calvin, M. and Wilson, K., *J. Am. Chem. Soc.*, **67**, 2003 (1945).
13. Van Uitert, L. and Haas, C., *J. Am. Chem. Soc.*, **75**, 451 (1953).
14. Van Uitert, L., Fernelius, W., and Douglas, B., *J. Am. Chem. Soc.*, **75**, 3577 (1953).

SUGGESTED SUPPLEMENTARY READING

Audrieth, L. and Kleinberg, J., "Non-Aqueous Solvents," John Wiley & Sons, New York, N.Y., 1953.
Harned, H. and Owen, B., "The Physical Chemistry of Electrolytic Solutions," 3rd ed., Reinhold Publishing Corp., New York, N.Y., 1958.

11 | *Theory of the Nucleus*

Around the turn of the century, several discoveries were made that completely reshaped the fields of chemistry and physics. One of these was the discovery of radioactivity by Henri Becquerel in 1896. Becquerel had been interested in studying phosphorescence in various compounds, and during his studies he noted the effect upon potassium uranyl sulfate of what he thought was light. After exposing the uranium salt to light, he noticed that it emitted a radiation that was capable of darkening a photographic plate even after the radiation had passed through thin layers of various opaque materials. This observation in itself might not be particularly surprising since an external source of energy had been used. However, with further study a quite amazing result was obtained. Becquerel found that the intensity of the rays emitted by the uranium salt did not depend on exposure to an external light source at all. Crystals that had been prepared and kept in the dark gave the same effect as those that had been exposed to the light. In addition, it was noted that the emission did not depend on any particular compound of uranium, but rather, merely on the presence of uranium. These observations led to an early realization that this new type of radiation was solely an atomic phenomenon and was independent of the chemical or physical state of the substance.

The mysterious character and source of energy of these *Becquerel rays* resulted in an immediate surge of interest, and by 1898, G. C. Schmidt and Mme. Curie, working independently, were able to show that thorium as well as uranium was capable of emitting these rays. In their further studies on the uranium ores, the Curies noted that some of the ores were more radioactive than an equivalent amount of the uranium compound prepared in the laboratory. This led to a search for possible new radioactive elements present in the ores. By using pitchblende, which is an ore

363

containing primarily U_3O_8, Mme. Curie was able to isolate one new source of activity by precipitating bismuth as the sulfide from a solution of the ore. Since bismuth itself is not radioactive, the activity that followed the bismuth sulfide must have been due to a new element whose sulfide is similar to that of bismuth. This new element was named polonium. In another separation, barium chloride was fractionally precipitated from the pitchblende residue, and another substance of extremely high activity was found to be present. This element, which behaved like barium, was called radium.

Although much of this very early work was devoted to the discovery of new sources of radioactivity, at the same time interest in the nature of the emitted rays could not help but grow. By using the techniques of absorption, Rutherford shed some light on the nature of these rays by separating them into what appeared to be two general types. The first type was found to be absorbed by very small amounts of aluminum while the second type showed a considerably greater penetrating ability. Accordingly, the first type was called *alpha* radiation, and the more penetrating one was termed *beta* radiation.

A somewhat better understanding of the nature of these emitted particles or rays came with the application of magnetic deflection techniques. As early as 1899, it was found that the beta rays could be deflected with a magnetic field, the nature of the deflection indicating that they very likely were high-energy electrons. As a result of these early studies, the alpha rays, on the other hand, appeared to be unaffected by a magnetic field. However, carrying on the investigation of these radiations, Rutherford was able, in 1903, to show that by means of a sufficiently strong magnetic field, the alpha particles could also be deflected. The direction of the deflection showed that they had the properties of positively charged particles, and calculations on the charge to mass ratio indicated that they could be doubly charged helium ions. This idea was substantiated by the consistent presence of helium in uranium ores and was subsequently proven by placing a radioactive sample next to an evacuated glass container with walls sufficiently thin for the alpha particles to pass through. In a matter of days sufficient helium had collected in the glass container to be detected spectroscopically.

A third component of the radioactive emissions was detected by Strutt at about the same time that Rutherford was studying the deflection of alpha radiation by a magnetic field. This third component was found to be extremely penetrating in comparison to the alpha and beta radiations, and it was completely unaffected by the presence of a magnetic field. From these and other experiments, this new radiation appeared to be of the same general character as the X ray, and it was given the name of *gamma* radiation.

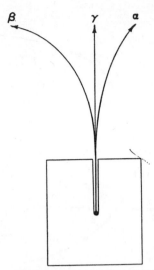

FIGURE 11–1. Resolution
of α, β, and γ Rays by
Means of a Magnetic
Field.

The resolution of these three components can readily be demonstrated
by means of the experiment shown schematically in Figure 11–1, in which
a radioactive source is placed in a small hole drilled into a lead block. As
the particles leave the hole, they are deflected by a magnetic field which,
in this case, is directed out of the page. Since the relative degree of deflection for the alpha and beta particles is dependent on the ratio of the charge
to the mass of the particles, a considerably greater deflection results for a
beta particle.

RADIOACTIVE DECAY CURVES

As a result of the discovery and study of a number of new radioactive
substances in the period from 1900 to 1903, a significant advance in the
understanding of radioactive processes came about. One of the more
important advances came in 1900, when Crookes obtained a new radioactive substance by a carbonate precipitation from a uranium solution.
It was found that if the uranium were precipitated with ammonium
carbonate and the resulting precipitate redissolved with excess ammonium
carbonate, a small amount of residue of very high activity remained. On
the other hand, it was found that the separated uranium was, at first,
relatively inactive. The interesting feature of this experiment was that
the new substance, which was named *uranium X*, lost its activity rather
quickly, while at the same time, it was observed to be regenerated in the

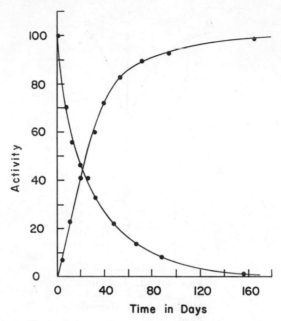

FIGURE 11–2. Decay and Regeneration of Uranium X.

uranium fraction. This would indicate that the activity initially observed in the uranium ore was due primarily to radioactive elements other than the uranium, and in the case of the carbonate precipitate, it was due primarily to the uranium X. Yet, these activities must all have their origin ultimately in some parent species which appears here to be uranium.

If a plot is made of the observed decay and growth relation for uranium X, the curves shown in Figure 11–2 are obtained. The daughter element, uranium X, has a relatively short lifetime, and if it is separated from the uranium parent, it is seen to decay out very rapidly. Yet, although it is removed from the uranium parent, it is found to be rapidly regenerated by the parent and an equilibrium state is soon attained where the decay of the uranium parent to uranium X and the decay of uranium X are proceeding at the same rate.

The shape of the decay curve for uranium X is typical of that for any pure radioactive substance, and it is found to be characteristic of an exponential process. The analytical expression for such a decay process may be obtained by assuming that the rate of decay, $-dN/dt$ is proportional to the number of undecayed atoms that are present at time, t. This leads to the differential equation

$$-\frac{dN}{dt} = \lambda N \tag{11-1}$$

where N is the number of undecayed atoms present at time t and λ is a proportionality constant known as the *decay constant*. On integration between the proper limits, in which N_0 is the number of undecayed atoms at time $t = 0$, we obtain

$$\int_{N_0}^{N} \frac{dN}{N} = - \int_{t=0}^{t=t} \lambda \; dt$$

$$\ln \frac{N}{N_0} = -\lambda t$$

or

$$N = N_0 \, e^{-\lambda t} \qquad\qquad (11\text{--}2)$$

The rate of decay proved to be an excellent means of characterizing a particular radioactive species. Some of these were observed to decay rather rapidly while others were found to decay quite slowly. However, in all cases, the rate of decay was found to be characteristic. The manner in which the decay rate can best be utilized is in terms of a quantity called the *half-life*. This is the time it takes for a radioactive species to decay to one half of its initial activity. We can obtain the expression for the half-life by setting the ratio N/N_0 equal to 1/2. This gives

$$\ln 2 = \lambda t_{\frac{1}{2}}$$

or

$$t_{\frac{1}{2}} = \frac{0.693}{\lambda} \qquad\qquad (11\text{--}3)$$

Another manner of expressing the decay rate is in terms of the *average* or *mean-lifetime* of the radioactive species. This is given by

$$\tau = \frac{1}{\lambda} \qquad\qquad (11\text{--}4)$$

and it can be seen to be related to the half-life by the factor 0.693.

Since it is found that each radioactive species has its own characteristic half-life, the identification of a radioactive isotope can be made by plotting the log of the disintegrations per unit time, that is, the log of the activity, *versus* the time as seen in Figure 11–3. In this particular example a *composite* curve is seen that results from the presence of two activities. Such a curve is readily resolved into its individual components when it is recognized that the decay curve for a pure species should be a straight line. Thus, after the short-lived activity has decayed out, the remaining curve is due to the long lived component. This curve can then be extrapolated back to zero time and subtracted from the composite curve. The sub traction then gives the decay curve of the short lived activity. The half-life of each component can be read directly from the curves by noting the time

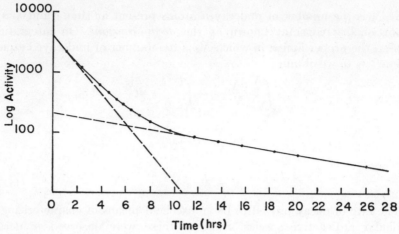

FIGURE 11–3. Resolution of a Composite Decay Curve into its Two Components.

necessary for the activity to decrease to one-half its value at any given time, t.

RADIOACTIVE CHAINS

As a result of the extensive studies on the naturally occurring radioactive elements, it was found that those of atomic number greater than 83 were members of one or another of three radioactive chains or series. The first of these series is the *uranium series* shown in Figure 11–4. The

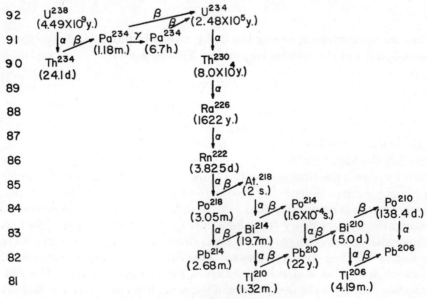

FIGURE 11–4. The Uranium Series.

parent member is ^{238}U, and by means of alpha and beta transformations, it ends with ^{206}Pb. It is interesting to note that the atomic weight of every member of this series can be represented by the relation "$4n + 2$", where n is an integer. For instance, the atomic weight of the second member of the series, UX_1, is 234. According to our relation, this is $(4 \times 58) + 2$. The basis for the relation lies, of course, in the fact that the relative weight of an alpha particle is 4. Because of this relation, the uranium series is sometimes referred to as the "$4n + 2$" series.

The *actinium series*, or "$4n + 3$" series, has ^{235}U as the parent, and its final product is the stable lead isotope, ^{207}Pb. The third of the naturally occurring series is the *thorium* or "$4n$" *series*. It begins with ^{232}Th and ends with the stable lead isotope, ^{208}Pb. Although, a "$4n + 1$" series does not occur in nature, such a series has been produced artificially. It is considered to begin with ^{237}Np and end with ^{209}Bi.

ISOTOPES

The first realization of the existence of isotopes came from an understanding of the radioactive chains. Decay by an alpha particle will decrease the atomic number by two units and the atomic weight by four units, whereas decay by a beta particle will increase the atomic number by one unit and, for all practical purposes, will not affect the atomic weight. In the uranium series, it is seen that ^{238}U decays in succession by an alpha particle and two beta particles to give the fourth member of the series In our present state of understanding, we are aware that this member of the series is the uranium isotope ^{234}U. In the early studies on the decay series, it was found that this member behaved chemically in an identical manner to the parent element. As a consequence, the parent was called uranium I and the other member was called uranium II. Knowing the relative masses of the alpha and beta particles, it was obvious that uranium I and uranium II could not have the same atomic weight in spite of their chemical identity. Observations such as this for several pairs of chemically similar species led Soddy[1] to the conclusion that a given element could have more than one atomic weight, and he gave such pairs the name of isotopes.

BINDING ENERGY

The discovery of isotopes and the closeness of isotopic masses to whole numbers brings to mind the hypothesis of Prout in which he proposed that all elements are built up from the hydrogen atom. We now know that this idea is not as far from the facts as was once thought. However, the accuracy of measurement possible with the mass spectrograph is sufficient to show that the mass of an element is not exactly equal to the sum of the masses of its constituent particles.

On the physical atomic weight scale, which is based on a defined weight of 16.000000 for the oxygen isotope 16 rather than a value of 16.000000 for the naturally occurring mixture of oxygen,* the mass of the hydrogen atom and the neutron are, respectively,

$$m_H = 1.008142 \text{ atomic mass units}$$

$$m_N = 1.008982 \text{ atomic mass units}$$

where an atomic mass unit is $1/N_0 = (6.023 \times 10^{23})^{-1} = 1.661 \times 10^{-24}$ g. If we now consider the atom $_2^4$He, it is seen that if its mass is simply the sum of its constituent particles, it should be

$$2 \times 1.008982 + 2 \times 1.008142 = 4.003425 \text{ amu}$$

Experimentally, however, it is found that the mass of the $_2^4$He atom is 4.00387 amu. It is apparent that there is a loss of mass which can be expressed by the relation

$$\Delta M = Zm_H + (A - Z)m_N - M_{ZA} \tag{11-5}$$

where Z represents the atomic number and A is the mass number of the particular isotope whose mass is M_{ZA}. This loss of mass that results from the formation of a nucleus is referred to as the *mass defect* and it is related to a quantity called the *binding energy*.** Ordinarily, we define the binding energy as *the energy released in an imaginary process in which the nucleons come together to form the nucleus, starting from large separations with negligible kinetic energies.* Thus, ΔM is the mass equivalent of the energy released in the formation of the nucleus from its constituent particles.

The energy equivalent of the mass defect can be determined from the Einstein relation $E = mc^2$. Since one atomic mass unit was seen to be 1.661×10^{-24} g, its energy equivalent is found to be $E = (1.661 \times 10^{-24})(2.998 \times 10^{10})^2$ ergs, or $E = 1.493 \times 10^{-3}$ ergs. Ordinarily, in nuclear processes, energy is expressed in terms of million electron volts rather than ergs. Thus, since the relation between mev and ergs is 1 mev $= 1.602 \times 10^{-6}$ ergs, it is found that 1 amu $= 931$ mev.

For the example of $_2^4$He, we find that $\Delta M = 4.03425 - 4.00387$, or $\Delta M = 0.03038$ amu. In terms of mev, the binding energy then becomes 28.3 mev, or 7.1 mev per *nucleon*, that is, per nuclear particle. If a plot is made of the average binding energy per nucleon as a function of the mass

---

* In order to convert an atomic weight on the physical scale to the chemical scale, it is necessary to multiply the physical atomic weight by 1.000279. Although it is not yet in general use, a new scale based on ^{12}C $= 12.00000$ is now in effect.

**Frequently, the packing fraction, which is defined as $(M - A)/A$, is tabulated instead of the binding energy.

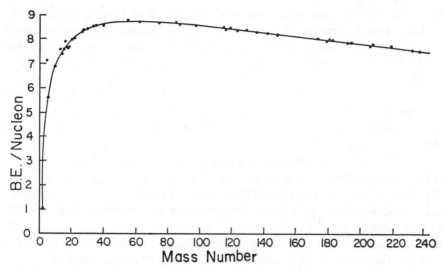

FIGURE 11–5. Binding Energy Curve.

number, the curve shown in Figure 11–5 is obtained. It is noted that the curve rises quite rapidly from relatively low values for the elements of very low atomic weight until it hits a maximum value of about 8.8 mev in the neighborhood of mass number 55. In this region it starts falling very slowly until it reaches a value of about 7.6 for ^{238}U. The change is found to be quite regular except for three very light elements, $^4_2$He, $^{12}_6$C, and $^{16}_8$O, all of which show abnormally high binding energies.

Although 8 or 9 mev may not appear to be a large amount of energy in itself, when we consider the energy involved in the binding energy of a mole of a substance, we can begin to appreciate the magnitude of the energies involved in nuclear processes.

STRUCTURE OF THE NUCLEUS

Before 1920, very little was known about the nucleus. In addition to the ability of some nuclei to emit alpha, beta, and gamma rays, it was known that the mass of an atom was concentrated primarily in the nucleus and the atomic number was a measure of the positive charge of the nucleus. Since the electron and proton were the only fundamental particles known at that time, it was only natural to imagine the nucleus to be composed of these particles. This resulted in a nuclear model known as the *proton-electron model*. According to this model, the nucleus contained a sufficient number of protons to account for the mass number, A. However, since the positive charge on the nucleus is equal to the atomic number, Z, it was necessary for the nucleus to also contain $(A - Z)$ electrons. Thus, there would be enough protons to account for the atomic number and the remaining mass of the nucleus would be made up of proton-electron pairs. This model had certain apparent advantages. For instance, radioactive decay involved two types of particles, the alpha particle and the beta particle. Both of these were observed to come out of the nucleus, and it would seem to be reasonable that they must have been inside of the nucleus. Or, in the case of the alpha particle, the constituents would at least be available for the formation of the particle.

In spite of some apparent advantages of the proton-electron model, several serious difficulties soon arose. Among the first of these was that of the *angular momentum* or *spin* of the nucleus. The idea of nuclear spin had been used by Pauli to explain the existence of hyperfine structure in certain spectral lines. Using spectral instruments of very high resolution, it had been observed that many spectral lines showed an extremely fine splitting that could not be explained in terms of the extranuclear electrons or the isotopic masses of the elements. Pauli was able to quantitatively account for these lines by treating the nucleus as if it had an angular momentum just as is found with the electrons. The source of this angular momentum of the nucleus was ascribed to both an intrinsic spin of $1/2(h/2\pi)$ for a fundamental particle such as a proton or an electron as well as an orbital angular momentum. The total angular momentum or spin of a nucleus is $I = L \pm S$, where L is the orbital angular momentum of the nucleus and S is the spin angular momentum of the nucleus. Since the orbital angular momentum will always be an integral multiple of $h/2\pi$, the number of fundamental particles present in the nucleus should determine if the nuclear spin, I, is an integral or half-integral multiple of $h/2\pi$. As a result of experimental studies, it was found that nuclei that have an *odd* mass number have spins that are odd half-integral multiples of $h/2\pi$ such that $I = 1/2, 3/2, 5/2, \cdots$, whereas, nuclei of *even* mass number have spins that are zero or integral multiples of $h/2\pi$, giving $I = 0, 1, 2, \cdots$. Now, if we consider the isotope $^{14}_{7}\text{N}$, it is seen that a conflict with the electron-proton model arises. According to this model, $^{14}_{7}\text{N}$ should contain 14 protons and 7 electrons. This gives a total of 21 particles and should result in an odd half-integral spin. However, experimentally the spin of $^{14}_{7}\text{N}$ has been determined to be 1.

Another difficulty with the electron-proton model can be seen when we consider the *statistics* of the $^{14}_{7}\text{N}$ nucleus. Whereas macroscopic properties such as the distribution of energies in gases can be treated by classical Boltzmann statistics, it has been found necessary to develop new statistical approaches for nuclei and fundamental particles. Two types of statistics, both based on quantum theory, have been developed. In terms of the quantum mechanical criterion, it is found that if the coordinates of two identical particles in a system can be interchanged without changing the sign of the wave function describing the system, the system obeys *Bose-Einstein* statistics. However, if the wave function is *antisymmetrical*, that is, if the sign of the wave function does change with this interchange of coordinates, the system follows *Fermi-Dirac* statistics; the difference being that the Pauli Exclusion Principle applies to those particles obeying Fermi-Dirac statistics.

All fundamental particles as well as nuclei having an odd number of nucleons obey Fermi-Dirac statistics. Those having an even number of nucleons are found to obey Bose-Einstein statistics. If we again consider the $^{14}_{7}N$ nucleus in the light of the electron-proton model, we note that the 21 fundamental particles should lead to Fermi-Dirac statistics. However, we again find a disagreement with experiment since $^{14}_{7}N$ obeys Bose-Einstein statistics.

Finally, a crude, but indicative quantum mechanical argument concerning the energy of the electron can also be used to discredit the electron-proton model of the nucleus. If the electron is treated as if it were confined in a box of nuclear dimensions, it is possible to obtain a fair approximation to its energy by means of a simple particle in a box treatment. The energy of an electron in a one dimensional rectangular box is given by $E = n^2 h^2 / 8 m a^2$, and by substituting the accepted values for the various terms, the energy is seen to be

$$E = \frac{(1)^2 \ (6.62 \times 10^{-27})^2}{8(9.11 \times 10^{-28}) \ (10^{-12})^2}$$

$$E = 6 \times 10^{-3} \text{ erg}$$

Although, this is admittedly a rather crude approach, it gives an idea of the general order of magnitude of the energy that might be expected for an electron confined to so small a volume. This value is several orders of magnitude greater than any ever observed in beta decay.

In an attempt to resolve this problem, Rutherford proposed in 1920, that an electron-proton pair might be so closely associated that they could be considered to be a neutral particle, which he called a *neutron*. Twelve years later, the neutron was discovered by Chadwick as a result of studies on nuclear transmutations from alpha particle bombardment. This led to a radically new model of the nucleus in which it was proposed that the nucleus is composed of only neutrons and protons. This solved the problems that had arisen with the electron-proton model, but as we shall see, it introduced new problems that, from a classical standpoint, are no less than paradoxical.

RADIOACTIVE DECAY

We generally think of radioactive decay in terms of alpha, beta, and gamma emission, as well as spontaneous fission. Although all of these have been experimentally observed and are well established, it is found that each offers its own paradox in terms of our classical or every-day experiences. One of the most obvious of these paradoxes can be seen in beta decay, where we go to great lengths to support a model of the nucleus that contains only neutrons and protons and thereby put ourselves in the position of observing a particle come from the nucleus that was never in it. It is not only in beta decay that we find our classical picture to break down. An equally disturbing situation is encountered in alpha decay. It is because of the failures of our classical treatment of decay processes such as these that quantum mechanics is introduced, and thus far, it would appear that it can be made to work.

Alpha Decay

The elements that are found to be alpha emitters are primarily restricted to the heavier atoms. Outside of the exceptional example of ^{8}Be, which breaks down with a half-life of 10^{-16} seconds to two helium atoms, ^{147}Sm is considered to be an unusually light alpha emitter. It would appear that all of the naturally occurring elements with atomic weight greater than ^{208}Pb are unstable with respect to alpha decay, and it is most likely that the elements with atomic weights between 190 and 208 are also energetically unstable toward alpha decay but have half-lives too long to be detected.

For some time it was thought that the alpha particles emitted from a given nucleus are *monoenergetic*. However, more accurate studies have shown that this is not necessarily true. In most instances, the decay will involve a spectrum of alpha particle energies composed of two or more closely spaced monoenergetic groups. In the decay of ^{222}Rn, for instance, a single monoenergetic alpha group of energy 5.484 mev is emitted, whereas ^{228}Th is found to emit five alpha groups with energies of 5.137, 5.173, 5.208, 5.338, and 5.421 mev.

The existence of these monoenergetic groups indicates that there is a possibility of energy levels in the nucleus just as is found in the extra-nuclear structure of the atom. The different alpha groups should correspond to transitions to the various nuclear energy levels. To support this view, it is observed that gamma-ray emission invariably accompanies the alpha decay of a nuclide with two or more alpha-ray groups. The observed gamma rays result from transitions between the various levels and will, therefore, give a measure of the relative energies of these levels. Consequently, it should be possible to construct nuclear energy diagrams, and this is found to be the case. An example of such a diagram, or *decay scheme*, is seen in

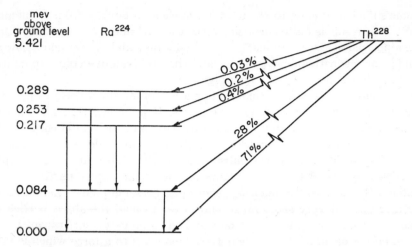

FIGURE 11–6. Decay Scheme of ^{228}Th. (After Stephens, F. S., Jr., Asaro, F., and Perlman, I., *Phys. Rev.*, **107**, 1091 (1957).)

Figure 11–6, where the decay of ^{228}Th to the product nucleus ^{224}Ra is shown. The alpha particles from highest energy alpha group will very likely go to the ground state of the product nucleus, and those of the lower energy alpha groups will go to the various excited states. It is highly improbable that alpha or beta decay will take place from an *excited state*, and therefore, the emission of a series of gamma rays from the excited states to the ground state would be expected. Measurement of the various gamma-ray energies substantiates this idea, and a decay scheme can be constructed from which the energy levels of the product nucleus can be determined.

One of the more interesting features of alpha decay is found in the relation between the half-life of the decay and the energy of the emitted alpha particle. It would be expected that as the energy of the alpha particle increases, the half-life for the decay would show a corresponding decrease. This is exactly what is observed. However, the magnitude of the effect is quite unexpected. For the isotope ^{232}Th, the alpha particles have an energy of about 4 mev, and for ^{212}Po, they have an energy of about 8.8 mev. Yet, the half-life of ^{232}Th is 1.4×10^{10} years, whereas the half-life of ^{212}Po is 3×10^{-7} seconds. Thus, we find a difference in half-life of about 10^{24} as a result of an energy difference of only slightly more than a factor of 2. Such an extreme dependence is rather difficult to understand in terms of our ordinary classical concepts.

Another feature of alpha decay that cannot readily be interpreted in terms of classical concepts arises from a study of the scattering of alpha particles by the heavy nuclei. When the ^{238}U nucleus is bombarded with 8.78 mev alpha particles from ^{212}Po, the scattered alpha particles do not come sufficiently close to the uranium nucleus to deviate from Coulomb's law. This result is quite surprising since the ^{238}U nucleus is known to emit an alpha particle with an energy of only 4.2 mev and one wonders how an alpha particle with an energy no greater than this can overcome a potential barrier that is at least 8.78 mev high.

Alpha-decay Model. In constructing a model for alpha decay, we find it necessary to consider two types of forces. It is known that like charges repel each other according to Coulomb's law, and such an effect must be considered to exist for the nucleus and the alpha particle at some distance from the nucleus. This was substantiated with the scattering of alpha particles by the ^{238}U nucleus. However, when an alpha particle comes sufficiently close to the nucleus, there must be some point where a much greater force of very short range takes over to hold the alpha particle in the nucleus. Such a force must be assumed to be very short range, therefore, falling off much faster than $1/r^2$. This leads to a force which is very strong at the surface of the nucleus but is equal to zero at small distances outside the surface. Such a model may be represented by a potential energy curve of the type shown in Figure 11–7. As the positively charged particle approaches the nucleus, only the coulombic repulsion is significant until it essentially reaches the surface of the nucleus at R_0. At this point, the short-range nuclear forces begin to take over to give a potential minimum inside of the nucleus. The hump just outside of the nucleus is known as the coulomb or *potential barrier*, and it is this barrier that an alpha particle must, in the classical sense, pass over in order to escape. Since the height of the potential barrier for ^{238}U was found to be at least 8.78 mev high, it is rather difficult to understand from a classical standpoint how a 4.2 mev alpha particle can get out of such a nucleus.

Actually, there are three different cases to consider for an alpha particle in a nucleus described by this potential well. These are the three cases

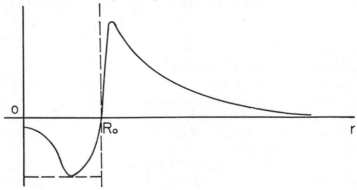

FIGURE 11–7. Schematic Representation of the Potential Barrier to Alpha Decay.

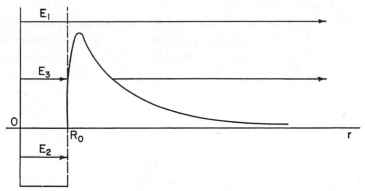

FIGURE 11–8. Potential Barrier to Alpha Decay for Three Different Energy Extremes.

indicated in Figure 11–8 by E_1, E_2, and E_3. For the first situation, represented by E_1, the energy of the alpha particle is greater than the potential barrier, and it will escape from the nucleus the first time it reaches the nuclear surface. This would lead to spontaneous decay with no measurable half-life. For the second case, E_2, the binding energy of the last alpha particle is greater than zero, and this results in a stable nucleus. Now, according to classical ideas, the nucleus with an alpha particle having an energy represented by E_3, would also be stable due to the activation energy necessary to get it over the potential barrier. Thus, according to this picture we are led to the conclusion that alpha decay is impossible. In spite of our classical conclusions, we nevertheless know that alpha decay does take place. The solution to the problem came in 1928, when Gamow and, independently, Gurney and Condon applied the methods of quantum mechanics.[2,3] Using the same general approach as they, we find that a first order quantum mechanical approximation can be carried out by treating the potential well as a *square well* such as shown in Figure 11–9, where the alpha particle is assumed to be moving freely inside the potential well. Actually, the idea that an alpha particle exists as such in the nucleus and

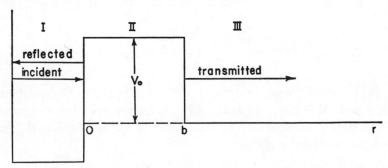

FIGURE 11–9. Square Well Approximation of the Alpha Decay Model.

sees the nucleus as a simple potential well, represents an extremely over-simplified model, and its only justification lies in the quite good results it gives. Nevertheless, if we consider the alpha particle with an energy, E_3, it is found that there is a finite probability that it can escape from the nucleus by *leaking* or *tunneling* through the potential barrier. This possibility arises from the fact that the wave equation for the particle has a solution inside the barrier wall and, for this reason, it has a finite probability of existence inside the barrier.

Mathematical Treatment of Alpha Decay. Mathematically, we assume that the alpha particle bounces back and forth inside the nucleus, hitting the opposite walls $v/2r$ times a second. Each time the alpha particle collides, there is a small probability that it will leak through the potential barrier rather than be reflected. If we represent the probability per unit time of leaking through the barrier by λ, it is seen that

$$\lambda = v/2r \times T \qquad (11\text{–}6)$$

where T is the *transmission coefficient*. That is, the probability of leakage per unit time is equal to the number of collisions per unit time multiplied by the probability of leakage for each collision. Quantitatively, the transmission coefficient is

$$T = \frac{\text{intensity of transmitted wave}}{\text{intensity of incident wave}} \qquad (11\text{–}7)$$

If we consider the wave equations in the three regions shown in Figure 11–9, it is seen that these are

$$\text{Region I:} \quad (V = 0) \quad \frac{d^2\psi_I}{dx^2} + \frac{8\,\pi^2 m}{h^2}\,E\psi_I \qquad = 0 \quad (11\text{–}8a)$$

$$\text{Region II:} \quad (V = V_0) \quad \frac{d^2\psi_{II}}{dx^2} - \frac{8\,\pi^2 m}{h^2}\,(V_0 - E)\psi_{II} = 0 \quad (11\text{–}8b)$$

$$\text{Region III:} \quad (V = 0) \quad \frac{d^2\psi_{III}}{dx^2} + \frac{8\,\pi^2 m}{h^2}\,E\psi_{III} \qquad = 0 \quad (11\text{–}8c)$$

It should be readily recognized that the solution to the wave equations in regions I and III is the same as the solution for the equation of a particle in a box. Here it turns out to be convenient to use the exponential form of the solution, thereby giving:

$$\text{Region I:} \ \psi_I = Ae^{i\alpha x} + Be^{-i\alpha x} \qquad (11\text{–}9)$$

where $Ae^{i\alpha x}$ represents the incident wave and $Be^{-i\alpha x}$ represents the reflected wave,

$$\text{Region III:} \quad \psi_{III} = Ce^{i\alpha x} \tag{11-10}$$

the negative term being omitted since there is no reflected wave. In region II, the wave equation can be put into the form

$$\frac{d^2\psi_{II}}{dx^2} - \beta^2\psi_{II} = 0 \tag{11-11}$$

where $\beta^2 = 8\pi^2 m(V_0 - E)/h^2$. The minus sign arises from the fact that V_0 is greater than E. It can easily be verified by substitution that the solution to a differential equation of this form is

$$\psi_{II} = Fe^{\beta x} + Ge^{-\beta x} \tag{11-12}$$

Knowing the wave functions in all three regions, we should now see that the transmission coefficient can be evaluated. The intensity of a wave can be represented by the square of the wave function, and from Eq. (11–7), we obtain

$$T = \frac{|Ce^{i\alpha x}|^2}{|Ae^{i\alpha x}|^2} = \frac{|C|^2}{|A|^2} \tag{11-13}$$

This leaves T dependent on the values of the constants C and A, and these can be determined by requiring the wave function to be of class Q. If the alpha particle is to follow a physically reasonable path in its leakage through the barrier, the wave function and its first derivative should be continuous. Thus, we can say that at the boundaries of the three regions,

$$\psi_I(0) = \psi_{II}(0) \qquad \psi_{II}(b) = \psi_{III}(b)$$
$$\text{and}$$
$$\psi'_I(0) = \psi'_{II}(0) \qquad \psi'_{II}(b) = \psi'_{III}(b)$$

where ψ' represents the first derivative of ψ with respect to x.

There are various mathematical means of connecting these functions at the boundaries, such as requiring the ratio of the slope to the amplitude of the wave to be continuous on both sides of the boundary. However, the difficulties are those of rather involved algebra and do not offer any conceptual difficulties. As a result, it is found that the transmission coefficient is given by

$$T = \frac{16\,E\,(V_0 - E)}{V_0^2} \exp\left\{-2\,\frac{(2m)^{\frac{1}{2}}}{h}\,\sqrt{V_0 - E}\,b\right\} \tag{11-14}$$

It is readily apparent that the evaluation of T will depend very critically on the height of the potential barrier above the alpha particle energy, $(V_0 - E)$, and on the barrier thickness, b. These factors, unfortunately, can only be estimated and consequently an accurate quantitative comparison with experiment is not possible. Additionally, we must recognize the extreme crudeness of our model. A somewhat better, but yet crude, treatment uses a quantum mechanical method of approximation known as the "WKB approximation," which allows the use of a rounded potential barrier. This method leads to the slightly different expression for the transmission coefficient,

$$T = \exp\left\{-\frac{4\pi}{h}(2m)^{\frac{1}{2}}\int_{r_1}^{r^2}\sqrt{V_{(r)}-E}\,dr\right\} \qquad (11\text{--}15)$$

Finally, to calculate the decay probability, we must know the frequency of collision of the alpha particle with the walls of the nucleus. Since we have already stated that it is unreasonable to expect the alpha particle to actually be bouncing back and forth in the nucleus, one may wonder what sort of frequency we are using. However, we can obtain fair agreement with experiment if we obtain the collision frequency by using the velocity of the alpha particle obtained from the momentum term of the uncertainty principle, $\Delta p\Delta x\sim h$, and assume that the radius of the nucleus is about 1.5×10^{-13} cm.

In spite of the naïve nature of this approach to alpha decay, the qualitative results are quite encouraging. By leakage through a potential barrier a mechanism for alpha decay is provided, and the most satisfying feature of this mechanism is that the approximated life-times of decay are of the proper order of magnitude. In addition, the unusual relationship between the half-life for decay and the energy of the alpha particle becomes quite reasonable. The exponential term in Eq. (11–14) leads to an extreme dependence of T, and therefore the half-life, on the energy of the alpha particle. Actual calculations in terms of this model show quite reasonable qualitative agreement in this respect. Thus, in spite of the fact that we do not know the shape of the potential barrier, the extent of the nuclear forces, or even the radius of the nucleus, it is still possible to obtain quite satisfactory results with this model due to the sensitivity of the transmission coefficient.

Beta Decay

Beta decay is usually thought to involve the emission of an electron with the resultant conversion of a neutron to a proton. This leads to an increase of one in the atomic number of the atom with no significant change in its mass. However, in addition to the emission of the conventional negative electron, a common variation of beta decay has been found in the emission of a *positive electron*. This results in the conversion of a proton to a neutron. The *positron* was first observed in 1933, by C. D. Anderson[4] while studying photographs of tracks in a Wilson cloud chamber. At that time, he noted a particle that behaved in the presence of a magnetic field in a manner analogous to that of a particle with the charge and mass of an electron. Yet, it had a direction of curvature that could be due only to a positively charged particle. Since that time, the positive electron, or positron, has been found to be a very common particle in the decay of the artificial radioisotopes. Although the decay properties of the positron are in many ways analogous to those of the negative electron, it has only a transitory existence. After emission, it is slowed down as a result of collisions and finally is *annihilated* by combination with a negative electron. This results in the production of two gamma rays, each having an energy of 0.511 mev, the energy equivalent of the mass of an electron.

A third mode of beta decay is found in *orbital electron capture*. This process involves the capture by the nucleus of an electron in the extra-nuclear structure of the atom and thereby gives the same net nuclear change as positron emission. As a result of the greater probability of its existence in the neighborhood of the nucleus, an electron from the K shell is usually captured. The detection of an electron-capture process is ordinarily more difficult than the detection of other decay processes. A gamma ray can be detected if the nucleus is left in an excited state as a result of the capture process, but frequently the only observable radiations are the characteristic X rays and *Auger* electrons that result from the vacancy in the K, L, M, etc., shell of the product nucleus.

From a classical standpoint, it is seen that beta decay is as unreasonable as is alpha decay. Two problems that immediately arise are (1) why are beta rays not monoenergetic as are alpha rays?, and (2) if it has been shown that the electron is not inside the nucleus, how does it come from the nucleus?

On considering the energies of the beta rays, we would expect those coming from a given nucleus to all have the same energy, or at least to belong to one of several monoenergetic groups. This, however, is not the case. A determination of the beta-ray energies from a given nucleus can readily be obtained by several means, such as with a magnetic lens spectrometer or with a scintillation spectrometer, and instead of monoenergetic groups, a *continuous* spectrum of energies is obtained. This is apparent from the beta spectrum of ^{32}P shown in Figure 11–10. Although the plot is a momentum plot, it is nevertheless apparent that the beta-ray energies from this nucleus can vary anywhere from zero to a maximum value of the order of 1.7 mev.

If we think of beta decay in terms of the usual two-body process, that is, a process involving only a beta particle and the nucleus, the decay may be represented as

$$Z^A \rightarrow (Z + 1)^A + e^- \qquad (11\text{–}16)$$

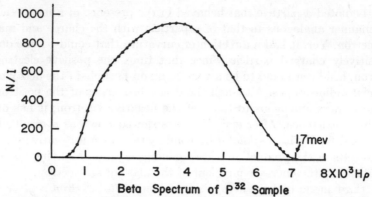

FIGURE 11–10. Beta-ray Spectrum of ^{32}P. (After Jensen, E. N., Nichols, R. T., Clement, J., and Pohm, A., *Phys. Rev.*, **85**, 112 (1952).)

Since the electron that leaves the nucleus of the parent atom must be replaced by an electron in the electronic shells of the product atom as a result of the increase in atomic number, we can express the mass-energy relation of this decay, neglecting the electronic binding energy, as

$$M (Z)^A = M (Z + 1)^A + T \qquad (11\text{–}17)$$

T represents the total kinetic energy of the system and is given by

$$T = T_\beta + T_R \qquad (11\text{–}18)$$

where T_β is the kinetic energy of the electron and T_R is the kinetic energy of recoil of the nucleus. For the case of ^{32}P, we find that

$$T = M(^{32}\text{P}) - M(^{32}\text{S}) = 31.98490 - 31.98226 \text{ amu}$$
$$= 0.00183 \text{ amu}$$

In terms of mev, this amounts to very nearly 1.7 mev. Continuing the calculations in terms of a two-body problem, the momentum of the recoiling nucleus must be equal to, and opposite in direction to, that of the electron, and the conservation of momentum determines T_β and T_R uniquely. It is readily shown that the kinetic energy of the beta particle is very nearly 1.7 mev, and the kinetic energy of the recoiling nucleus is only 0.078 mev. Energywise, we should then expect all of the beta particles from ^{32}P to have an energy of about 1.7 mev. Yet it can be seen from the beta spectrum that they can take on any energy from zero to 1.7 mev, with an average energy of the beta particles being only about one third of the maximum energy.

The Neutrino. The solution to this dilemma can be approached in two ways. First, it can be assumed that the laws of conservation, such as conservation of momentum, do not hold in the realm of the nucleus; or secondly, it can be assumed that the decay actually involves a third as yet undetected particle which is capable of carrying off the remaining energy. This latter approach was suggested in 1927 by Pauli, and was later used by Fermi in his formulation of a theory of beta decay. This new particle was called a *neutrino,* and in order to maintain the laws of conservation and explain its undetectable nature, it was necessary to assign to it the properties of no charge, a very small magnetic moment, very nearly zero rest mass, a spin of one half, and Fermi-Dirac statistics. The probability of a particle with no charge, magnetic moment, or rest mass interacting with matter is essentially zero. In fact, it has been calculated that if the only reaction of a neutrino is

$$\nu + {}_1^1\text{H} \rightarrow {}_0^1n + e^+$$

its mean free path in lead will be about 3 light-years.

Using the idea of a three-body decay mechanism, a successful theory of beta decay was developed by Enrico Fermi in 1934.[5] In terms of this approach, the various modes of beta decay can be represented as

$${}_0^1n \rightarrow {}_1^1\text{H} + e^- + \nu' \quad \text{(negatron emission)}$$

$${}_1^1\text{H} \rightarrow {}_0^1n + e^+ + \nu \quad \text{(positron emission)}$$

$${}_1^1\text{H} + e^- \rightarrow {}_0^1n + \nu \quad \text{(electron capture)}$$

In order to bring about these transformations, Fermi utilized the mathematical approach of quantum mechanics in a manner analogous to that used for the treatment of electromagnetic radiation in the atomic realm. Using the time-dependent wave equation, it is possible to create and annihilate photons at the time of their emission or absorption in extra-nuclear processes. And inasmuch as the electron does not exist as such in the nucleus, according to the neutron-proton model, an extension of this approach to the problem of beta emission would appear promising. This may not, at first, seem to be too reasonable. We are prone to expect the properties of a wave to be quite different from those of a particle. Consequently, we may not be disturbed to see a photon created, but we find it difficult to visualize a similar process for an electron. However, in the light of our past experiences with the wave-particle dualism of quantum mechanics, we should not by now be particularly surprised to find that an equivalent approach should apply for both systems.

As a result of the Fermi theory, an equation is obtained for the energy distribution of the emitted beta particles having the form

$$N(\gamma)d\gamma = G^2|m|^2 f(Z,\gamma)(\gamma_0 - \gamma)^2(\gamma^2 - 1)^{\frac{1}{2}}\gamma d\gamma \qquad (11\text{–}19)$$

where γ is the energy in units of mc^2, that is, $\gamma = E/mc^2$. $N(\gamma)d\gamma$ represents the fraction of the nuclei that emit a beta particle with energy between γ and $\gamma + d\gamma$ per unit time, G represents a constant, $f(Z,\gamma)$ is a function expressing the effect of the *coulomb field* of the nucleus on the emitted beta particle, and the relative probability of beta decay is given by the square of the *matrix element*, $|m|^2$. The remaining factors are statistical factors describing the sharing of energy between the beta particle, the nucleus, and the neutrino, with the maximum or *end-point energy* of the beta group being γ_0.

According to the Fermi theory, it should be possible to predict both the probability of decay and the shape of the beta spectrum. The decay probability is usually expressed in terms of the decay constant, λ, or the mean life, τ, either of which can be obtained by integrating Eq. (11–19) over all possible values of the kinetic energy. Thus, we find that

$$\lambda = \frac{1}{\tau} = \int_0^{\gamma_0} N(\gamma)\, d\gamma \qquad (11\text{–}20)$$

Transition Probabilities. Just as certain transitions in atomic spectra are observed to take place and others are observed to be forbidden, we can also speak of *allowed* and *forbidden transitions* in beta decay. Instead of actually being forbidden, it would be more nearly correct to say that transitions between certain nuclear levels are more probable than others. The more likely transitions are said to be allowed transitions and the less probable transitions are considered to be forbidden to various degrees. The most obvious indication of the existence of these degrees of forbiddenness is to be seen in the half-life of a beta-emitter. The half-life for an allowed transition would, in general, be relatively short, whereas the half-life of a forbidden transition would be considerably longer.

The actual probability of decay is dependent on the matrix element of Eq. (11–19). According to the theory, it is possible to express the matrix element in an infinite series, and although it is not usually possible to evaluate the matrix element, it can be shown that each nonvanishing term of the series is roughly 100 times larger than the next following term. That is, if the first term is not equal to zero, it will be approximately 100 times larger than the second term, and so on. Because of the magnitude of this difference, all but the first nonvanishing term can be neglected. From the form of Eq. (11–19), it can be seen that the larger the value of the matrix element, the greater will be the probability of decay. Since the largest possible value of the matrix element is found when the first term of the series is nonvanishing, this term should lead to the greatest decay probability and correspondingly, the shortest half-life. Such a transition is said to be an allowed transition. When the first term of the expansion is zero, and the second term is nonvanishing, we then have a first forbidden transition. Since the value of the matrix element is approximately 100 times smaller than in the allowed case, it is quite obvious that a first forbidden transition will not be as probable as an allowed transition.

Similarly, if it is found that the third term of the matrix expansion is the first nonvanishing term, the transition probability is yet smaller and the transition is said to be second forbidden, and so on.

The disappearance of the various leading terms in the expansion of the matrix element is not without some basis in theory. The total spin change of the nucleus for a transition, ΔI, must be an integral multiple of $h/2\pi$, and just as is found for atomic transitions, certain selection rules that determine the magnitude of the spin change also exist for nuclear transformations. According to the original theory of Fermi, the selection rule $\Delta I = 0$ was used for allowed transitions. This particular selection rule resulted from the use of the simplest of five different basic forms of the nucleon interaction that are consistent with the theory. It turned out that some disagreement existed between theory and experiment in terms of this simple type of interaction, and a more complicated form was used by Gamow and Teller, which led to the selection rule $\Delta I = 0$, ± 1. Although, there is no theoretical justification for the interaction form chosen by Gamow and Teller, it is found that the agreement between theory and experiment is quite good.

Another factor affecting the transition probability of a nuclear transition is the *parity change* of the system. A nuclear state has an odd or even parity depending on whether or not the wave function changes in sign when the signs of all the space coordinates of the system are changed. Actually, the parity is a more general form of the angular momentum quantum number, l, and just as an electron transition will depend on the angular momentum quantum number, a nuclear transition will depend on the parity change. Rather than consider s, p, d, f, etc., states, we can speak of *even* or *odd* parity; the even l states such as s, d, g, have even parity and the p, f, h, states have odd parity. Thus, when considering transitions between different nuclear states, one of the quantum conditions will be concerned with whether there is a change in parity.

ft Values. Because of the large difference in the magnitude of the various terms in the matrix element expansion which determines the degree of forbiddenness of a transition, it is possible to make a rather good theoretical classification of the decay type in terms of the degree of forbiddenness. By combining Eq. (11–19) and Eq. (11–20) we can obtain the equation

$$\frac{1}{\tau} = G^2 |m|^2 \int_0^{\gamma_0} f(Z, \gamma)(\gamma_0 - \gamma)^2(\gamma^2 - 1)^{\frac{1}{2}}\gamma d\gamma \qquad (11\text{--}21)$$

Since, after integration and substitution of the limits, the terms under the integral will become $f(Z, \gamma_0)$, we can make this substitution to give

$$\frac{1}{\tau} = G^2 |m|^2 f(Z, \gamma_0)$$

If, for simplicity, we represent $f(Z,\gamma_0)$ as merely f, we can obtain on rearrangement

$$f\tau = \frac{1}{G^2|m|^2}$$

or, in terms of half-life, rather than mean-life

$$ft = 0.693\,f\tau = \frac{1}{(G')^2|m|^2} \qquad (11\text{--}22)$$

Since G or G' is a constant, it is apparent that the ft value will reflect a change in $|m|$. And, since $|m|$ was shown to determine the degree of forbiddenness of a beta transition, the ft value will then indicate a difference in an allowed and a forbidden transition. It also should be apparent that the ft value can be determined from the integral in Eq. (11–21) if we know the atomic number of the nuclide and its measured beta end-point energy along with the half-life of the transition. Now, since the magnitude of $|m|^2$ is about 100 times smaller for a first forbidden transition than it is for an allowed transition, we should then expect the ft value for an allowed transition to be about 100 times smaller than it would be for a first forbidden transition, and so on. This is found to be the case, and a large number of beta transformations have been classified in terms of the ft values, or more commonly, in terms of log ft values. The general range of log ft values are given in Table 11–1, for some decay types along with the presently accepted selection rules and parity changes. It can be seen that the relationship is not completely unique. Nevertheless, a more or less general correlation does exist.

TABLE 11–1. / **Selection Rules for Beta Decay.**

Classification	Spin Change	Parity Change	Log ft
Allowed (favored)	0 or 1	no	3
Allowed (normal)	0 or 1	no	4 – 7
Allowed (1 - forbidden)	1	no	6 – 9
First forbidden	0 or 1	yes	6 – 8
First forbidden (unique)	2	yes	9
Second forbidden	2	no	10 – 14
Second forbidden (unique)	3	no	14
Third forbidden	3	yes	18
Third forbidden (unique)	4	yes	20

Kurie Plot. For the determination of the shape of the beta spectrum as well as of the beta end-point energy, it is found that direct employment of the beta spectrum is essentially useless. For instance, if an ordinary spectrum such as that of ^{32}P seen in Figure 11–10, is used for the determination of the end-point energy, it will not be possible to determine the intercept, due to the asymptotic approach of the curve to the energy axis. For this reason, the data is usually put in the form of a *Kurie* or *Fermi plot*. This can be done by rearranging Eq. (11–19) to the form

$$\left[\frac{N(\gamma)}{f(Z,\gamma)\,(\gamma^2 - 1)^{\frac{1}{2}}\gamma}\right]^{\frac{1}{2}} = G\,|m|\,(\gamma_0 - \gamma) \qquad (11\text{–}23)$$

If a plot is now made of the left side of the equation against the energy, a straight line will be obtained that intersects the energy axis at the value of the beta end-point energy. This, of course, leads to a much more accurate determination of the maximum energy of the beta-ray group as can be seen in Figure 11–11, where a Kurie plot of the ^{127}Te beta group is shown.

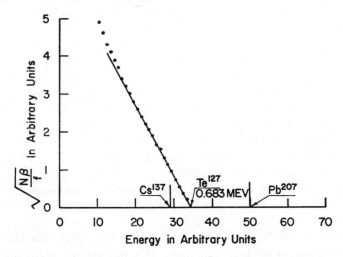

FIGURE 11–11. Kurie Plot of the ^{127}Te Beta Group. (After Day, M. C., Eakins, G. W., and Voigt, A. F., *Phys. Rev.*, **100**, 796 (1955).)

Gamma Decay

When a nucleus is left in an excited state, we can expect it to decay to a more stable state by means of gamma emission. It is for this reason that we find gamma emission associated with virtually all alpha or beta transitions. These usually leave the product nucleus in an excited state which then decays to a more stable state of the same nucleus by means of a gamma ray. Since a gamma ray is a form of electromagnetic radiation and thus has no charge or rest mass, there will be no change in the isotopic identity between the parent and the product nucleus.

There are actually three forms that gamma emission can take. The first of these is the simple emission of a gamma ray. A very common alternative, however, is *internal conversion*. In a rather naïve sense, this can be thought to involve the collision of the emitted gamma ray with an electron in the external structure of the atom. As a result of this collision, the energy of the gamma ray is supposed to be transferred completely to the electron, and the electron is then emitted with an energy equal to that of the initial gamma ray minus the binding energy of the electron. In spite of the desirable simplicity of this picture, it loses its appeal when we consider the probability of such a collision. We now think of internal conversion to be an alternative and competing process with gamma emission in which an electron from one of the electron shells of the atom is emitted by the nucleus. Most commonly, an electron from the K or L shell is emitted, since the probability is quite high that these electrons will be in sufficiently close proximity to the nucleus to allow the process of electron emission to take place.

The ratio of the number of electrons converted to the number of emitted gamma rays is known as the *internal conversion coefficient*. Since electrons can be emitted from the various shells, we can have K conversion coefficients, L conversion coefficients, and so on. In general, it is found that the conversion coefficient increases with an increase in atomic number of the gamma emitter and with an increase in spin change, ΔI, between the initial and final states. The extent of conversion decreases with an increase in energy of the gamma ray. In fact, very few emitters show internal conversion to a measurable extent when the gamma ray energy is greater than about 0.5 mev. A very notable exception is the case of ^{207m}Pb which has a high conversion ratio with a gamma-ray energy of 0.976 mev.

The third mode by which the available energy of the excited nucleus may be removed is by *pair formation*. This process can occur only if the gamma-ray energy is greater than 1.02 mev, the energy equivalent of the mass of two electrons. Here the excited nucleus can simultaneously create one new electron and one new positron, that is, an electron-positron pair, and emit them with kinetic energies equal to the original excitation energy minus the 1.02 mev necessary for the creation of the electron-positron pair. Although, this mode of gamma decay is not common, it has been observed and must be considered along with the two more common modes.

Isomeric Transitions. Alpha and beta decay processes are usually followed by gamma emission, and it is generally found that the time interval between the emission of an alpha or beta particle and the emission of a gamma ray is too short to be measured. Experimentally, a time interval of 10^{-9} or 10^{-10} seconds can be detected. However, gamma emission is usually more rapid than this, and consequently, the gamma rays appear to be emitted simultaneously with the alpha or beta particle. In some instances this is not true. Transitions do take place between different energy levels in some nuclei with measurable half-lives. The species in these two different energy states of the same nucleus are termed *nuclear isomers*, and the transitions are referred to as *isomeric transitions*. One very common example of such an isomeric transition is observed in the decay of ^{80m}Br to ^{80}Br which takes place with the emission of a gamma ray and has a half-life of 4.5 hours. Isomeric transitions have been observed for numerous pairs, and the number of such transitions observed will increase as the ability to measure shorter half-lives improves. Possibly, if we attain the ability to detect gamma-ray half-lives of the order of 10^{-14} seconds or less, virtually all gamma transitions will fit the description of an isomeric transition.

The quantum mechanical theory of isomeric transitions leads to, at the least, a semiquantitative understanding of their nature. It can be shown that the decay probability is dependent primarily on the energy available for the transition and the nuclear spin change, ΔI, in going from the initial state to the final state of the nucleus. If the energy of the gamma ray is small and the spin change is large, the transition probability will be small. We can draw the general conclusion that such long-lived isomeric pairs have large spin differences between their energy states. Frequently, we find spin changes as large as four or five for the rather long-lived isomeric transitions.

One very interesting aspect of decay processes involving the electrons in the atom, is the effect the chemical state of the element might have on the decay half-life. Ordinarily, we consider the half-life of a radioactive element to be unalterable. However, one might expect a K-capture process would depend on the distribution of the K electrons around the nucleus, and if this distribution could be altered, the half-life might also be altered. The same general argument will apply to decay by internal conversion, where the emission of an electron from an extranuclear shell is involved. Again, if the distribution of these electrons can be altered, it would be expected that the half-life of the element might be altered. Variations in half-lives have actually been observed for processes involving both electron capture and internal conversion. For the case of ^7Be, which decays by electron capture, it has been shown by Segré that the half-life of the isotope in the compound BeF_2 is 0.08 per cent greater than it is in the pure metal.[6] In the same manner, it is found[7] that the half-life of ^{99m}Tc, which shows a high conversion of M and N electrons, is 0.027 per cent greater in Tc_2S_7 than it is in $KTcO_4$.

DECAY SCHEMES

When a radioactive species decays by alpha or beta emission, the decay is usually followed by gamma emission. This indicates that the initial decay leaves the product nucleus in an excited state. More likely than not, the excited nucleus does not decay to its ground state by the emission of a single gamma ray. In fact, it may reach its final ground state by emitting a rather large number of gamma rays. Each of these gamma rays will be the result of a transition between two energy states of the product nucleus and, if we could determine the energies of the various transitions, we would know the relative energies of the levels.

For beta emission, there are instances where a beta transition leads directly to the ground state of the product nucleus. As can be seen in Figure 11–12, this is the case of ^{49}Sc which decays by the emission of a

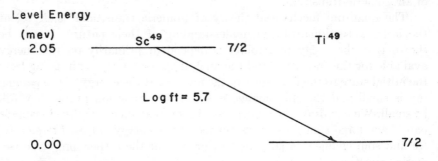

FIGURE 11–12. Decay Scheme of ^{49}Sc. (After O'Kelley, G. D., Lazar, N. H., and Eichler, E., *Phys. Rev.*, **101**, 1059 (1956).)

single beta group to the ground state of ^{49}Ti. The information that would be of interest for this decay would be the energy of the beta transition, the classification of the transition as allowed or forbidden, and the spin assignments of the two levels involved. The energy of the transition is the same as the end-point energy of the beta group, and this can be determined from a Fermi plot of the beta spectrum. It turns out that for this particular case, the level assignments can be deduced from alternative information and are found to be $f_{7/2}$ for both the ^{49}Sc and for the ^{49}Ti. However, it is still possible to determine if this assignment is in agreement with the decay classification. Since the levels are both f levels, there is no parity change, and the spin change is seen to be $\Delta I = 0$. This means that the transition must be of the allowed type. Now, if the theory is correct, the log ft value will be in the allowed range. The calculated log ft value is

5.7. This falls within the allowed range, and we conclude that theory and experiment are in agreement in this particular instance.

A great number of more complicated decay schemes have been determined,[8] and a few of these, including the isomeric transition of ^{97m}Nb, are shown in Figure 11–13. It might be noted that level assignments are given in terms of the spin, along with a plus or minus. The plus represents an even parity state and a minus represents an odd parity state. Since we are interested primarily in the parity change, it is not necessary to show whether the state is an *s*, *p*, *d*, *f*, etc., state.

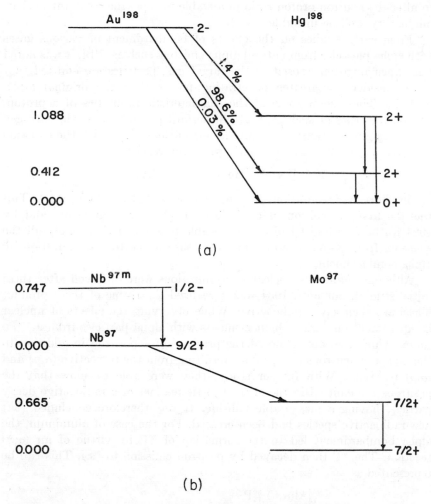

(a)

(b)

FIGURE 11–13.   Decay Schemes of **(a)**, ^{198}Au and **(b)**, ^{97m}Nb. (After Strominger, D., Hollander, J., and Seaborg, G., *Rev. Mod. Phys.*, **30**, 585 (1958).)

INDUCED RADIOACTIVITY

A nuclear decay can be considered to result from an unstable arrangement of neutrons and protons in a nucleus. When the arrangement is, for some reason, unfavorable, the nucleus will transform to a more favorable structure by one or more of the available modes of decay. Thus, we assume that the isotopes we observe in nature either have a stable nuclear configuration, or else their decay rates are sufficiently low that all of the species has not yet decayed out. The large majority of the elements that are lighter than bismuth fall into this first class. However, if it were possible to alter the neutron-proton ratio in a stable isotope, the resultant nucleus might very well be unstable.

From early studies on the effects of bombardment of various gases with alpha particles from natural alpha emitters such as ^{214}Bi, it was noted that when nitrogen is used as the target gas, particles are emitted that have considerably greater penetrating power than the original alpha particles. These show some of the characteristic properties of a proton, and on the basis of such studies, Rutherford proposed that the nitrogen nucleus might be transformed into a new nucleus along with the emission of a proton. Accordingly, we can express the reaction as

$$\,^{14}_{7}\text{N} + \,^{4}_{2}\text{He} \rightarrow \,^{17}_{8}\text{O} + \,^{1}_{1}\text{H}$$

or, in short hand notation, it can be represented as $^{14}_{7}\text{N}(\alpha,p)^{17}_{8}\text{O}$. This was the first recognition of an induced nuclear transmutation, and by 1924 Rutherford and Chadwick were able to show that virtually all the elements from boron to potassium were susceptible to transmutation by alpha bombardment.

Although numerous nuclear transmutations were observed after these initial studies, not until 1934 was it realized that some of these product nuclei are themselves radioactive. While observing the effects of nuclear bombardment on various light elements with alpha particles from a ^{214}Po source, Curie and Joliot[9] noted the presence of a positron in addition to the expected neutrons and protons resulting from the respective (α,n) and (α,p) reactions. With further study, they were able to show that the positrons are emitted in the characteristic manner of a radioactive decay particle, having a measurable half-life. It was therefore concluded that new radioactive species had been created. For the case of aluminum, the alpha bombardment led to the formation of ^{30}P by virtue of an (α,n) reaction. The ^{30}P then decayed by positron emission to ^{30}Si. This can be represented as

$$^{27}_{13}\text{Al}(\alpha,n)\;^{30}_{15}\text{P}$$

$$^{30}_{15}\text{P} \rightarrow \,^{30}_{14}\text{Si} + \beta^+ \qquad t_{\frac{1}{2}} = 2.5 \text{ min}$$

Since this initial observation of the creation of a new radioactive species, more than a thousand radionuclides have been made. However, the large majority of these have depended on the development of accelerating instruments capable of developing considerably greater energies than are obtainable from natural radioactive sources.

The energy requirements of a nuclear transmutation depend on several factors. If we again consider the transmutation of the $^{14}_{7}N$ nucleus, we note that an amount of energy, Q, is involved in the over-all reaction. That is,

$$^{14}_{7}N + {}^{4}_{2}He \rightarrow {}^{17}_{8}O + {}^{1}_{1}H + Q$$

This energy is usually referred to as simply the "Q" of the reaction, and it is a measure of the energy that is either absorbed or released in the nuclear process. The Q can be determined from the over-all mass balance for the reaction, and for this particular case, it is seen to be

$$14.007515 + 4.00387 = 17.004533 + 1.008142 + Q$$

or, $Q = -0.001264$ amu $= -1.18$ mev. From this we see that it will be necessary to put 1.18 mev into the system in order to bring about the indicated transmutation.

Threshold Energies

Although, the Q value for the reaction $^{14}_{7}N(\alpha,p)^{17}_{8}O$ is only -1.18 mev, a considerably greater amount of energy is actually necessary to bring about the change. In order to maintain the conservation of momentum, 4/18 of the kinetic energy of the incident alpha particle must go into the kinetic energy of the products. This means that $(18/14)(1.18$ mev) or 1.49 mev will be necessary to satisfy the energy requirements of the Q value and the conservation of momentum. Thus, an incident alpha particle must have, at least, this amount of energy before the transmutation can take place. This is the *threshold energy* for the $^{14}_{7}N(\alpha,p)$ reaction, that is, the kinetic energy just necessary to make the transmutation energetically possible.

From a classical standpoint, it would appear that a threshold energy as determined from the Q value would be quite valid for bombardment with uncharged particles such as gamma rays or neutrons. On the other hand, if the bombarding particles do have a charge, it would appear that their minimum energy should be greater than the potential barrier of the target nucleus before a nuclear transmutation could be expected to take place. This, however, is not quite the case. Just as there is a finite probability of an alpha particle escaping from the nucleus by tunneling through the potential barrier, there is a finite probability that a bombarding charged particle may also tunnel through the barrier. However, in one significant way the two processes are quite different. According to the decay model, an alpha particle in the nucleus is colliding with the barrier walls with an extremely high frequency. Yet, a bombarding alpha particle collides with the barrier only once. It would appear that this should lead to a vanishingly small probability of penetration. The difference lies in the thickness and the height of the barrier at the point of collision. As can be seen in Figure 11-7, the barrier thickness decreases rather significantly near the top, and if an incident charged particle collides with the barrier near its top, it has a fair probability of tunneling through. Nevertheless, we find that the penetration probability for such a charged particle will be very small unless its energy is somewhat greater than the *Q* value. Consequently, we may recognize the *Q* value as a theoretical threshold for such bombardments, but from the practical side, we recognize that it is essential to have energies considerably in excess of this.

Nuclear Cross-Sections

In addition to the energy of a bombarding particle, it is also necessary to consider the probability that a particle with a sufficiently great energy will actually bring about a nuclear transmutation. This probability is expressed in terms of a quantity called the *cross-section* and is represented by the symbol σ. The first factor to be considered is the probability that the bombarding particle will, in fact, collide with the target nucleus. For this, we can merely calculate the geometrical cross-sectional area that the target nucleus presents to the incident particle. This, however, is not the only factor that must be considered. Nuclear cross-sections have been observed with values from a fraction of the geometrical cross-section up to several hundred thousand times its value.

Carrying over the original picture of a geometrical area as a basis for comparison, we can define a unit for the measurement of the cross-section. This will be called a *barn*, and it will have a value of 10^{-24}cm^2. This is of the order of magnitude of the actual geometrical area of a heavy nucleus. Since the radius of such a nucleus is in the neighborhood of 10^{-12}cm, its area would be about 10^{-24}cm^2. It is actually found that the nuclear cross-section for high-energy uncharged particles such as fast neutrons is always less, but frequently of the same magnitude, as the geometrical cross-sectional area of the target nucleus. On the other hand, the cross-sections for charged particles as well as for slow neutrons show quite divergent values.

It turns out to be extremely rare for a target to yield only one particular type of nuclear reaction. Quite to the contrary, a given nucleus will be susceptible to several different types of nuclear reactions such as (α,n) and (α,p), as well as numerous other less probable reactions as a result of alpha bombardment. In addition, a variety of other reactions may be induced by other types of bombarding particles such as neutrons, protons, deuterons, photons, and even heavier charged ions. Each of these processes will have its own partial cross-section that exists for a given bombardment. As an example, we might consider the irradiation of tellurium by photons having an energy up to 70 mev. Such an irradiation will lead primarily to a (γ,n) and a (γ,p) reaction with the (γ,n) reaction being the most prominent. However, a rather large number of less common reactions can also be observed. These might range from a not-so-uncommon reaction, such as a $(\gamma,2n)$, to such a comparatively exotic reaction as a $(\gamma,3p3n)$. The total cross-section for transmutation will be primarily made up of the first two reaction types. Nevertheless, the other reactions will also make their contributions. If now a new photon energy range is used, it will be found that the ratio of cross-sections for the various reactions will also change. If the photon energy is lowered, we would expect the (γ,n) reaction to become even more prominent, and if the photon energy is increased, the other possible reactions would be expected to show some tendency to increase. In general, it would be expected that a decrease in the energy of the incident particle would favor the emission of an uncharged particle. This can be attributed to an increase in the potential barrier for the emitted particle as its charge is increased. It is generally observed that lower

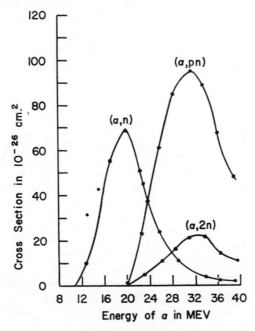

FIGURE 11-14. Cross-sections for Alpha-induced Reactions in ^{60}Ni. (After Ghoshal, S. N., *Phys. Rev.*, **80**, 939 (1950).)

energies of the incident particles will lead to simple products such as the emission of a single neutron or proton. These trends are well illustrated in Figure 11–14, where the energy dependence of the cross-sections for alpha-induced reactions of ^{60}Ni are given. Here we see that the nuclear cross-section is not only a function of the target nucleus and the type of reaction, but it is also a function of the energy of the bombarding particle.

Nuclear Fission

In addition to the various nuclear transmutations mentioned, there is another type of transmutation that is of particular importance. This is nuclear *fission*. Fission involves the splitting of a heavy nucleus into two or more fragments of intermediate size, along with the emission of several neutrons. The fission process has been observed only among the heavier elements, and it has been induced by virtually all of the various types of bombarding particles. Of these, the neutron-induced fissions are by far the most important.

Neutron-induced fission has been observed with both fast and slow neutrons. In the early studies on nuclear fission, it was observed that the fission cross-sections for certain nuclei were greatly enhanced when a hydrogenous material such as paraffin was present. It was concluded that the fast neutrons were slowed to thermal energies as a result of collisions with the hydrogen atoms, and the fission processes involved then the interaction of *thermal* or slow neutrons with the target nuclei. The majority of the fissionable nuclides are susceptible only to fast-particle fission.

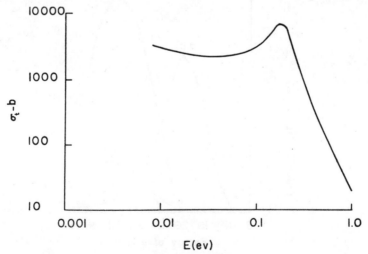

FIGURE 11–15. Slow Neutron Absorption Cross-Sections for Cadmium. (After Rainwater, L. J., Havens, W. W., Jr., Wu, C. S., and Dunning, J. R., *Phys. Rev.*, **71**, 65 (1947).)

Several nuclides, however, are found to fission with thermal neutrons as well as with fast neutrons, and the fission cross-sections in these cases are considerably greater than the corresponding fast-particle cross-sections. For ^{235}U, the thermal-neutron fission cross-section with 2200 m/sec neutrons is 580 barns, and for ^{238}U, the major constituent of naturally occurring uranium, the fission cross-section for thermal neutrons is zero. The value of 580 barns is considerably greater than would be expected for fast-particle cross-sections, which will be less than the geometrical cross-sectional area of the target nucleus.

To emphasize the extreme difference in cross-sections between thermal and fast neutrons, it is worthwhile to consider neutron-induced reactions other than fission. Thermal neutrons can be captured by virtually all nuclei, and the capture usually leads to a (n, γ) reaction. This process, known as *radiative capture*, can occur in fissionable as well as nonfissionable atoms and is, therefore, a competitive process with fission. Cross-sections

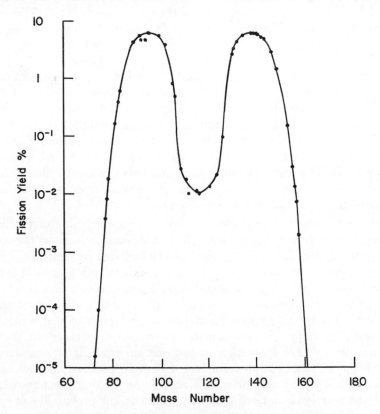

FIGURE 11–16. Fission Yield Curve for ^{235}U. (*J. Am. Chem. Soc.*, **68**, 2411 (1946).)

for such reactions are frequently very high, and as can be seen from the example of cadmium shown in Figure 11–15, the cross-sections may fall off radically with an increase in energy of the incident neutron.

It might be thought that a nuclear fission would split an atom into two essentially equally sized fragments. This is not the case. It can be seen in Figure 11–16, that unsymmetrical fission is observed with peaks in the neighborhood of A equal to 95 and 139. Symmetrical fission takes place only to the extent of 0.01 to 0.02 per cent. An unsymmetrical yield curve is observed for both thermal-neutron fission and for fast-neutron fission if the neutron energies are not too high. However, at very high particle energies, for instance 200 or 300 mev, the yield curve takes on a quite different shape, approaching a symmetrical-type curve but having a rather flat peak.

The great practical value of the fission process lies in the tremendous amount of energy that is released in each nuclear fission. This can be appreciated from the binding energy curve shown in Figure 11–5. The fission of a heavy element like ^{235}U results in fragments having mass numbers ranging from about 80 to 150. We can see from the binding-energy curve that the elements in this mass range all have binding energies in the neighborhood of 8.4 mev per nucleon. But the binding energy per nucleon for uranium is around 7.6 mev. This leads to a difference of about 0.8 mev per nuclear particle that will be given up in a fission process. Since the ^{235}U nucleus plus the thermal neutron gives us a total of 236 particles, we see that approximately 200 mev is released in a single fission. The major portion of this energy appears as kinetic energy of the fission fragments, with substantially lesser amounts going towards the kinetic energy of the fission neutrons, the emission of prompt gamma rays, and the decay products of the radioactive species formed.

In addition to the very great energy release, the value of the fission process is equally dependent on the fact that neutron-induced fission can be self-sustaining. The fission process can be initiated by neutrons, and for ^{235}U, an average of about 2.5 neutrons are emitted per fission. If each of the emitted neutrons leads to an additional fission, along with the accompanying emission of more neutrons, it is obvious that a chain reaction will be set up. On the other hand, if the mean free path of the neutrons is sufficiently great to allow the neutrons to escape from the system, the reaction will die out. For a reaction to just sustain itself, it is necessary for an average of one neutron from each fission to produce another fission. Thus, there is a minimum or *critical size* of the fissioning material, below which the reaction is not self-sustaining. That is, the probability of escape by the neutron is greater than the probability of inducing a fission. From the practical standpoint of a nuclear explosion, it should be apparent that if two *subcritical masses* are brought together, a critical mass could be formed that would lead to the desired explosive effect.

NUCLEAR RECOIL

When a source is obtained by irradiation, only an extremely small percentage of the target atoms are actually transformed to radioactive atoms. Consequently, if a radioactive source of high specific activity is desired, it is obviously necessary that the radioactive atoms be separable from the bulk of the target material. Frequently, this is not too difficult a problem. If the atomic number of the product nucleus is different from that of the target nucleus, then a simple chemical separation is possible. This situation arises in virtually all instances where either the incident or the emitted particle is charged. If, on the other hand, the atomic number does not change, it will be necessary to use an entirely different approach. For instance, if ^{129}Sb is to be obtained from a (γ,p) reaction on ^{130}Te, the antimony can readily be separated from the tellurium target material by chemical means. However, if ^{129}Te is to be obtained from a (γ,n) reaction on ^{130}Te, it is apparent that we are confronted with a quite different problem.

The first solution to this problem came in 1934, when L. Szilard and T. A. Chalmers[10] discovered that the iodine activity formed from a neutron irradiation of ethyl iodide could be separated from the organic target material. The apparent result of the irradiation was the conversion of inactive iodine atoms in the ethyl iodide molecules to free radioactive iodide ions, which could then be extracted from the organic phase with water. In order for this to take place, the carbon-iodine bond must be broken. If thermal neutrons are used as the irradiating particles, they will have essentially zero kinetic energy, and the bond breakage must arise from the recoil of the nucleus resulting from the emission of the usual gamma ray. Calculations of the energy involved in this type of process indicate that such a mechanism is quite reasonable. In order to conserve momentum, the recoiling nucleus must have an equal and opposite momentum to that of the emitted gamma ray. Since the energy of a gamma ray can be expressed as $E = mc^2$, the momentum of the gamma ray, which is represented by the symbol p, will be

$$p_\gamma = mc = \frac{E_\gamma}{c} \tag{11--24}$$

Now, for the nucleus, the recoil energy will be

$$E_r = \frac{1}{2} mv^2 = \frac{m^2v^2}{2m} = \frac{p_\gamma^{\,2}}{2m} \tag{11--25}$$

and since the momenta of the gamma ray and the recoil nucleus must be equal and opposite, it is legitimate to use the momentum of the gamma ray in Eq. (11–25). If we express the mass in atomic mass units rather than grams, and express the energy in mev rather than ergs, we obtain the equation for the recoil energy by combining Eq. (11–24) and Eq. (11–25):

$$E_r = \frac{E_\gamma{}^2}{1862m} \qquad (11\text{–}26)$$

A covalent bond energy would not be expected to exceed 5 ev, and it can be seen from Eq. (11–26) that a 2-mev gamma ray will impart a considerably greater recoil energy than this in even a very heavy atom.

In order for a *Szilard-Chalmers reaction* to be successful, it is necessary that the radioactive atom does not recombine with an alkyl or molecular fragment, and that it will not exchange with an inactive atom in a target molecule. Szilard-Chalmers reactions have been studied quite extensively in the solid, liquid, and gaseous states with the alkyl halides, using mostly (n,γ) and (γ,n) type processes. As a result of these studies, models have been proposed,[11,12] primarily by Libby and his coworkers, to explain the properties of these so-called *hot-atom* reactions.

In addition to the usual alkyl halide studies, some work has been done on the irradiation of inorganic compounds. It is sometimes found that, after an irradiation, the oxidation state of the radioactive product atoms is different from that of the inactive target atoms. The energies involved in the collision and recoil of a nucleus should be sufficiently great to disrupt the electrons in the atom, and we would in general expect the atom to rearrange to its most stable configuration. A good example of a separation based on an oxidation state change is that of tellurium. Tellurium can be irradiated by either neutrons or gamma rays in the form of H_6TeO_6, and the active tellurium atoms resulting from the (γ,n) or (n,γ) reaction are found to be in the +4 oxidation state. Since the +4 state is more easily reduced than the +6 state, SO_2 can be used to selectively reduce the lower state to the metal, and thereby separate the two. This technique has been used for several elements other than tellurium, and it could probably be used any time the less stable oxidation state of an element does not exchange too rapidly with the more stable oxidation state of that element.

A very important application of these enrichment reactions is found in the preparation of radioactive sources. For instance, in the determination of a beta spectrum, it is observed that the shape of the spectrum will depend on the thickness of the source. This is due to the energy loss of the beta rays as they pass through the bulk of the sample. In fact, low-energy beta rays may be completely absorbed in a thick source. For this reason, we sometimes use sources of *infinite thickness*. These, at least, will show a consistency in the absorption of beta rays. However, if we are interested in energies of the beta rays, it is necessary to have samples of high specific activity. It is for the preparation of these that the Szilard-Chalmers type reaction is of extreme importance.

CHEMICAL APPLICATIONS

The use of radioactive isotopes in the various phases of chemistry has become so widespread that no attempt will be made here to give an accounting of them. These include such a diversity of problems as the determination of a reaction mechanism to the following of an earthworm as it responds to various stimuli. And radioactive tracers have found as much use in the industrial world as they have in the academic world. This success can be attributed primarily to two factors. Firstly, except for the very light elements, the chemistry of a radioactive atom is no different from that of any other atom of the same element, and secondly, the fate of an individual radioactive atom can be followed by virtue of its decay properties.

One of the first problems that arises in any radiochemical study is that of *isotopic exchange*. At times this can be a curse, and at other times it may be the basis for a successful experiment. Basically, isotopic exchange is a reaction in which the atoms of an element interchange between two or more different chemical forms of that element. Although exchange may be taking place continually, it is not detectable unless some of the atoms are *tagged*.

Probably the most common type of exchange reaction involves the formation of a transition state which will give a rearrangement of chemical bonds on decomposition. This may be represented as

$$X - X + X^{*-} = (X - X - X^*)^- = X^- + X - X^*$$

where X^* represents the tagged atom. If the exchange is complete, we would find the tagged atoms distributed proportionally between $X - X$ and X^-. Another type of exchange that is of considerable importance is that of *electron transfer*. This type of exchange might be observed when an element is present in two different oxidation states, such as Tl^+ and Tl^{+++}. In this type of exchange, we might add tagged Tl^+ to a solution containing both oxidation states, and if electron exchange takes place, we would then find the tagged atoms distributed between the two states. The rate of electron exchange is found to vary considerably with the different species, depending on such factors as the number and type of electrons involved, the geometry of the ion, etc.

One rather useful application of isotopic exchange has been in the study of substitution reactions in coordination compounds. It has been possible to correlate the exchange rate between the coordinated ions and the radioactive ions in solution to the electron configuration of the central metal atom. Many complexes exchange their anions very rapidly, whereas other complexes show a very slow exchange rate. This can be related to the occupation of the d orbitals in the central metal ion.[13,14]

The development of radiochemical techniques has led to two basic contributions in the field of kinetics. By tagging atoms in certain positions in a molecule, it is possible to determine their ultimate fate in a reaction. Secondly, the techniques make it possible to determine reaction rates at equilibrium. This offers an advantage over the usual methods which require that rates be determined far from equilibrium. An example of the use of a tagged atom can be seen in the oxidation of fumaric acid to formic acid. A question arises as to whether the formic acid comes from a methenyl carbon atom or a carboxyl carbon atom. By tagging only the carboxylic carbons with ^{11}C, and carrying out the oxidation, the source of the formic acid carbon atom can be determined by noting if the resultant formic acid is radioactive. It turns out that it is not, and it can, therefore, be concluded that the formic acid originates from the methenyl carbon atoms in the fumaric acid. From this work, it is possible to propose a reasonable mechanism for the oxidation.

There are numerous applications of radiochemical techniques to the field of analytical chemistry. The most obvious of these is the direct determination of a radioactive species. This is rather straightforward when the species is naturally radioactive. The major difficulty arises from the problems of *absolute counting*. That is, it must be possible to account for every particle that is emitted from the source. This involves questions in geometry, scattering, absorption in the source, and counter efficiency. All of these can be solved to a certain extent, but we could hardly hope for an error of less than 1 or 2 per cent. Nevertheless, there are times when this error is justified because of convenience or difficulty of conventional chemical separations.

A qualitative, and even semiquantitative determination of radioactive elements can be made quite rapidly if the gamma transitions for the isotopes are known. Ordinarily, the determination of the presence of a given radioactive isotope is made on the basis of its half-life. This can be prohibitive if the half-life is long, and at least annoying if it is of the order of several hours. However, if the gamma transitions have been evaluated, the isotope can be recognized in a matter of minutes by means of a scintillation spectrometer.

Another very interesting and useful analytical application is that of *activation analysis*. Knowing the type of reaction to be expected, a sample may be bombarded in order to transmute some of the nuclei in the sample. If the transmuted nuclei are radioactive, they can be observed by the usual methods. By careful calibration, this method can be reasonably accurate for the determination of trace impurities.

We find that the applications of radiochemical techniques are almost unlimited. Many of these are very straightforward and many are extremely clever. However, they will not, in general, involve new concepts as much as applications of a useful tool to conventional problems.

BIBLIOGRAPHY

1. Soddy, F., *Nature*, **91**, 57 (1913).
2. Gamow, G., *Z. Phys.*, **51**, 204 (1928).
3. Gurney, R. and Condon, E., *Nature*, **122**, 439 (1928); *Phys. Rev.*, **33**, 127 (1929).
4. Anderson, C., *Science*, **76**, 238 (1932); *Phys. Rev.*, **43**, 491 (1933).
5. Fermi, E., *Z. Physik*, **88**, 161 (1934).
6. Segré, E. and Wiegand, C., *Phys. Rev.*, **75**, 39 (1949).
7. Bainbridge, K., Goldhaber, M., and Wilson, E., *Phys. Rev.*, **90**, 430 (1935).
8. Strominger, D., Hollander, J., and Seaborg, G., *Rev. Mod. Phys.*, **30**, 585 (1958).
9. Curie, I. and Joliot, F., *Compt. rend.*, **196**, 1885 (1933); **198**, 254 (1934).
10. Szilard, L. and Chalmers, T., *Nature*, **134**, 462 (1934).
11. Libby, W., *J. Am. Chem. Soc.*, **69**, 2523 (1947).
12. Richardson, A. and Voigt, A., *J. Chem. Phys.*, **28**, 854 (1958).
13. Taube, H., *Chem. Revs.*, **50**, 69 (1952).
14. Stranks, D. and Wilkins, R., *Chem. Revs.*, **57**, 743 (1957).

SUGGESTED SUPPLEMENTARY READING

Friedlander, G. and Kennedy, S., "Nuclear and Radio Chemistry," John Wiley & Sons, New York, N.Y., 1955.

Wahl, A. and Bonner, N., "Radioactivity Applied to Chemistry," John Wiley & Sons, New York, N.Y., 1955.

Kaplan, I., "Nuclear Physics," Addison-Wesley Publishing Co., Cambridge, 1955.

Fermi, E., "Nuclear Physics," University of Chicago Press, Chicago, Ill., 1950.

Halliday, D., "Introductory Nuclear Physics," John Wiley & Sons, New York, N.Y., 1950.

Index